PALEARCTIC BIRDS

A CHECKLIST OF THE BIRDS

OF

EUROPE, NORTH AFRICA AND ASIA

north of the foothills of the Himalayas

MARK BEAMAN

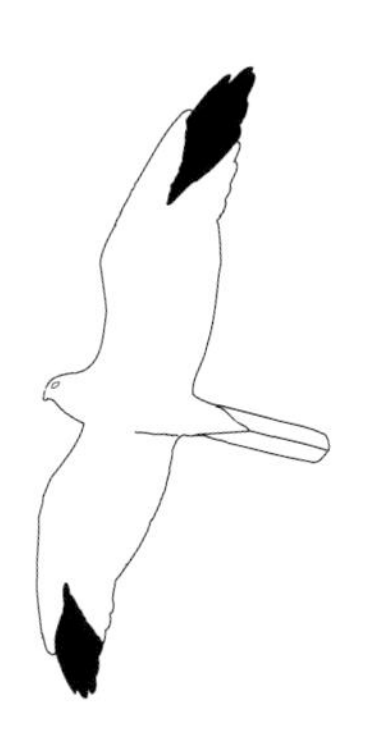

1994

Harrier Publications, Stonyhurst, England

Palearctic Birds

A Checklist of the Birds of Europe, North Africa and Asia
north of the foothills of the Himalayas.

ISBN 0 9523391 0 2

British Library Cataloguing-in-Publication Data.
A catalogue record for this book is available from the British Library.

Cover illustration: Pallas's Sandgrouse by Nik Borrow

Published by Harrier Publications, Two Jays, Kemple End, Birdy Brow, Stonyhurst,
Lancashire BB7 9QY, England, U.K. Tel: 01254-826317. Fax: 01254-826780.

Printed by Lords Printers, Sandygate House, Sandygate, Burnley BB11 1TE.

CONTENTS

INTRODUCTION

Vaurie's milestone work *The Birds of the Palearctic Fauna* (1959a, 1965a), was followed by Voous's much appreciated and widely followed *List of Recent Holarctic Bird Species* (1977). However, many changes in taxonomy have occurred during the intervening period and, in particular, there has been a rapidly gathering movement towards standardizing the English names of birds on a worldwide basis, so there would seem to be a real need for an updated checklist of Palearctic birds that incorporates these taxonomic changes and makes a sensible contribution to the on-going debate about which English names should be adopted as standard.

In this checklist I have adopted a conservative approach towards the sequence and composition of families as I wanted to produce a list which could be used with ease and familiarity by current students of Palearctic birds. The radical new treatment of families proposed by Sibley & Ahlquist (1990) and adopted by Sibley & Monroe (1990) in their magisterial *Distribution and Taxonomy of Birds of the World* remains highly controversial and has not been followed in the *Handbook of the Birds of the World* (del Hoyo *et al.* 1992) nor in any of the important regional works now in production or recently completed, yet these are likely to be the standard works of reference for most ornithologists for many years to come.

As has been pointed out by Mayr & Bock (1994), there are considerable advantages to be had in maintaining a 'standard' order of families, which would not only greatly ease communication between ornithologists working in all fields (not just systematics), but would also remove the need for never-ending upheavals to data storage and indexing systems, and indeed the layouts of avifaunas, checklists and field guides, in order to make these coincide with the latest, most experimental views of systematists. I can appreciate the sheer common sense of this argument, provided there is no attempt to imply that a standard order indicates taxonomic relationships.

As the 'Voous order' is now so well-entrenched and well-liked as the standard for the Palearctic region, I have followed the same modified Wetmore order adopted by Voous. For the same reason the order of species within families generally follows Voous, with only a few exceptions.

Taxonomy at the level of genus and species mostly follows Voous, although there are quite a few changes which take into account recent taxonomic revisions. In general I have not followed those splits adopted by Sibley & Monroe (1990, 1993) where published supporting evidence is either sparse or lacking, or to my mind unconvincing. Further research may well, however, show some of these treatments to be justified.

ENGLISH NAMES

A more radical approach has been adopted for English names, which may distress some people. I believe that a standardized world list of 'official' English names is both an inevitable development and something to be welcomed by English-speaking ornithologists everywhere as a means to easier communication. It is important to remember that the introduction of standardized names in the literature and for other formal purposes does not in any way prevent ornithologists from continuing to use traditional names in conversation.

Standardization requires that modifiers (such as 'common' or 'Eurasian') be added to many traditional English names for Palearctic birds (e.g. Wigeon, Hobby, Cuckoo, Nuthatch, Treecreeper) in order to avoid ambiguity. I also accept that some otherwise perfectly adequate names should change to avoid conflict with identical or partly overlapping names for other species. In addition, where two or more names are currently in widespread use in different parts of the world, only one can become the standard, necessitating some painful choices.

Such changes are self-evidently required if the goal of a standardized worldwide list of English bird names is to be achieved. Most unfortunately, however, the waters have been muddied by a simultaneous attempt to change numerous Old World bird names that are already unique and perfectly adequate. These attempts, which are nothing to do with the changes that are required for standardization, have nonetheless been widely confused with the latter and have only served to enhance the level of opposition to standardization as such.

I do not accept that many existing English names that are unique, satisfactory and often well-established should be changed *en masse* just because authors feel they can come up with newly-coined alternatives they see as being more appropriate. Even the process of adapting to the many revised or new names for species where the addition of modifiers or other name changes are essential for standardization will put a great burden on the English-speaking ornithological community, and I feel that most people will share my belief that numerous further, purely gratuitous, changes which suit the subjective preferences of their proponents should be strongly resisted.

Some English names will undoubtedly continue to change, especially where major taxonomic revisions make this unavoidable or at least greatly preferable, but if we accept that any name should be changed where this will better indicate field characters, family or generic relationships, or geographic distribution then there will be no end to the upheaval: Montagu's Harrier will become 'Bar-winged Harrier', Fieldfare will become 'Fieldfare Thrush', Eleonora's Falcon will become 'Mediterranean Falcon' (or perhaps 'Island Falcon') and Brambling will become ... well, who knows what?

'Tidying up' names to try to better indicate taxonomic affinities (as in renaming 'Dunnock' as 'Hedge Accentor', or changing the universally-liked and most apt 'Red-flanked Bluetail' to 'Orange-flanked Bush Robin') is a classic example of unnecessary change. Short of the most wide-reaching orgy of name changing, English vernacular names are never going to become a parallel version of the scientific nomenclature. In any case, do we really want this? Surely it is the role of the taxonomic categories and the scientific nomenclature to point up relationships, or the lack of them?

Another example of unnecessary change is the substitution of newly invented alternatives for English names that honour illustrious ornithologists. Why should these be unceremoniously dumped when there is no pressing need? The latter problem has not been significant in the case of European or North American birds, where too much outrage would inevitably follow any attempt to remove all traces of the likes of Audubon, Montagu, Pallas, Ross or Wilson, but is a real threat in Asia where names that commemorate such famous pioneers of eastern Palearctic ornithology as Hume, Kozlov, Père David, Przevalski and Roborovski disappear at a stroke in Sibley & Monroe (1990), yet no convincing argument has been put forward to justify these changes. The argument that in some cases the people in question are celebrated by the scientific name is unimpressive to me: we are dealing here with vernacular names, which are used for most verbal communication between today's English-speaking ornithologists, and only by retaining these English names will we be regularly reminded of the important role played by these historic personalities.

My main aim, so far as English names is concerned, has been to try to resolve existing nomenclatural problems while maintaining as much stability as possible. I have therefore resisted name changes that I feel are unnecessary and I have only resorted to newly-coined names where all the existing names are positively inaccurate or where there was some nomenclatural problem that could not be simply solved by other means (e.g. adding a modifier). Some of the names I have adopted I personally dislike, but I accept that many compromises are necessary to achieve the goal of worldwide standardization.

The majority of the English names adopted in this checklist coincide with those used by Sibley & Monroe (1990, 1993), who in turn were much influenced by the sterling work on the names of Western Palearctic species by the British Ornithologists' Union's Records Committee (1988) and Inskipp & Sharrock (1992). Where I differ from these authors, the names they use are given as alternatives, as are many other alternative names that are presently in widespread use. In most instances, an explanation as to why a particular English name was chosen is given in the 'Notes on English names'.

In general I have:

1. Chosen what I regard as the more appropriate name where there are two or more unique names for the species that are already in frequent use. I have tried to be as even-handed as possible when considering the relative merits of names that are well established in Europe, North America, Asia or Africa but, where the decision was difficult, more weight was usually given to better-known names in the interests of stability.

(Note: descriptions such as 'better-known' or 'more widely used' in the 'Notes on English names' refer to knowledge of, and use of, the name by a greater number of today's English-speaking ornithologists and not necessarily to its adoption in a majority of ornithological works, many of which relate to areas of the world with few resident English-speakers. Inevitably, such an assessment is something of a 'guesstimate'.)

2. Adopted newly-coined names (or resurrected former names) only where none of the names already in widespread use are unique and at least reasonably appropriate.

3. Added modifiers to well-established and appropriate existing names which happen to clash with the names for species elsewhere in the world rather than adopt newly-coined names or unsatisfactory former names.

4. Simplified existing names, provided this does not lead to confusion, rather than add modifiers to the names of other, well-known species.

5. Avoided coining entirely new names or modifiers, as there are already more than enough on offer, apart from a very few instances where I felt this was the best solution.

6. Tried to minimize the use of the word Eurasian. I share the commonly held view that this is an unattractive word, but there is no denying that it is an appropriate description for some species that are distributed across the entire breadth of Eurasia. I have generally avoided using it for species that are primarily 'western' in distribution, with a breeding range extending only as far as central Siberia or central Asia (and often a winter range that is purely in subsaharan Africa). In particular I feel its use should be avoided when there is a widespread species in eastern Asia that shares the group name (e.g. marsh harriers, scops owls, nightjars, jackdaws). On the other hand, it is a more precise term than 'northern' and often preferable as a modifier for species that are widespread in Eurasia but not circumpolar.

7. Tended, in closely balanced cases, to favour English names that reflect the scientific name, since this can be mutually beneficial. I have not, however, followed this principle slavishly, as scientific names are themselves sometimes inappropriate or even misleading.

Inevitably, personal preferences and the need to solve unusually problematical cases have led to some inconsistency, but I have tried to keep this to a minimum.

Worst of all has been the problem of trying to reconcile differences between British Isles (or Old World) and North American usage at the generic level. These differences are diver *v.* loon for *Gavia* species, buzzard *v.* hawk for *Buteo* species, grouse *v.* ptarmigan for *Lagopus lagopus*, skua *v.* jaeger for *Stercorarius* species, guillemot *v.* murre for *Uria* species and bunting *v.* longspur for *Calcarius* species. At first I planned to steer clear of this minefield, as have all past authors who, understandably enough, opted to follow their own local practice. Unfortunately this problem will not go away and, with worldwide standardization of English names well on the way, it does need to be resolved.

After much consideration, and indeed agonizing, I have opted for loon, buzzard (for the circumpolar Rough-legged Buzzard *Buteo lagopus* at least), ptarmigan, jaeger, murre and longspur. I fully expect these decisions to bring howls of outrage from some quarters, but I hope that those willing to approach this subject with an open mind will accept that these name differences have to be reconciled at some stage if a worldwide standardization is to be achieved and that they will take note of the arguments for and against these rival names under the relevant entries in 'Notes on English names'. We all become attached to familiar names, but so equally do others with a different tradition. When a decision has to be made as to which name should be the world 'standard', we should try to prevent gut prejudice from clouding our assessments.

Another difficult and contentious area is group names that are shared between families. In this Palearctic checklist (including alternative names) there are two families sharing the names 'petrel', 'snipe', 'owl', 'blackbird', 'warbler', 'grosbeak' and 'oriole', three families sharing 'sparrow' and 'finch' and no less than four families sharing 'plover' and 'tit'. Changing the English group names for entire families, or large groups of species, is a gloomy prospect. Do we really want to see something like 'neo-warbler' adopted for the members of the New World Parulidae so that no one will think they are related to the Old World warblers of the family Sylviidae? While few people would advocate such wholesale change, the real problem is deciding where to draw the line. What about single species which have English names that suggest that they are members of another family entirely? Although I am generally in favour of English name stability, and believe it is the role of the taxonomic categories rather than English names to show taxonomic relationships, there are occasions where a change of English name is clearly desirable. Renaming species whose existing English name gives a grossly misleading indication of its taxonomic position has been common practice in the past: otherwise we would still find, for example, that *Cercotrichas galactotes* (Rufous-tailed Scrub Robin) was being called 'Rufous Warbler' long after it had been moved from the Sylviidae to the Turdidae. It is only common sense to be pragmatic in such instances and look at each individual case on its merits.

Lastly, since I find the current fashion for introducing hyphens into bird names both inconsistent and ugly, I have not gone further than I considered necessary down this awkward road. I have no quarrel with hyphenating family names (e.g. 'storm-petrel', 'painted-snipe', 'cuckoo-shrike') to point up the fact that these are distinct entities, but within families the use of hyphenation is often much less helpful. Although some combinations (e.g. 'pygmy-goose', 'sparrow-lark', 'wren-babbler') are often used and generally considered to enhance clarity, widespread use of hyphens to try to indicate taxonomic differences is simply going to create a morass of subtle name variations which for most people will have no obvious significance (and thus be instantly forgettable). For example, one can convert the name 'European Honey Buzzard' for *Pernis apivorus* into 'European Honey-buzzard' to try to indicate that this particular species is not a true buzzard of the genus *Buteo*, but hyphens cannot be employed in the parallel case of the name 'Grey-faced Buzzard' for *Butastur indicus*. As for hyphenated constructions like 'Great Crested-Tern' for *Sterna bergii* that try to ensure that no one gains the impression that this species has a larger crest, as opposed to a larger overall size, than 'Lesser Crested-Tern' *S. bengalensis*, this sort of thing often causes confusion (suggesting, in this instance, that these species differ in some way from other *Sterna* species) and is best avoided.

GEOGRAPHICAL LIMITS

The southern boundary of the Palearctic region is impossible to determine with any great precision. As a result two approaches are possible when treating its avifauna. The first approach (as followed by Vaurie 1959a, 1965a) is to be liberal with the boundaries of the region, but then deliberately exclude many purely Afrotropical and especially Oriental species that are found in the periphery of the chosen area on the grounds that the work is a treatment of the Palearctic avifauna *per se*, rather than an attempt to produce a precise list of species recorded from a specified geographical area. Even though this approach has the advantage of concentrating on the clearly Palearctic elements of the avifauna, without any need to include vagrants and peripheral species, there are still considerable problems involved in deciding what to include or exclude. Thus one finds Vaurie including such clearly Oriental species as Plain Prinia *Prinia inornata* because this lowland form extends up the deep valleys into Sikang (now western Sichuan) and thus occurs within his geographical (if not altitudinal) limits, while montane species like Long-billed Thrush *Zoothera monticola* that reach to between 3000-4000m in the Himalayas, and thus also reach his area of coverage, are excluded.

The second approach is to try, so far as is possible in a very complex situation, to compile a complete list of species, including all vagrants and rare visitors, that have occurred inside Palearctic limits (or, in the case of Voous 1977, Holarctic limits). This places the onus on the author to determine appropriate geographical limits for the Palearctic which coincide with the points at which a predominantly Palearctic avifauna gives way to a predominantly Afrotropical or Oriental avifauna. Unfortunately in Asia there is nothing straightforward about the interface between the Palearctic and Oriental regions, either in terms of geography or flora, and this makes for all sorts of anomalies. In central China, for example, numerous Oriental elements extend northwards in the plains and lower valleys, many reaching as far as extreme southern Gansu and the Han Shui valley of southern Shaanxi, yet many Palearctic birds in effect leap-frog southwards across middle China in the many 'islands' of montane forest. This creates a nightmare situation for anyone trying to determine a meaningful boundary between the regions.

As this checklist is intended to be a complete list of species recorded from the Palearctic region, I have followed the second line of approach. I prefer to take an inclusive rather than an exclusive stance, so I have included areas with mixed avifaunas such as southwestern Arabia and the upper temperate broadleaf forests of the Himalayas and the eastern ramparts of the Tibetan plateau. These areas do not clearly belong to the Palearctic but neither do they clearly belong to the Afrotropical or Oriental regions respectively. As with so many aspects of the natural world, they are complex interfaces which are not conducive to the human predilection for drawing precise limits. Including species found in these interfaces between avifaunas helps to link this checklist with works treating the Afrotropical and Oriental regions. Inevitably any choice of artificial geographical limits for the Palearctic results in inconsistencies and this list will certainly have its share. No author is immune from this problem.

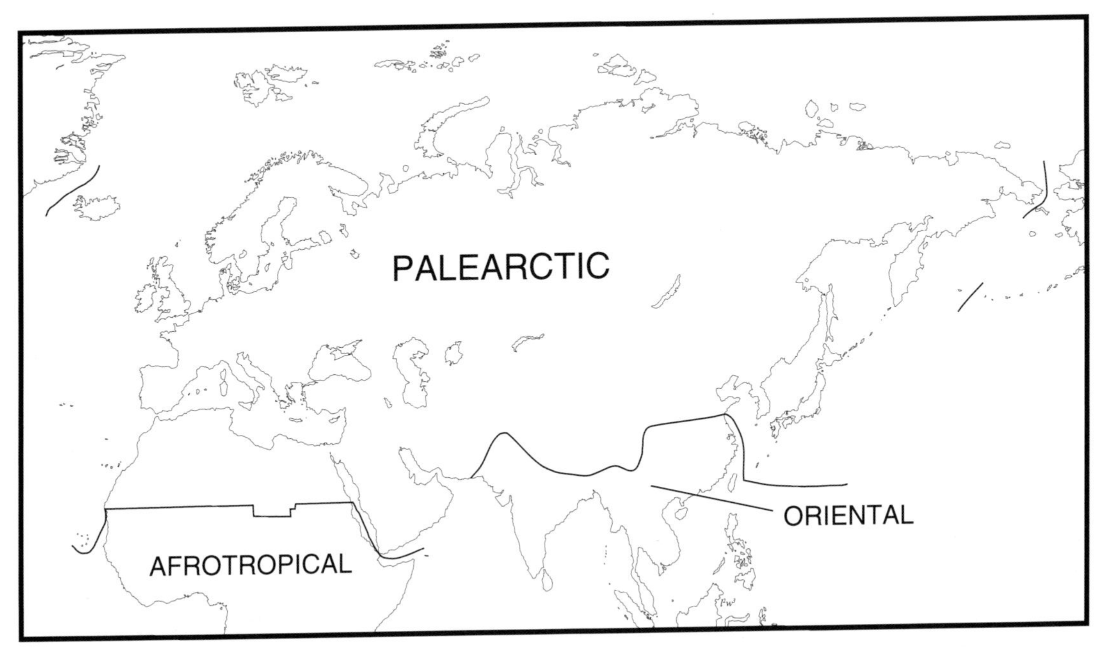

Fig. 1. The Palearctic Region

By and large I have adopted very similar geographical limits to those followed by both Vaurie (1959a, 1965a) and Voous (1977), but there are some small differences.

In the west, Jan Mayen, Iceland, the Azores and the Cape Verde Islands are included, but not eastern Greenland (included by Vaurie).

In Africa the boundary is identical to that adopted by Cramp & Simmons (1977) for *The Birds of the Western Palearctic* from the Atlantic coast as far as northwestern Chad, but to the east it runs a little further to the south. I have mostly followed the 21°N line of latitude from the Baie du Lévrier on the Atlantic coast to the Red Sea coast of Sudan, but extended the area of coverage southwards to include all of Libya and Chad north of 19°N and thereby take in the whole of the Tibesti. I thus include in the Palearctic the whole of the Cap Blanc peninsula, the Hoggar and the Tibesti, but exclude the Mauritanian Adrar, the Adrar des Ifora, the Aïr, the Ennedi, the Nile in the vicinity of Dongola and the area north of Port Sudan. The northern limits of the *Acacia* savanna zone reach to about 19-20°N in parts of subsaharan Africa (notably northern Mauritania, the Aïr, the Ennedi and the Red Sea hills north of Port Sudan) and Afrotropical species clearly predominate in these areas. A few Afrotropical species penetrate to 22°N or even further, but Palearctic elements predominate north of about 21°N. In addition, the islands of the Banc d'Arguin are included, but not the adjacent mainland coast of Mauritania.

Voous states that he roughly followed a line through the middle of the Sahara at 19°N, but in reality he must have adopted a more northerly boundary (at least in most areas of the Sahara) as he excluded a series of Afrotropical species that are known to occur between 19-21°N. Vaurie included the entire southern fringe of the Sahara, including the Aïr, the Ennedi, the region of Dongola and the Red Sea hills north of Port Sudan in his area of coverage, but deliberately excluded most Afrotropical elements occurring in these areas.

The southern tip of Arabia is problematical and has been excluded from the Palearctic by some authors (e.g. Vaurie; Dowsett & Forbes-Watson 1993) but included by others (e.g. Voous). While Afrotropical forms (of limited diversity) predominate in the coastal lowlands and foothills, Palearctic forms predominate in the interior. The endemic species of the area show both Afrotropical and Palearctic affinities, with Arabian Accentor *Prunella fagani* being the most southerly representative of this purely Palearctic family. Faced with such a difficult situation and such a small physical area, I prefer, for the sake of geographical simplicity, to include the whole Arabian peninsula.

The Palearctic boundary in southern Asia is broadly obvious, in that the Himalayas and their associated ranges provide such a profound ecological boundary to the spread of Oriental elements to the north and at the same time allow Palearctic species to spread southwards at higher altitudes in the temperate zone forests. The precise limits are, however, far more difficult to identify. I have tried to settle on a boundary that excludes lowland and foothill areas with their predominantly Oriental influences while including higher areas with a more mixed avifauna.

The chosen boundary initially runs from the Makran coast of Pakistan at Ras Ormara northwards to the Harboi Hills and the mountains east of Quetta, and thence along the Sulaiman Range and the mountainous borderlands of Pakistan and Afghanistan to the Himalayas. Both Vaurie and Voous included the southeastern corner of Baluchistan in the Palearctic, but more recent studies indicate that quite a number of Oriental species, even including Common Tailorbird *Orthotomus sutorius*, occur in this area (Roberts 1991, 1992) and so I prefer to exclude areas such as Sonmiani Lagoon and the lower Hab Valley. In addition I have only included species known to occur above 2000m in northwestern Pakistan and adjacent Afghanistan, the same altitudinal limit adopted for the Himalayas in Pakistan (see below), and in consequence lower-lying areas such as Kohat and the Kabul valley are excluded.

The line then runs along the main range of the Himalayas and onwards to the mountains at the extreme northernmost tip of Burma, the Lijiang Range in northern Yunnan and the mountainous western margins of the Red Basin of Sichuan. Voous states that, as a rule, he followed Vaurie in including species that inhabit the zone of temperate mixed deciduous forest and upwards. Due to the influences of geography, latitude and climate, the height at which such forest commences shows considerable variation. In Pakistan and northern Sichuan this forest type occurs as low as 1500-1800m, but in the highest rainfall areas from eastern Nepal to Arunachal Pradesh it is usually only found upwards of 2600m (see Stainton 1972). Consequently I have been unable to use a constant altitudinal 'cut-off point' throughout the region and instead have interpreted the available data on altitudinal distribution and habitat preferences as best I could. As a rule I have included species known to occur at or above 2000m in the northwestern Himalayas (Pakistan and Kashmir) and central and northern Sichuan, 2500m in the western Himalayas (Himachal Pradesh to Garhwal), northern Yunnan and southern Sichuan, and 2800m in the eastern Himalayas (Nepal to Arunachal Pradesh) and northernmost Burma. These are rather arbitrary boundaries that, because there is so much variation in the altitudes at which different forest types occur, include the upper edge of the evergreen broadleaf forest in places, but they effectively serve to exclude many obviously Oriental elements that reach moderate altitudes. It should be noted that in this region of remarkable altitudinal variations many deep valleys penetrate far into the mountain massifs, allowing Oriental species to extend well into the Himalayas and especially the eastern edge of the Tibetan plateau, but these lower-lying areas are best considered as being outwith Palearctic limits.

The Palearctic boundary in eastern China is particularly difficult to determine. Many clearly Oriental species extend northwards across the lowlands and lower mountains of eastern China as far as the Yangtze River (or Chang Jiang) or beyond, but their westward spread is conspicuously halted by the high mountain massif of the Tibetan plateau. The Yangtze forms no barrier to the northward spread and a fair number of Oriental species are found right across the Red Basin of Sichuan as far as the adjacent and contiguous lowlands of southeasternmost Gansu, often also reaching the low-lying valley of the Han Shui (a tributary of the Yangtze) in southernmost Shaanxi. Very few such species extend further north than this, however, so the high mountains of southern Gansu and the Qinling Shan range in southern Shaanxi clearly represent a significant barrier. Some Palearctic species, on the other hand, extend southwards through the mountains of southern Shaanxi, Southern Gansu and northeastern Sichuan as far as western Guizhou and eastern Yunnan. Faced with such a situation I decided to take as the boundary the Yangtze/Huang Ho watershed in southern Gansu and the Qinling Shan in Shaanxi. This is a slightly more northerly boundary than that adopted by Vaurie, but does, I feel, better represent the boundary between the Palearctic and Oriental regions.

Further to the east, few Oriental forms extend further north than the lowlands around the mouth of the Yangtze or the hills of southern Anhui and southern Henan. In this area I have adopted the 34°N line of latitude from the Yellow Sea coast, just south of the Shandong peninsula, inland to the Qinling Shan as a convenient if rather arbitrary boundary.

On the Pacific fringe, the Nansei (or Ryukyu) Islands, the Daito (or Borodino) Islands, the Kazan (or Volcano) Islands and the Ogasawara (or Bonin) Islands are included. Taiwan and its associated islands have been excluded, although a case could be made for including the highest regions of this mountainous island in the Palearctic, harbouring as they do such clearly Palearctic elements as Alpine Accentor *Prunella collaris* and Spotted Nutcracker *Nucifraga caryocatactes*. Conversely a case can be made for excluding the southernmost Nansei islands because of the marked Oriental influence in their avifauna.

In the Bering Sea region the Komandor Islands are included and so is Ratmanova Island (or Big Diomede Island) in the Bering Strait. (The latter is included for purely administrative convenience since it is the last outpost of Russian territory: neither of the Diomede islands has any faunistic significance.)

In addition to the naturally occurring breeding species of the Palearctic region and peripheral regions, as defined above, the checklist includes all regular non-breeding visitors, vagrants, rare visitors and established introductions (including species that have escaped from captivity and established apparently viable breeding populations in the wild).

For the most part, the following references have been used to determine which species to include and their status:

Palearctic: Vaurie (1959a, 1965a)

Western Palearctic: Cramp (1985-1992), Cramp & Perrins (1993-1994), Cramp & Simmons (1977-1983).

North Africa and the Atlantic Islands: Anon. (1993), Brown *et al.* (1982), Duff (1979), Fry *et al.* (1988), Goodman & Meininger (1989), Hall & Moreau (1970), Hazevoet (in press), Hollom *et al.* (1988), Jepson & Zonfrillo (1988), Keith *et al.* (1992), Lamarche (1988), Nikolaus (1987), Snow (1978), Urban *et al.* (1986).

Arabia, Israel, Iran and Afghanistan: Ash *et al.* (1989), Bear (1991), Gallagher & Woodcock (1980), Hirschfeld & King (1992), Hollom *et al.* (1988), Hüe & Etchécopar (1970), Kirwan (1993), Niethammer & Niethammer (1967), Oman Bird Record Committee (1994), Paludan (1959), Richardson (1990, 1992), Shirihai (in press), Stagg (1992), Symens *et al.* (1994).

Indian subcontinent: Ali (1962), Ali & Ripley (1971-1987), Inskipp & Inskipp (1991), Martens & Eck (1991), Redman (1992), Ripley (1982), Roberts (1991, 1992).

Burma: Smythies (1986).

China and Tibet: Alström *et al.* (1992), Cheng (1987), Cheng *et al.* (1963), Meyer de Schauensee (1984), Roselaar (1992, 1994), Vaurie (1972).

Korea: Gore & Won (1971).

Japan: Brazil (1991), Ornithological Society of Japan (1974).

Former USSR: Stepanyan (1990).

Information about the reasons for including certain species can be found in the 'Notes on distributional status'. Information is also provided about species that were excluded for one reason or another: see 'Omitted species'. The great majority of extralimital vagrants have been recorded from the Western Palearctic or Japan, and details of occurrence are not usually given for vagrant species that have occurred in either or both these areas and which are included in Cramp *et al.* (1977-1994) or Brazil (1991).

ACKNOWLEDGEMENTS

I would like to sincerely thank the following for their many helpful comments on, and criticisms of, earlier drafts of this checklist, for their assistance in general and for their endless encouragement: P. Alström, W. R. P. Bourne, G. Carey, S. J. M. Gantlett, S. C. Harrap, T. P. Inskipp, K. Kaufman, P. R. Kennerley, B. King, A. G. Knox, H. B. Lee, I. Lewis, S. C. Madge, K. Mild, M. E. Morton, U. Olsson, N. J. Redman, C. Robson, D. A. Scott, J. T. R. Sharrock, L. Svennson, K. H. Voous, J. A. Wolstencroft and D. A. Zimmerman. I would also like to thank the following for their kind assistance and encouragement: P. Exley, M. Martin, R. P. Martins, B. Mercer, D. Mitchell, H. Shirihai, W. Suter, M. Van Beirs and P. Yésou.

KEY TO SYSTEMATIC LIST

Scientific names: an asterisk after the scientific name (or family name) signifies that an entry about the species (or family) can be found in the 'Taxonomic notes'.

Some species are given a status code after the scientific name, as follows:

V = vagrant or rare visitor
A = altitudinal wanderer (in the Himalayas or mountains of Yunnan and Sichuan)
NB = regular non-breeding visitor
I = introduced (and apparently established)
E = extinct
EP = extinct in the Palearctic

The category NB applies to a number of seabird species from outside the region that regularly oversummer in Palearctic waters (although often far offshore).

English names: An asterisk after the English name signifies that an explanation about the name selected can be found in the 'Notes on English names'.

Alternative English names are given a code as follows:

1 = names adopted by Sibley & Monroe (1990), or as modified in the '*Supplement*' (1993).
2 = names proposed by Inskipp & Sharrock (1992).
3 = names proposed by the British Ornithologists' Union when different from those proposed by *British Birds* in Inskipp & Sharrock (1992).
4 = names proposed by *British Birds* when different from those proposed by the British Ornithologists' Union in Inskipp & Sharrock (1992).

(Note: these codes are also employed, where appropriate, in the notes sections of this checklist.)

SYSTEMATIC LIST

Scientific Name	English Name	Alternative Name(s)
STRUTHIONIDAE		
Struthio camelus	Ostrich	
GAVIIDAE		
Gavia stellata	Red-throated Loon*	Red-throated Diver[2]
*Gavia arctica**	Black-throated Loon*	Arctic Loon[1], Arctic Diver[4], Black-throated Diver[3]
*Gavia pacifica**	Pacific Loon*	Pacific Diver
Gavia immer	Great Northern Loon*	Common Loon[1], Great Northern Diver[2]
*Gavia adamsii**	Yellow-billed Loon*	Yellow-billed Diver[2], White-billed Diver
PODICIPEDIDAE		
Podilymbus podiceps (V)	Pied-billed Grebe	
*Tachybaptus ruficollis**	Little Grebe	Dabchick
Podiceps cristatus	Great Crested Grebe	
Podiceps grisegena	Red-necked Grebe	
Podiceps auritus	Horned Grebe*	Slavonian Grebe[2]
Podiceps nigricollis	Black-necked Grebe*	Eared Grebe
DIOMEDEIDAE*		
Diomedea melanophris (V)	Black-browed Albatross	
Diomedea chlororhynchos (V)	Yellow-nosed Albatross	
Diomedea cauta (V)	Shy Albatross	White-capped Albatross
Diomedea nigripes	Black-footed Albatross	
Diomedea immutabilis	Laysan Albatross	
Diomedea albatrus	Short-tailed Albatross	
Diomedea exulans (V)	Wandering Albatross	

PROCELLARIIDAE		
Fulmarus glacialis	Northern Fulmar	Fulmar
Daption capense (V)	Cape Petrel	Pintado Petrel
Pterodroma neglecta (V)	Kermadec Petrel	
*Pterodroma feae**	Fea's Petrel*	Cape Verde Petrel[1], Gon-gon
*Pterodroma madeira**	Zino's Petrel*	Madeira Petrel[1], Freira
Pterodroma mollis (V)	Soft-plumaged Petrel	
Pterodroma inexpectata (NB)	Mottled Petrel	
Pterodroma solandri (NB)	Providence Petrel*	Solander's Petrel
Pterodroma incerta (V)	Atlantic Petrel*	Schlegel's Petrel[2]
Pterodroma hasitata (V)	Black-capped Petrel*	Capped Petrel[2]
Pterodroma hypoleuca	Bonin Petrel	
Pterodroma nigripennis (NB)	Black-winged Petrel	
*Pterodroma phaeopygia** (V)	Dark-rumped Petrel*	Hawaiian Petrel
incl. *sandwichensis* (V)	Hawaiian Petrel	
*Pterodroma cervicalis** (V)	White-necked Petrel	
Pterodroma longirostris (NB)	Stejneger's Petrel	
Bulweria bulwerii	Bulwer's Petrel	
*Bulweria fallax**	Jouanin's Petrel	
*Calonectris diomedea**	Cory's Shearwater	
incl. *edwardsii*	Cape Verde Shearwater	
*Calonectris leucomelas**	Streaked Shearwater	White-faced Shearwater
Puffinus carneipes (NB)	Flesh-footed Shearwater*	Pale-footed Shearwater[4]
Puffinus gravis (NB)	Great Shearwater	Greater Shearwater
Puffinus pacificus	Wedge-tailed Shearwater	
Puffinus bulleri (V)	Buller's Shearwater	New Zealand Shearwater
Puffinus griseus (NB)	Sooty Shearwater	
Puffinus tenuirostris (NB)	Short-tailed Shearwater	
Puffinus nativitatis (V)	Christmas Shearwater*	Christmas Island Shearwater[1]
Puffinus puffinus	Manx Shearwater	
*Puffinus yelkouan**	Mediterranean Shearwater*	Yelkouan Shearwater, Levantine Shearwater
incl. *mauretanicus*	Balearic Shearwater	
Puffinus assimilis	Little Shearwater	
*Puffinus lherminieri**	Audubon's Shearwater	
incl. *persicus*	Persian Shearwater	
incl. *bannermani*	Bannerman's Shearwater	
HYDROBATIDAE*		
Oceanites oceanicus (NB)	Wilson's Storm-petrel	Wilson's Petrel
Pelagodroma marina	White-faced Storm-petrel	White-faced Petrel, Frigate Petrel
Fregetta grallaria (V)	White-bellied Storm-petrel	
Fregetta tropica (NB)	Black-bellied Storm-petrel	
Hydrobates pelagicus	European Storm-petrel*	British Storm-petrel, Storm Petrel
Oceanodroma furcata	Fork-tailed Storm-petrel	

Oceanodroma leucorhoa	Leach's Storm-petrel	Leach's Petrel
*Oceanodroma monorhis**	Swinhoe's Storm-petrel	Swinhoe's Petrel
Oceanodroma castro	Madeiran Storm-petrel*	Band-rumped Storm-petrel[1], Harcourt's Storm-petrel, Madeiran Petrel
Oceanodroma matsudairae	Matsudaira's Storm-petrel	
*Oceanodroma tristrami**	Tristram's Storm-petrel	
PHAETHONTIDAE		
Phaethon aethereus	Red-billed Tropicbird	
Phaethon rubricauda	Red-tailed Tropicbird	
Phaethon lepturus (V)	White-tailed Tropicbird	
SULIDAE		
Sula sula	Red-footed Booby	
Sula dactylatra	Masked Booby	Blue-faced Booby
Sula leucogaster	Brown Booby	
*Morus capensis** (V)	Cape Gannet	
*Morus bassanus**	Northern Gannet	Gannet
PHALACROCORACIDAE		
*Phalacrocorax carbo**	Great Cormorant	Cormorant
incl. *lucidus*	White-breasted Cormorant	
Phalacrocorax capillatus	Temminck's Cormorant*	Japanese Cormorant[1]
Phalacrocorax perspicillatus (E)	Pallas's Cormorant	
Phalacrocorax pelagicus	Pelagic Cormorant	
Phalacrocorax urile	Red-faced Cormorant	
Phalacrocorax auritus (V)	Double-crested Cormorant	
Phalacrocorax aristotelis	European Shag	Shag
Phalacrocorax nigrogularis	Socotra Cormorant	
*Phalacrocorax pygmeus**	Pygmy Cormorant	
Phalacrocorax africanus	Long-tailed Cormorant*	Reed Cormorant
ANHINGIDAE		
*Anhinga rufa**	African Darter*	Darter[2]
PELECANIDAE		
Pelecanus onocrotalus	Great White Pelican*	Eastern White Pelican, White Pelican, Rosy Pelican
*Pelecanus crispus**	Dalmatian Pelican	
Pelecanus rufescens	Pink-backed Pelican	

FREGATIDAE

Fregata minor (V)	Great Frigatebird	Greater Frigatebird
Fregata magnificens	Magnificent Frigatebird	
Fregata ariel (V)	Lesser Frigatebird	Least Frigatebird

ARDEIDAE

Botaurus stellaris	Great Bittern*	Eurasian Bittern, Bittern
Botaurus lentiginosus (V)	American Bittern	
Ixobrychus exilis (V)	Least Bittern	
Ixobrychus minutus	Little Bittern	
Ixobrychus sinensis	Yellow Bittern	Chinese Little Bittern
Ixobrychus eurhythmus	Schrenck's Bittern	Schrenck's Little Bittern
Ixobrychus cinnamomeus	Cinnamon Bittern	Chestnut Bittern
*Ixobrychus sturmii** (V)	Dwarf Bittern	
*Dupetor flavicollis** (V)	Black Bittern	
Gorsachius melanolophus	Malayan Night Heron	
Gorsachius goisagi	Japanese Night Heron	
Nycticorax nycticorax	Black-crowned Night Heron	Night Heron
Nycticorax caledonicus (EP)	Rufous Night Heron	
Butorides striatus	Striated Heron*	Green-backed Heron, Little Green Heron, Little Heron
*Butorides virescens** (V)	Green Heron	
*Bubulcus ibis**	Cattle Egret*	
incl. *coromanda*	Eastern Cattle Egret	
Ardeola ralloides	Squacco Heron	
Ardeola grayii	Indian Pond Heron	
Ardeola bacchus	Chinese Pond Heron	
*Egretta caerulea** (V)	Little Blue Heron	
*Egretta tricolor** (V)	Tricolored Heron	Louisiana Heron
*Egretta ardesiaca** (V)	Black Heron*	Black Egret
Egretta thula (V)	Snowy Egret	
Egretta eulophotes	Chinese Egret	Swinhoe's Egret
Egretta sacra	Pacific Reef Egret	Eastern Reef Heron
*Egretta gularis**	Western Reef Egret*	Western Reef Heron
Egretta garzetta	Little Egret	
*Egretta intermedia**	Intermediate Egret*	Yellow-billed Egret, Plumed Egret
*Egretta alba**	Great Egret*	Great White Egret
*Ardea cinerea**	Grey Heron	Heron
incl. *monicae*	Mauritanian Heron	
*Ardea herodias** (V)	Great Blue Heron	
Ardea melanocephala (V)	Black-headed Heron	
*Ardea purpurea**	Purple Heron	
incl. *bournei*	Bourne's Heron	
Ardea goliath	Goliath Heron	

SCOPIDAE

Scopus umbretta	Hamerkop*	Hammerkop

CICONIIDAE

Mycteria leucocephala (V)	Painted Stork	
Mycteria ibis (V)	Yellow-billed Stork	
Ciconia nigra	Black Stork	
Ciconia abdimii	Abdim's Stork	
Ciconia episcopus (V)	Woolly-necked Stork	White-necked Stork
Ciconia ciconia	White Stork	
*Ciconia boyciana**	Oriental Stork*	Oriental White Stork
Leptoptilos crumeniferus (V)	Marabou Stork	Marabou

THRESKIORNITHIDAE

Plegadis falcinellus	Glossy Ibis	
Geronticus eremita	Northern Bald Ibis*	Waldrapp[1], Hermit Ibis[4], Bald Ibis
Nipponia nippon (EP)	Crested Ibis	Japanese Crested Ibis
Threskiornis aethiopicus	Sacred Ibis	
*Threskiornis melanocephalus**	Black-headed Ibis	White Ibis
Platalea leucorodia	Eurasian Spoonbill	White Spoonbill, Spoonbill
Platalea minor	Black-faced Spoonbill	
Platalea alba (V)	African Spoonbill	

PHOENICOPTERIDAE

*Phoenicopterus ruber**	Greater Flamingo*	American Flamingo
incl. *roseus*	Greater Flamingo	Rosy Flamingo
*Phoenicopterus minor** (V)	Lesser Flamingo	

ANATIDAE

*Dendrocygna bicolor** (V)	Fulvous Whistling Duck	Fulvous Tree Duck
*Dendrocygna javanica** (EP/V)	Lesser Whistling Duck	Lesser Tree Duck
*Dendrocygna viduata** (V)	White-faced Whistling Duck	White-faced Tree Duck
Cygnus olor	Mute Swan	
Cygnus atratus (I)	Black Swan	
*Cygnus columbianus**	Tundra Swan*	Whistling Swan, Bewick's Swan
incl. *bewickii*	Bewick's Swan	
Cygnus cygnus	Whooper Swan	
*Cygnus buccinator** (V)	Trumpeter Swan	
*Anser cygnoides**	Swan Goose	
Anser fabalis	Bean Goose	
*Anser brachyrhynchus**	Pink-footed Goose	

Anser albifrons	Greater White-fronted Goose	White-fronted Goose
Anser erythropus	Lesser White-fronted Goose	
Anser anser	Greylag Goose	
*Anser indicus**	Bar-headed Goose	
*Anser caerulescens**	Snow Goose	Blue Goose (blue morph)
*Anser rossii** (V)	Ross's Goose	
*Anser canagica**	Emperor Goose	
*Branta canadensis** (I/V)	Canada Goose	
incl. *hutchinsii*	Hutchins's Goose	
Branta leucopsis	Barnacle Goose	
*Branta bernicla**	Brent Goose*	Brant
incl. *nigricans*	Black Brant	
*Branta ruficollis**	Red-breasted Goose	
Alopochen aegyptiacus	Egyptian Goose	
Tadorna ferruginea	Ruddy Shelduck	
Tadorna cristata (E?)	Crested Shelduck	
Tadorna tadorna	Common Shelduck	Shelduck
Plectropterus gambensis (V)	Spur-winged Goose	
Sarkidiornis melanotos (V)	Comb Duck	Knob-billed Duck
Nettapus coromandelianus (V)	Cotton Pygmy-goose	Cotton Teal
Aix sponsa (V)	Wood Duck	
Aix galericulata	Mandarin Duck	Mandarin
Anas penelope	Eurasian Wigeon	Wigeon
Anas americana (V)	American Wigeon	
Anas falcata	Falcated Duck	Falcated Teal
Anas strepera	Gadwall	
Anas formosa	Baikal Teal	
*Anas crecca**	Common Teal*	Green-winged Teal, Teal
incl. *carolinensis* (V)	Green-winged Teal	
Anas capensis (V)	Cape Teal	
Anas platyrhynchos	Mallard	
*Anas rubripes** (V)	American Black Duck	Black Duck
*Anas poecilorhyncha**	Spot-billed Duck*	Spotbill Duck
incl. *zonorhyncha*	Eastern Spot-billed Duck	
Anas luzonica (V)	Philippine Duck	
Anas acuta	Northern Pintail	Common Pintail, Pintail
Anas erythrorhyncha (V)	Red-billed Teal*	Red-billed Duck[1,2]
Anas querquedula	Garganey	
Anas discors (V)	Blue-winged Teal	
Anas smithii (V)	Cape Shoveler	
Anas clypeata	Northern Shoveler	Shoveler
*Marmaronetta angustirostris**	Marbled Duck*	Marbled Teal[1]
Netta rufina	Red-crested Pochard	
Aythya valisineria (V)	Canvasback	
Aythya ferina	Common Pochard	Pochard
Aythya americana (V)	Redhead	

Aythya collaris (V)	Ring-necked Duck	
Aythya baeri	Baer's Pochard	
Aythya nyroca	Ferruginous Duck*	Ferruginous Pochard[1], White-eyed Pochard
Aythya fuligula	Tufted Duck	
Aythya marila	Greater Scaup	Scaup
Aythya affinis (V)	Lesser Scaup	
Somateria mollissima	Common Eider	Eider
Somateria spectabilis	King Eider	
Somateria fischeri	Spectacled Eider	
Polysticta stelleri	Steller's Eider	
Histrionicus histrionicus	Harlequin Duck	Harlequin
Clangula hyemalis	Long-tailed Duck*	Oldsquaw
*Melanitta nigra**	Common Scoter*	Black Scoter[1,2]
incl. *americana*	Black Scoter	American Scoter[1]
Melanitta perspicillata	Surf Scoter	
*Melanitta fusca**	Velvet Scoter*	White-winged Scoter[1]
incl. *deglandi*	White-winged Scoter	
Bucephala albeola (V)	Bufflehead	
Bucephala islandica	Barrow's Goldeneye	
Bucephala clangula	Common Goldeneye	Goldeneye
*Lophodytes cucullatus** (V)	Hooded Merganser	
*Mergellus albellus**	Smew	
Mergus serrator	Red-breasted Merganser	
Mergus squamatus	Scaly-sided Merganser	Chinese Merganser
Mergus merganser	Goosander*	Common Merganser[1]
Oxyura jamaicensis (I)	Ruddy Duck	
Oxyura leucocephala	White-headed Duck	

ACCIPITRIDAE

Pernis apivorus	European Honey Buzzard*	Eurasian Honey Buzzard, Honey Buzzard
*Pernis ptilorhyncus**	Crested Honey Buzzard*	Oriental Honey Buzzard[1]
Elanus caeruleus	Black-winged Kite*	Black-shouldered Kite[2]
Chelictinia riocourii (V)	African Swallow-tailed Kite*	Scissor-tailed Kite[1], Swallow-tailed Kite
*Milvus migrans**	Black Kite	
incl. *lineatus*	Black-eared Kite	
incl. *aegyptius*	Yellow-billed Kite	
*Milvus milvus**	Red Kite	
Haliastur indus (V)	Brahminy Kite	
Haliaeetus vocifer (V)	African Fish Eagle	
Haliaeetus leucoryphus	Pallas's Fish Eagle*	Pallas's Sea Eagle[1]
Haliaeetus albicilla	White-tailed Eagle	
Haliaeetus leucocephalus (EP/V)	Bald Eagle	

*Haliaeetus pelagicus**	Steller's Sea Eagle	
Gypaetus barbatus	Lammergeier	Lammergeyer, Bearded Vulture
Neophron percnopterus	Egyptian Vulture	
Necrosyrtes monachus (V)	Hooded Vulture	
*Gyps bengalensis**	Indian White-backed Vulture*	White-rumped Vulture[1]
Gyps fulvus	Eurasian Griffon Vulture*	Eurasian Griffon[1], Griffon Vulture
*Gyps himalayensis**	Himalayan Griffon Vulture*	Himalayan Griffon[1]
Gyps rueppellii (V)	Rüppell's Griffon Vulture*	Rueppell's Griffon[1], Rüppell's Vulture
Sarcogyps calvus (A)	Red-headed Vulture	Indian Black Vulture
Torgos tracheliotus	Lappet-faced Vulture	
Aegypius monachus	Eurasian Black Vulture*	Cinereous Vulture[1,3], Monk Vulture[4], Black Vulture
*Circaetus gallicus**	Short-toed Eagle*	Short-toed Snake Eagle[1,2], Black-breasted Snake Eagle
Terathopius ecaudatus	Bateleur	
*Spilornis cheela**	Crested Serpent Eagle	
incl. *perplexus*	Ryukyu Serpent Eagle	
Circus aeruginosus	Western Marsh Harrier*	Eurasian Marsh Harrier[2], Marsh Harrier
*Circus spilonotus**	Eastern Marsh Harrier	
Circus cyaneus	Hen Harrier*	Northern Harrier[1]
Circus macrourus	Pallid Harrier	
Circus pygargus	Montagu's Harrier	
*Circus melanoleucos**	Pied Harrier	
Melierax metabates	Dark Chanting Goshawk	
*Micronisus gabar** (V)	Gabar Goshawk	
Accipiter gentilis	Northern Goshawk	Goshawk
Accipiter virgatus	Besra	Besra Sparrowhawk
*Accipiter gularis**	Japanese Sparrowhawk	
Accipiter nisus	Eurasian Sparrowhawk	Sparrowhawk
Accipiter soloensis	Chinese Goshawk	Horsfield's Sparrowhawk
Accipiter badius	Shikra	Little Banded Goshawk
*Accipiter brevipes**	Levant Sparrowhawk	
Butastur teesa	White-eyed Buzzard	
Butastur indicus	Grey-faced Buzzard	
Buteo swainsoni (V)	Swainson's Hawk*	Swainson's Buzzard[4]
Buteo buteo	Common Buzzard	Buzzard
*Buteo rufinus**	Long-legged Buzzard	
*Buteo hemilasius**	Upland Buzzard	
Buteo lagopus	Rough-legged Buzzard*	Rough-legged Hawk[1]
Ictinaetus malayensis	Black Eagle	
Aquila pomarina	Lesser Spotted Eagle	
Aquila clanga	Greater Spotted Eagle	Spotted Eagle
*Aquila nipalensis**	Steppe Eagle	

*Aquila rapax**	Tawny Eagle*	
incl. *vindhiana*	Asian Tawny Eagle	
*Aquila heliaca**	Imperial Eagle*	
incl. *adalberti*	Spanish Imperial Eagle*	Adalbert's Eagle[1]
Aquila chrysaetos	Golden Eagle	
Aquila verreauxii	Verreaux's Eagle*	Black Eagle
*Hieraaetus pennatus**	Booted Eagle	
*Hieraaetus fasciatus**	Bonelli's Eagle	
Spizaetus nipalensis	Mountain Hawk Eagle	Hodgson's Hawk Eagle

PANDIONIDAE*

Pandion haliaetus	Osprey	

FALCONIDAE

Falco naumanni	Lesser Kestrel	
Falco tinnunculus	Common Kestrel	Eurasian Kestrel, Kestrel
Falco sparverius (V)	American Kestrel	
Falco chicquera	Red-necked Falcon	Red-headed Merlin
Falco vespertinus	Red-footed Falcon	Western Red-footed Falcon
*Falco amurensis**	Amur Falcon	Manchurian Red-footed Falcon, Eastern Red-footed Falcon
Falco columbarius	Merlin	
Falco subbuteo	Eurasian Hobby*	Northern Hobby, Hobby
Falco eleonorae	Eleonora's Falcon	
Falco concolor	Sooty Falcon	
Falco biarmicus	Lanner Falcon	Lanner
*Falco jugger**	Laggar Falcon	Laggar
*Falco cherrug**	Saker Falcon	Saker
incl. *altaicus*	Altai Falcon	
Falco rusticolus	Gyr Falcon*	Gyrfalcon[1]
Falco peregrinus	Peregrine Falcon	Peregrine
*Falco pelegrinoides**	Barbary Falcon	

TETRAONIDAE*

*Dendragapus falcipennis**	Siberian Grouse*	Siberian Spruce Grouse
*Bonasa bonasia**	Hazel Grouse	
*Bonasa sewerzowi**	Severtzov's Grouse*	Chinese Grouse[1]
*Lagopus lagopus**	Willow Ptarmigan*	Willow Grouse, Red Grouse
incl. *scoticus*	Red Grouse	
Lagopus mutus	Rock Ptarmigan*	Ptarmigan
*Tetrao tetrix**	Black Grouse	
*Tetrao mlokosiewiczi**	Caucasian Grouse*	Caucasian Black Grouse

Tetrao parvirostris	Black-billed Capercaillie	
Tetrao urogallus	Western Capercaillie	Capercaillie

PHASIANIDAE

*Callipepla californica** (I)	California Quail	
*Colinus virginianus** (I)	Northern Bobwhite	Bobwhite Quail, Bobwhite
Lerwa lerwa	Snow Partridge	
Tetraophasis obscurus	Verreaux's Monal Partridge*	Chestnut-throated Partridge[1], Verreaux's Pheasant Partridge
*Tetraophasis szechenyii**	Széchenyi's Monal Partridge*	Buff-throated Partridge[1], Széchenyi's Pheasant Partridge
Tetraogallus caucasicus	Caucasian Snowcock	
Tetraogallus caspius	Caspian Snowcock	
Tetraogallus himalayensis	Himalayan Snowcock	
Tetraogallus tibetanus	Tibetan Snowcock	
Tetraogallus altaicus	Altai Snowcock	
*Alectoris chukar**	Chukar*	Chukar Partridge[4], Chukor Partridge
*Alectoris magna**	Przevalski's Partridge*	Rusty-necklaced Partridge[1], Przevalski's Rock Partridge
Alectoris graeca	Rock Partridge	
Alectoris rufa	Red-legged Partridge	
Alectoris barbara	Barbary Partridge	
*Alectoris philbyi**	Philby's Partridge	Philby's Rock Partridge
Alectoris melanocephala	Arabian Partridge	Arabian Red-legged Partridge
Ammoperdix griseogularis	See-see Partridge*	See-see
Ammoperdix heyi	Sand Partridge	
Francolinus francolinus	Black Francolin	Black Partridge
Francolinus pondicerianus	Grey Francolin	Grey Partridge
Francolinus bicalcaratus	Double-spurred Francolin	
Perdix perdix	Grey Partridge	Common Partridge, Partridge
*Perdix dauurica**	Daurian Partridge	
Perdix hodgsoniae	Tibetan Partridge	
Coturnix coturnix	Common Quail	Quail
*Coturnix japonica**	Japanese Quail	
Coturnix delegorguei	Harlequin Quail	
Arborophila torqueola	Hill Partridge	Common Hill Partridge
Bambusicola thoracica (I)	Chinese Bamboo Partridge	Bamboo Partridge
Ithaginis cruentus	Blood Pheasant	
Tragopan melanocephalus	Western Tragopan	
Tragopan satyra	Satyr Tragopan	Crimson Tragopan
Tragopan blythii	Blyth's Tragopan	Grey-bellied Tragopan
Tragopan temminckii	Temminck's Tragopan	
Pucrasia macrolopha	Koklass Pheasant	
Lophophorus impejanus	Himalayan Monal	Impeyan Pheasant
Lophophorus sclateri	Sclater's Monal	

Lophophorus lhuysii	Chinese Monal	
*Lophura leucomelanos**	Kalij Pheasant	
Crossoptilon crossoptilon	White Eared Pheasant	
*Crossoptilon harmani**	Tibetan Eared Pheasant	Elwes's Eared Pheasant
Crossoptilon mantchuricum	Brown Eared Pheasant	
Crossoptilon auritum	Blue Eared Pheasant	
Catreus wallichii	Cheer Pheasant	
Syrmaticus soemmerringii	Copper Pheasant	
Syrmaticus reevesii	Reeves's Pheasant	
*Phasianus colchicus**	Common Pheasant*	Ring-necked Pheasant, Pheasant
incl. *versicolor*	Green Pheasant	Japanese Pheasant
Chrysolophus pictus	Golden Pheasant	
Chrysolophus amherstiae	Lady Amherst's Pheasant	

NUMIDIDAE

Numida meleagris	Helmeted Guineafowl	

MELEAGRIDIDAE*

Meleagris gallopavo (I)	Wild Turkey	

TURNICIDAE

Turnix sylvatica	Small Button-quail*	Little Button-quail, Kurrichane Button-quail, Andalusian Hemipode
Turnix tanki	Yellow-legged Button-quail	
Turnix suscitator	Barred Button-quail	

RALLIDAE

Rallina eurizonoides	Slaty-legged Crake	Banded Crake
*Gallirallus okinawae**	Okinawa Rail	
*Gallirallus striatus** (V)	Slaty-breasted Rail	Blue-breasted Banded Rail
Rallus aquaticus	Water Rail	
Porzana porzana	Spotted Crake	
Porzana carolina (V)	Sora*	Sora Crake[4], Sora Rail
Porzana parva	Little Crake	
Porzana pusilla	Baillon's Crake	
Porzana cinerea (EP)	White-browed Crake	Ashy Crake
Porzana fusca	Ruddy-breasted Crake	Ruddy Crake
Porzana paykullii	Band-bellied Crake	Siberian Ruddy Crake
*Porzana bicolor**	Black-tailed Crake	Elwes's Crake
*Aenigmatolimnas marginalis** (V)	Striped Crake	

*Coturnicops exquisitus**	Swinhoe's Rail*	Swinhoe's Yellow Rail, Asian Yellow Rail
Crex crex	Corn Crake*	Corncrake
Amaurornis akool (A)	Brown Crake	
Amaurornis phoenicurus	White-breasted Waterhen	
*Amaurornis flavirostra** (V)	Black Crake	
Gallinula chloropus	Common Moorhen	Common Gallinule, Moorhen
Gallinula angulata (V)	Lesser Moorhen	
*Porphyrula alleni** (V)	Allen's Gallinule	Lesser Gallinule
*Porphyrula martinica** (V)	Purple Gallinule*	American Purple Gallinule[4]
*Porphyrio porphyrio**	Purple Swamp-hen*	Purple Gallinule
Gallicrex cinerea	Watercock	
Fulica atra	Eurasian Coot*	Common Coot[1,2], European Coot, Coot
Fulica americana (V)	American Coot	
Fulica cristata	Red-knobbed Coot*	Crested Coot
GRUIDAE		
Grus grus	Common Crane	Crane
Grus nigricollis	Black-necked Crane	
Grus monacha	Hooded Crane	
Grus canadensis	Sandhill Crane	
Grus vipio	White-naped Crane	White-necked Crane
Grus japonensis	Red-crowned Crane*	Japanese Crane, Manchurian Crane
Grus leucogeranus	Siberian Crane*	Siberian White Crane
*Anthropoides virgo**	Demoiselle Crane	
OTIDIDAE		
*Tetrax tetrax**	Little Bustard	
Neotis denhami (V)	Denham's Bustard*	Stanley Bustard[1]
Neotis nuba	Nubian Bustard	
Chlamydotis undulata	Houbara Bustard*	Houbara
Ardeotis arabs	Arabian Bustard	
Otis tarda	Great Bustard	
JACANIDAE		
Hydrophasianus chirurgus (V)	Pheasant-tailed Jacana	
ROSTRATULIDAE		
Rostratula benghalensis	Greater Painted-snipe*	Painted Snipe

HAEMATOPODIDAE*		
Haematopus ostralegus	Eurasian Oystercatcher	Common Oystercatcher, Oystercatcher
*Haematopus meadewaldoi** (E?)	Canary Islands Oystercatcher*	Canary Oystercatcher
IBIDORHYNCHIDAE*		
Ibidorhyncha struthersii	Ibisbill	
RECURVIROSTRIDAE*		
*Himantopus himantopus**	Black-winged Stilt	
incl. *leucocephalus* (V)	White-headed Stilt	
Recurvirostra avosetta	Pied Avocet	Avocet
DROMADIDAE*		
Dromas ardeola	Crab-plover*	Crab Plover[1]
BURHINIDAE		
Burhinus oedicnemus	Stone-curlew*	Eurasian Thick-knee[1,4], Northern Thick-knee, Stone Curlew
Burhinus senegalensis	Senegal Thick-knee	
Burhinus capensis	Spotted Thick-knee	Spotted Dikkop
*Esacus recurvirostris**	Great Thick-knee	Great Stone Plover
GLAREOLIDAE		
Pluvianus aegyptius (EP?)	Egyptian Plover*	Crocodile Bird[1], Egyptian Courser[2]
Cursorius cursor	Cream-coloured Courser	
Glareola pratincola	Collared Pratincole	Pratincole
*Glareola maldivarum**	Oriental Pratincole	Eastern Collared Pratincole
*Glareola nordmanni**	Black-winged Pratincole	
Glareola lactea (V)	Small Pratincole	Little Pratincole
CHARADRIIDAE		
Charadrius dubius	Little Ringed Plover*	Little Plover[3]
Charadrius hiaticula	Common Ringed Plover*	Ringed Plover[3], Great Ringed Plover[4]
*Charadrius semipalmatus** (V)	Semipalmated Plover	
*Charadrius placidus**	Long-billed Plover	
Charadrius vociferus (V)	Killdeer*	Killdeer Plover[4]
Charadrius pecuarius	Kittlitz's Plover	Kittlitz's Sand Plover

Charadrius tricollaris (V)	Three-banded Plover	
Charadrius alexandrinus	Kentish Plover*	Snowy Plover
Charadrius mongolus	Lesser Sand Plover*	Mongolian Plover[1]
Charadrius leschenaultii	Greater Sand Plover	Large Sand Plover
Charadrius asiaticus	Caspian Plover	
*Charadrius veredus**	Oriental Plover	
*Charadrius morinellus**	Eurasian Dotterel*	Mountain Dotterel[4], Dotterel
*Pluvialis dominica** (V)	American Golden Plover*	Lesser Golden Plover
*Pluvialis fulva**	Pacific Golden Plover	
Pluvialis apricaria	European Golden Plover*	Eurasian Golden Plover[1], Greater Golden Plover, Golden Plover
Pluvialis squatarola	Grey Plover*	Black-bellied Plover
*Vanellus spinosus**	Spur-winged Lapwing*	Spur-winged Plover
*Vanellus tectus** (V)	Black-headed Lapwing*	Black-headed Plover
*Vanellus cinereus**	Grey-headed Lapwing*	Grey-headed Plover
*Vanellus indicus**	Red-wattled Lapwing*	Red-wattled Plover
*Vanellus gregarius**	Sociable Lapwing*	Sociable Plover
*Vanellus leucurus**	White-tailed Lapwing*	White-tailed Plover
Vanellus vanellus	Northern Lapwing	Lapwing

SCOLOPACIDAE

Calidris tenuirostris	Great Knot	
Calidris canutus	Red Knot	Knot
*Calidris alba**	Sanderling	
Calidris pusilla (V)	Semipalmated Sandpiper	
Calidris mauri	Western Sandpiper	
Calidris ruficollis	Red-necked Stint*	Rufous-necked Stint[1]
Calidris minuta	Little Stint	
Calidris temminckii	Temminck's Stint	
*Calidris subminuta**	Long-toed Stint	
Calidris minutilla (V)	Least Sandpiper	
Calidris fuscicollis (V)	White-rumped Sandpiper	
Calidris bairdii	Baird's Sandpiper	
Calidris melanotos	Pectoral Sandpiper	
Calidris acuminata	Sharp-tailed Sandpiper	
Calidris ferruginea	Curlew Sandpiper	
Calidris maritima	Purple Sandpiper	
*Calidris ptilocnemis**	Rock Sandpiper	
Calidris alpina	Dunlin	
Eurynorhynchus pygmeus	Spoon-billed Sandpiper*	Spoonbill Sandpiper[1,2]
Limicola falcinellus	Broad-billed Sandpiper	
Micropalama himantopus (V)	Stilt Sandpiper	
Tryngites subruficollis	Buff-breasted Sandpiper	
Philomachus pugnax	Ruff	

Lymnocryptes minimus	Jack Snipe	
*Gallinago gallinago**	Common Snipe	Snipe
Gallinago media	Great Snipe	
*Gallinago stenura**	Pintail Snipe*	Pin-tailed Snipe
*Gallinago megala**	Swinhoe's Snipe	
*Gallinago hardwickii**	Latham's Snipe	
*Gallinago solitaria**	Solitary Snipe	
*Gallinago nemoricola**	Wood Snipe	
Limnodromus griseus (V)	Short-billed Dowitcher	
*Limnodromus scolopaceus**	Long-billed Dowitcher	
Limnodromus semipalmatus	Asian Dowitcher*	Asiatic Dowitcher
Scolopax rusticola	Eurasian Woodcock	Woodcock
*Scolopax mira**	Amami Woodcock	
Limosa limosa	Black-tailed Godwit	
Limosa haemastica (V)	Hudsonian Godwit	
Limosa lapponica	Bar-tailed Godwit	
*Numenius minutus**	Little Curlew*	Little Whimbrel
Numenius borealis (V)	Eskimo Curlew	
Numenius phaeopus	Whimbrel	
Numenius tahitiensis (V)	Bristle-thighed Curlew	
Numenius tenuirostris	Slender-billed Curlew	
Numenius arquata	Eurasian Curlew*	European Curlew, Western Curlew, Curlew
Numenius madagascariensis	Far Eastern Curlew*	Eastern Curlew
Bartramia longicauda (V)	Upland Sandpiper	Upland Plover
Tringa erythropus	Spotted Redshank	
Tringa totanus	Common Redshank	Redshank
Tringa stagnatilis	Marsh Sandpiper	
Tringa nebularia	Common Greenshank	Greenshank
Tringa guttifer	Nordmann's Greenshank	Spotted Greenshank
Tringa melanoleuca (V)	Greater Yellowlegs	
Tringa flavipes (V)	Lesser Yellowlegs	
Tringa solitaria (V)	Solitary Sandpiper	
Tringa ochropus	Green Sandpiper	
Tringa glareola	Wood Sandpiper	
*Xenus cinereus**	Terek Sandpiper	
*Actitis hypoleucos**	Common Sandpiper	
*Actitis macularia** (V)	Spotted Sandpiper	
*Heteroscelus brevipes**	Grey-tailed Tattler	Grey-rumped Tattler, Grey-rumped Sandpiper
*Heteroscelus incanus**	Wandering Tattler	
Catoptrophorus semipalmatus (V)	Willet	
Arenaria interpres	Ruddy Turnstone	Turnstone
*Steganopus tricolor** (V)	Wilson's Phalarope	
Phalaropus lobatus	Red-necked Phalarope	Northern Phalarope
*Phalaropus fulicaria**	Red Phalarope*	Grey Phalarope[2]

STERCORARIIDAE*		
Stercorarius pomarinus	Pomarine Jaeger*	Pomarine Skua[2]
Stercorarius parasiticus	Parasitic Jaeger*	Arctic Skua[3], Parasitic Skua[4], Arctic Jaeger
Stercorarius longicaudus	Long-tailed Jaeger*	Long-tailed Skua[2]
*Catharacta skua**	Great Skua	
*Catharacta antarctica** (V)	Southern Skua*	Antarctic Skua
incl. *lonnbergi* (V)	Brown Skua	
*Catharacta maccormicki** (NB)	South Polar Skua*	McCormick's Skua
LARIDAE		
Larus hemprichii	Sooty Gull	Hemprich's Gull
Larus leucophthalmus	White-eyed Gull	
Larus ichthyaetus	Pallas's Gull*	Great Black-headed Gull[1]
*Larus relictus**	Relict Gull	Central Asian Gull
Larus melanocephalus	Mediterranean Gull	
Larus atricilla (V)	Laughing Gull	
Larus pipixcan (V)	Franklin's Gull	
Larus minutus	Little Gull	
*Larus sabini**	Sabine's Gull	
Larus saundersi	Saunders's Gull	
Larus philadelphia (V)	Bonaparte's Gull	
Larus ridibundus	Black-headed Gull*	Common Black-headed Gull[1]
Larus brunnicephalus	Brown-headed Gull	
Larus cirrocephalus	Grey-headed Gull	Grey-hooded Gull
Larus genei	Slender-billed Gull	
Larus crassirostris	Black-tailed Gull	
Larus audouinii	Audouin's Gull	
Larus delawarensis (V)	Ring-billed Gull	
*Larus canus**	Mew Gull*	Common Gull
incl. *kamtschatschensis*	Kamchatka Gull	
*Larus fuscus**	Lesser Black-backed Gull	
Larus argentatus	Herring Gull	
*Larus cachinnans**	Yellow-legged Gull	
*Larus armenicus**	Armenian Gull	
*Larus heuglini**	Heuglin's Gull*	Siberian Gull
incl. *vegae*	Vega Gull	
*Larus schistisagus**	Slaty-backed Gull	
*Larus glaucescens**	Glaucous-winged Gull	
*Larus glaucoides**	Iceland Gull	
incl. *kumlieni* (V)	Kumlien's Gull	
incl. *thayeri* (V)	Thayer's Gull	
Larus hyperboreus	Glaucous Gull	
Larus marinus	Great Black-backed Gull	

Rhodostethia rosea	Ross's Gull	
Rissa tridactyla	Black-legged Kittiwake	Kittiwake
Rissa brevirostris	Red-legged Kittiwake	
Pagophila eburnea	Ivory Gull	
STERNIDAE*		
*Sterna nilotica**	Gull-billed Tern	
*Sterna caspia**	Caspian Tern	
Sterna maxima	Royal Tern	
*Sterna bergii**	Greater Crested Tern*	Great Crested Tern[1], Crested Tern, Swift Tern
*Sterna bengalensis**	Lesser Crested Tern	
*Sterna bernsteini**	Chinese Crested Tern	
*Sterna sandvicensis**	Sandwich Tern	
Sterna elegans (V)	Elegant Tern	
Sterna sumatrana	Black-naped Tern	
Sterna dougallii	Roseate Tern	
Sterna hirundo	Common Tern	
Sterna paradisaea	Arctic Tern	
Sterna aleutica	Aleutian Tern	
Sterna forsteri (V)	Forster's Tern	
Sterna repressa	White-cheeked Tern	
Sterna lunata	Grey-backed Tern*	Spectacled Tern
Sterna anaethetus	Bridled Tern	
Sterna fuscata	Sooty Tern	
*Sterna albifrons**	Little Tern	
incl. *saundersi*	Saunders's Tern	Saunders's Little Tern
Chlidonias hybridus	Whiskered Tern	
Chlidonias niger	Black Tern	
Chlidonias leucopterus	White-winged Tern*	White-winged Black Tern
Procelsterna cerulea (V)	Blue-grey Noddy	Blue Noddy
*Anous minutus**	Black Noddy	White-capped Noddy
Anous tenuirostris (NB)	Lesser Noddy*	Black Noddy
Anous stolidus	Brown Noddy	Common Noddy
Gygis *alba* (V)	White Tern*	Common White Tern[1], Fairy Tern
RYNCHOPIDAE*		
Rynchops flavirostris (V)	African Skimmer	
Rynchops albicollis (V)	Indian Skimmer	

ALCIDAE*		
Uria aalge	Common Murre*	Common Guillemot[2], Guillemot
Uria lomvia	Brünnich's Murre*	Thick-billed Murre[1], Brünnich's Guillemot[2]
Alca torda	Razorbill	
Pinguinus impennis (E)	Great Auk	
Cepphus grylle	Black Guillemot	
*Cepphus columba**	Pigeon Guillemot	
Cepphus carbo	Spectacled Guillemot	
*Brachyramphus marmoratus**	Marbled Murrelet	
incl. *perdix*	Long-billed Murrelet	
Brachyramphus brevirostris	Kittlitz's Murrelet	
Synthliboramphus antiquus	Ancient Murrelet	
Synthliboramphus wumizusume	Japanese Murrelet	
*Alle alle**	Little Auk*	Dovekie[1]
Ptychoramphus aleuticus (V)	Cassin's Auklet	
Aethia cristatella	Crested Auklet	
Aethia pygmaea	Whiskered Auklet	
Aethia pusilla	Least Auklet	
Cyclorrhynchus psittacula	Parakeet Auklet	
Cerorhinca monocerata	Rhinoceros Auklet	
Fratercula arctica	Atlantic Puffin	Puffin
Fratercula corniculata	Horned Puffin	
*Lunda cirrhata**	Tufted Puffin	
PTEROCLIDAE*		
*Pterocles lichtensteinii**	Lichtenstein's Sandgrouse	
Pterocles coronatus	Crowned Sandgrouse	Coronetted Sandgrouse
Pterocles senegallus	Spotted Sandgrouse	
Pterocles exustus	Chestnut-bellied Sandgrouse	
Pterocles orientalis	Black-bellied Sandgrouse	
Pterocles alchata	Pin-tailed Sandgrouse	
Syrrhaptes paradoxus	Pallas's Sandgrouse	
Syrrhaptes tibetanus	Tibetan Sandgrouse	
COLUMBIDAE		
Columba livia	Rock Dove*	Rock Pigeon[1,2]
Columba rupestris	Hill Pigeon	Blue Hill Pigeon
Columba leuconota	Snow Pigeon	
Columba oenas	Stock Dove*	Stock Pigeon[1,2]
Columba eversmanni	Yellow-eyed Dove*	Pale-backed Pigeon[1], Yellow-eyed Pigeon[2], Yellow-eyed Stock Dove
Columba palumbus	Common Wood Pigeon	Wood Pigeon

Columba trocaz	Trocaz Pigeon*	Long-toed Pigeon
*Columba bollii**	Bolle's Pigeon	Bolle's Laurel Pigeon
Columba junoniae	Laurel Pigeon	
Columba arquatrix	African Olive Pigeon	Rameron Pigeon, Olive Pigeon
Columba hodgsonii	Speckled Wood Pigeon	
Columba pulchricollis	Ashy Wood Pigeon	
Columba janthina	Japanese Wood Pigeon	
Columba versicolor (E)	Bonin Wood Pigeon	
Columba jouyi (E)	Ryukyu Wood Pigeon*	Ryukyu Pigeon[1], Jouyi's Wood Pigeon
Streptopelia decaocto	Eurasian Collared Dove	Collared Dove
*Streptopelia roseogrisea**	African Collared Dove*	Rose-grey Dove, Pink-headed Dove
Streptopelia decipiens	African Mourning Dove*	Mourning Collared Dove[1], Mourning Dove
Streptopelia semitorquata	Red-eyed Dove	
*Streptopelia tranquebarica**	Red Turtle Dove*	Red Collared Dove[1]
Streptopelia turtur	European Turtle Dove	Turtle Dove
Streptopelia lugens	Dusky Turtle Dove	Pink-breasted Turtle Dove
Streptopelia orientalis	Oriental Turtle Dove*	Rufous Turtle Dove
Streptopelia senegalensis	Laughing Dove	Palm Dove
*Streptopelia chinensis**	Spotted Dove	
Oena capensis	Namaqua Dove	Long-tailed Dove
Chalcophaps indica	Emerald Dove*	Emerald Ground Dove, Green-winged Pigeon
Zenaida macroura (V)	American Mourning Dove*	Mourning Dove[1,2]
Treron waalia	Bruce's Green Pigeon	Yellow-bellied Green Pigeon
Treron sphenura (A)	Wedge-tailed Green Pigeon*	Wedge-tailed Pigeon
Treron sieboldii	White-bellied Green Pigeon*	White-bellied Pigeon, Japanese Green Pigeon
Treron formosae	Whistling Green Pigeon	Formosa Green Pigeon

PSITTACIDAE

Psittacula eupatria (I)	Alexandrine Parakeet	
Psittacula krameri	Rose-ringed Parakeet*	Ring-necked Parakeet
Psittacula derbiana	Lord Derby's Parakeet*	Derbyan Parakeet[1]
Psittacula himalayana	Slaty-headed Parakeet	
*Psittacula finschii**	Grey-headed Parakeet	
Myiopsitta monachus (I)	Monk Parakeet	

CUCULIDAE

*Clamator jacobinus**	Jacobin Cuckoo*	Pied Cuckoo[1]
Clamator coromandus	Chestnut-winged Cuckoo	Red-winged Cuckoo
Clamator glandarius	Great Spotted Cuckoo	

*Hierococcyx fugax**	Hodgson's Hawk Cuckoo	Fugitive Hawk Cuckoo
*Hierococcyx varius** (V)	Common Hawk Cuckoo	
*Hierococcyx sparverioides**	Large Hawk Cuckoo	
Chrysococcyx klaas	Klaas's Cuckoo	
Chrysococcyx caprius	Didric Cuckoo*	Dideric Cuckoo[1], Diederik Cuckoo
Cuculus micropterus	Indian Cuckoo	
Cuculus canorus	Common Cuckoo	European Cuckoo, Cuckoo
Cuculus saturatus	Oriental Cuckoo	Himalayan Cuckoo
Cuculus poliocephalus	Lesser Cuckoo	Little Cuckoo
Surniculus lugubris (V)	Drongo Cuckoo	
Eudynamys scolopacea (V)	Common Koel*	Asian Koel[1]
*Coccyzus erythropthalmus** (V)	Black-billed Cuckoo	
*Coccyzus americanus** (V)	Yellow-billed Cuckoo	
*Centropus senegalensis**	Senegal Coucal	
*Centropus superciliosus**	White-browed Coucal	Burchell's Coucal

TYTONIDAE

Tyto alba	Barn Owl*	Common Barn Owl
*Tyto capensis** (V)	Grass Owl*	
incl. *longimembris* (V)	Eastern Grass Owl	

STRIGIDAE

Otus spilocephalus	Mountain Scops Owl	
*Otus bakkamoena**	Collared Scops Owl*	Indian Scops Owl
incl. *lempiji*	Collared Scops Owl	
*Otus brucei**	Pallid Scops Owl*	Striated Scops Owl[4], Bruce's Scops Owl
Otus scops	European Scops Owl*	Common Scops Owl[1], Eurasian Scops Owl[2], Scops Owl
*Otus senegalensis**	African Scops Owl	
*Otus sunia**	Oriental Scops Owl	Indian Scops Owl
*Otus elegans**	Ryukyu Scops Owl*	Elegant Scops Owl[1]
*Bubo bubo**	Eurasian Eagle Owl*	Northern Eagle Owl, Eagle Owl
incl. *ascalaphus*	Pharaoh Eagle Owl	Desert Eagle Owl
incl. *bengalensis*	Rock Eagle Owl	
Bubo africanus	Spotted Eagle Owl	
Ketupa blakistoni	Blakiston's Fish Owl	
Ketupa zeylonensis	Brown Fish Owl	
Nyctea scandiaca	Snowy Owl	
Surnia ulula	Northern Hawk Owl	Hawk Owl
Glaucidium passerinum	Eurasian Pygmy Owl	Pygmy Owl
Glaucidium brodiei	Collared Owlet	
Glaucidium cuculoides	Asian Barred Owlet	Barred Owlet
Ninox scutulata	Brown Hawk Owl	

Athene noctua	Little Owl	
Athene brama	Spotted Owlet	Spotted Little Owl
Strix leptogrammica	Brown Wood Owl	
Strix aluco	Tawny Owl	
Strix butleri	Hume's Owl	Hume's Tawny Owl
*Strix uralensis**	Ural Owl	
incl. *davidi*	Père David's Owl*	Sichuan Wood Owl[1]
Strix nebulosa	Great Grey Owl	
Asio otus	Long-eared Owl	
Asio flammeus	Short-eared Owl	
Asio capensis	Marsh Owl	
Aegolius funereus	Tengmalm's Owl*	Boreal Owl[1]

CAPRIMULGIDAE

Caprimulgus inornatus	Plain Nightjar	
Caprimulgus poliocephalus	Mountain Nightjar*	Montane Nightjar[1], Abyssinian Nightjar
Caprimulgus nubicus	Nubian Nightjar	
Caprimulgus centralasicus	Vaurie's Nightjar	
Caprimulgus mahrattensis	Sykes's Nightjar	
Caprimulgus asiaticus	Indian Nightjar	
Caprimulgus indicus	Grey Nightjar	Jungle Nightjar
Caprimulgus europaeus	European Nightjar*	Eurasian Nightjar[1], Nightjar
Caprimulgus ruficollis	Red-necked Nightjar	
Caprimulgus aegyptius	Egyptian Nightjar	
Chordeiles minor (V)	Common Nighthawk	Nighthawk

APODIDAE

Collocalia brevirostris	Himalayan Swiftlet	
Chaetura pelagica (V)	Chimney Swift	
Hirundapus caudacutus	White-throated Needletail*	White-throated Needletail Swift[4], Needle-tailed Swift
*Apus alexandri**	Cape Verde Swift*	Alexander's Swift[1], Cape Verde Islands Swift
*Apus unicolor**	Plain Swift	
Apus apus	Common Swift	Swift
Apus pallidus	Pallid Swift	
Apus pacificus	Fork-tailed Swift*	Pacific Swift[2]
*Apus melba**	Alpine Swift	
Apus caffer	White-rumped Swift	African White-rumped Swift
*Apus affinis**	Little Swift*	House Swift
incl. *nipalensis*	House Swift	
Cypsiurus parvus	African Palm Swift	Palm Swift

TROCHILIDAE		
Selasphorus rufus (V)	Rufous Hummingbird	
TROGONIDAE		
Harpactes wardi	Ward's Trogon	
ALCEDINIDAE		
*Halcyon coromanda**	Ruddy Kingfisher	
*Halcyon smyrnensis**	White-throated Kingfisher*	Smyrna Kingfisher[2], White-breasted Kingfisher
*Halcyon pileata**	Black-capped Kingfisher	
*Halcyon leucocephala**	Grey-headed Kingfisher*	Chestnut-bellied Kingfisher
*Halcyon chloris**	Collared Kingfisher	White-collared Kingfisher
*Halcyon cinnamomina** (EP)	Micronesian Kingfisher	
incl. *miyakoensis* (E)	Miyako Kingfisher*	Ryukyu Kingfisher[1]
Alcedo atthis	Common Kingfisher*	European Kingfisher, River Kingfisher, Kingfisher
Alcedo cristata (V)	Malachite Kingfisher	
*Ceryle rudis**	Pied Kingfisher	Lesser Pied Kingfisher
*Ceryle alcyon** (V)	Belted Kingfisher	
*Ceryle lugubris**	Crested Kingfisher	Himalayan Pied Kingfisher
MEROPIDAE		
Merops albicollis	White-throated Bee-eater	
Merops orientalis	Green Bee-eater*	Little Green Bee-eater[1,2]
*Merops persicus**	Blue-cheeked Bee-eater	
Merops ornatus (V)	Rainbow Bee-eater	
Merops apiaster	European Bee-eater	Bee-eater
CORACIIDAE		
Coracias garrulus	European Roller	Roller
Coracias abyssinicus	Abyssinian Roller	
Coracias caudata (V)	Lilac-breasted Roller	
*Coracias noevia** (V)	Rufous-crowned Roller	Purple Roller
Coracias benghalensis	Indian Roller	
Eurystomus glaucurus (V)	Broad-billed Roller	African Broad-billed Roller
Eurystomus orientalis	Dollarbird	Broad-billed Roller
UPUPIDAE		
*Upupa epops**	Eurasian Hoopoe*	Hoopoe[2]

BUCEROTIDAE		
Tockus nasutus	African Grey Hornbill	Grey Hornbill
CAPITONIDAE		
*Megalaima virens**	Great Barbet	
INDICATORIDAE		
Indicator xanthonotus	Yellow-rumped Honeyguide	Orange-rumped Honeyguide
PICIDAE		
Jynx torquilla	Eurasian Wryneck*	Northern Wryneck, Wryneck
Picumnus innominatus	Speckled Piculet	
Colaptes auratus (V)	Northern Flicker	Yellow-shafted Flicker
Picus canus	Grey-headed Woodpecker*	Grey-faced Woodpecker[1], Black-naped Green Woodpecker
*Picus viridis**	European Green Woodpecker*	Eurasian Green Woodpecker[1], Green Woodpecker[3]
*Picus vaillantii**	Levaillant's Green Woodpecker*	Levaillant's Woodpecker[1,3], North African Green Woodpecker
Picus awokera	Japanese Green Woodpecker*	Japanese Woodpecker[1]
Picus squamatus	Scaly-bellied Woodpecker	Scaly-bellied Green Woodpecker
Sapheopipo noguchii	Okinawa Woodpecker*	Pryer's Woodpecker
Dryocopus martius	Black Woodpecker	Great Black Woodpecker
Dryocopus javensis	White-bellied Woodpecker	White-bellied Black Woodpecker
Sphyrapicus varius (V)	Yellow-bellied Sapsucker	
*Dendrocopos major**	Great Spotted Woodpecker	
*Dendrocopos leucopterus**	White-winged Woodpecker	White-winged Spotted Woodpecker
*Dendrocopos syriacus**	Syrian Woodpecker	
*Dendrocopos assimilis**	Sind Woodpecker	Sind Pied Woodpecker
*Dendrocopos himalayensis**	Himalayan Woodpecker	Himalayan Pied Woodpecker
*Dendrocopos darjellensis**	Darjeeling Woodpecker	Darjeeling Pied Woodpecker
*Dendrocopos cathpharius**	Crimson-breasted Woodpecker	Lesser Pied Woodpecker
*Dendrocopos medius**	Middle Spotted Woodpecker	
*Dendrocopos leucotos**	White-backed Woodpecker	
incl. *lilfordi*	Lilford's Woodpecker	Greek Pied Woodpecker
*Dendrocopos hyperythrus**	Rufous-bellied Woodpecker	
*Dendrocopos auriceps**	Brown-fronted Woodpecker	Brown-fronted Pied Woodpecker
*Dendrocopos minor**	Lesser Spotted Woodpecker	
*Dendrocopos canicapillus**	Grey-capped Woodpecker	Grey-capped Pygmy Woodpecker
*Dendrocopos kizuki**	Japanese Pygmy Woodpecker*	Pygmy Woodpecker[1]
*Dendrocopos dorae**	Arabian Woodpecker	
Picoides tridactylus	Three-toed Woodpecker	Northern Three-toed Woodpecker
Blythipicus pyrrhotis	Bay Woodpecker	Red-eared Bay Woodpecker

TYRANNIDAE

Sayornis phoebe (V)	Eastern Phoebe	
Empidonax virescens (V)	Acadian Flycatcher	

PITTIDAE

Pitta sordida (V)	Hooded Pitta	
*Pitta nympha**	Fairy Pitta	

ALAUDIDAE

*Mirafra cantillans**	Singing Bush Lark*	Singing Lark[1]
Eremopterix signata (V)	Chestnut-headed Sparrow-lark	
Eremopterix nigriceps	Black-crowned Sparrow-lark	Black-crowned Finch-lark
Eremalauda dunni	Dunn's Lark	
*Ammomanes cincturus**	Bar-tailed Lark	Bar-tailed Desert Lark
Ammomanes deserti	Desert Lark	
Alaemon alaudipes	Greater Hoopoe Lark*	Hoopoe Lark
Chersophilus duponti	Dupont's Lark	
Ramphocoris clotbey	Thick-billed Lark	
Melanocorypha calandra	Calandra Lark	
Melanocorypha bimaculata	Bimaculated Lark	Eastern Calandra Lark
Melanocorypha maxima	Tibetan Lark*	Long-billed Calandra Lark
Melanocorypha mongolica	Mongolian Lark	
Melanocorypha leucoptera	White-winged Lark	
Melanocorypha yeltoniensis	Black Lark	
*Calandrella cinerea**	Red-capped Lark	
incl. *blanfordi*	Blanford's Lark	
*Calandrella brachydactyla**	Greater Short-toed Lark	Short-toed Lark
Calandrella acutirostris	Hume's Short-toed Lark*	Hume's Lark[1]
*Calandrella rufescens**	Lesser Short-toed Lark	
incl. *cheleensis*	Asian Short-toed Lark	Eastern Short-toed Lark
Calandrella raytal	Sand Lark*	Indian Short-toed Lark[1], Indian Sand Lark
Galerida cristata	Crested Lark	
*Galerida theklae**	Thekla Lark	
Lullula arborea	Wood Lark*	Woodlark
Alauda gulgula	Oriental Skylark*	Oriental Lark[2], Small Skylark
*Alauda arvensis**	Eurasian Skylark*	Sky Lark[2], Common Skylark, Skylark
incl. *japonica*	Japanese Skylark	
Alauda razae	Raso Lark*	Razo Lark[1], Razo Island Lark
Eremophila alpestris	Horned Lark*	Shore Lark
Eremophila bilopha	Temminck's Lark	Temminck's Horned Lark

HIRUNDINIDAE

Riparia paludicola	Plain Martin*	Brown-throated Sand Martin, African Sand Martin
*Riparia riparia**	Sand Martin*	Common Sand Martin, Bank Swallow
incl. *diluta*	Pale Sand Martin	Eastern Sand Martin
Riparia cincta (V)	Banded Martin	
Tachycineta bicolor (V)	Tree Swallow	
*Hirundo fuligula**	Rock Martin	African Rock Martin
incl. *obsoleta*	Pale Crag Martin	
*Hirundo rupestris**	Eurasian Crag Martin*	Northern Crag Martin, Crag Martin
Hirundo rustica	Barn Swallow	Swallow
Hirundo tahitica	Pacific Swallow	
Hirundo aethiopica (V)	Ethiopian Swallow	
Hirundo smithii	Wire-tailed Swallow	
Hirundo abyssinica (V)	Lesser Striped Swallow	
Hirundo daurica	Red-rumped Swallow	
*Hirundo pyrrhonota** (V)	American Cliff Swallow*	Cliff Swallow[1,2]
Delichon nipalensis	Nepal House Martin*	Nepal Martin
*Delichon dasypus**	Asian House Martin*	Asian Martin
Delichon urbica	Common House Martin*	Northern House Martin[1], House Martin[2]

MOTACILLIDAE*

*Anthus richardi**	Richard's Pipit	
*Anthus rufulus** (A)	Paddyfield Pipit	
*Anthus godlewskii**	Blyth's Pipit	
Anthus campestris	Tawny Pipit	
Anthus berthelotii	Berthelot's Pipit	
Anthus similis	Long-billed Pipit	Brown Rock Pipit
*Anthus sylvanus**	Upland Pipit	
Anthus hodgsoni	Olive-backed Pipit*	Olive Tree Pipit, Indian Tree Pipit
Anthus trivialis	Tree Pipit*	Brown Tree Pipit
*Anthus gustavi**	Pechora Pipit	Petchora Pipit
incl. *menzbieri*	Menzbier's Pipit	
Anthus pratensis	Meadow Pipit	
Anthus cervinus	Red-throated Pipit	
Anthus roseatus	Rosy Pipit	Vinaceous-breasted Pipit
*Anthus petrosus**	Rock Pipit*	
Anthus spinoletta	Water Pipit	
*Anthus rubescens**	Buff-bellied Pipit*	American Pipit[1]
Tmetothylacus tenellus (V)	Golden Pipit	
Dendronanthus indicus	Forest Wagtail	

*Motacilla flava**	Yellow Wagtail	
incl. *feldegg*	Black-headed Wagtail	
incl. *lutea*	Yellow-headed Wagtail	
incl. *taivana*	Green-headed Wagtail	
Motacilla citreola	Citrine Wagtail*	Yellow-hooded Wagtail, Yellow-headed Wagtail
Motacilla cinerea	Grey Wagtail	
*Motacilla alba**	White Wagtail*	Pied Wagtail[4]
incl. *personata*	Masked Wagtail	
incl. *lugens*	Black-backed Wagtail	
*Motacilla grandis**	Japanese Wagtail	
*Motacilla aguimp**	African Pied Wagtail*	African Wagtail[4]
CAMPEPHAGIDAE*		
Coracina melaschistos	Black-winged Cuckoo-shrike	Smaller Grey Cuckoo-shrike
Pericrocotus ethologus	Long-tailed Minivet	
Pericrocotus solaris (A)	Grey-chinned Minivet	Yellow-throated Minivet
Pericrocotus cinnamomeus (V)	Small Minivet	
Pericrocotus divaricatus	Ashy Minivet	
*Pericrocotus tegimae**	Ryukyu Minivet	
PYCNONOTIDAE		
Spizixos canifrons	Crested Finchbill	Crested Finch-billed Bulbul
Spizixos semitorques	Collared Finchbill	Collared Finch-billed Bulbul
Pycnonotus sinensis	Chinese Bulbul*	Light-vented Bulbul[1]
Pycnonotus leucogenys	Himalayan Bulbul*	White-cheeked Bulbul[2]
*Pycnonotus leucotis**	White-eared Bulbul	
Pycnonotus cafer (I)	Red-vented Bulbul	
*Pycnonotus xanthopygos**	White-spectacled Bulbul*	Yellow-vented Bulbul
Pycnonotus barbatus	Common Bulbul*	Garden Bulbul[1,2]
*Hypsipetes amaurotis**	Brown-eared Bulbul	
*Hypsipetes leucocephalus**	Black Bulbul	
BOMBYCILLIDAE		
Bombycilla japonica	Japanese Waxwing	
Bombycilla garrulus	Bohemian Waxwing	Waxwing
*Hypocolius ampelinus**	Grey Hypocolius	Hypocolius
CINCLIDAE		
Cinclus cinclus	White-throated Dipper	Dipper
Cinclus pallasii	Brown Dipper	

TROGLODYTIDAE*		
Troglodytes troglodytes	Winter Wren*	Northern Wren, Wren
MIMIDAE		
Mimus polyglottos (V)	Northern Mockingbird	Mockingbird
Toxostoma rufum (V)	Brown Thrasher	
Dumetella carolinensis (V)	Grey Catbird	
PRUNELLIDAE		
Prunella immaculata	Maroon-backed Accentor	
Prunella rubida	Japanese Accentor	
Prunella modularis	Dunnock*	Hedge Accentor[1,2]
Prunella strophiata	Rufous-breasted Accentor	
Prunella montanella	Siberian Accentor	
Prunella fulvescens	Brown Accentor	
*Prunella ocularis**	Radde's Accentor	Spot-throated Accentor
*Prunella fagani**	Arabian Accentor*	Yemen Accentor[1]
Prunella atrogularis	Black-throated Accentor	
Prunella koslowi	Kozlov's Accentor*	Mongolian Accentor[1]
Prunella rubeculoides	Robin Accentor	
Prunella himalayana	Altai Accentor*	Rufous-streaked Accentor[1], Himalayan Accentor
Prunella collaris	Alpine Accentor	
TURDIDAE		
*Cercotrichas galactotes**	Rufous-tailed Scrub Robin*	Rufous Scrub Robin, Rufous Bush Robin, Rufous Bush Chat
Cercotrichas podobe	Black Scrub Robin*	Black Bush Robin
Brachypteryx stellata	Gould's Shortwing	
Brachypteryx hyperythra	Rusty-bellied Shortwing	
Brachypteryx montana	White-browed Shortwing	
Erithacus rubecula	European Robin	Robin
Erithacus akahige	Japanese Robin	
Erithacus komadori	Ryukyu Robin	
*Luscinia sibilans**	Rufous-tailed Robin	
Luscinia luscinia	Thrush Nightingale	Sprosser
Luscinia megarhynchos	Common Nightingale*	Rufous Nightingale[4], Nightingale
Luscinia calliope	Siberian Rubythroat	
Luscinia svecica	Bluethroat	
Luscinia pectoralis	White-tailed Rubythroat	Himalayan Rubythroat
Luscinia ruficeps	Rufous-headed Robin	

*Luscinia obscura**	Blackthroat*	Black-throated Blue Robin[1], Black-throated Robin
Luscinia pectardens	Firethroat	
Luscinia brunnea	Indian Blue Robin	
Luscinia cyane	Siberian Blue Robin	
Tarsiger cyanurus	Red-flanked Bluetail*	Orange-flanked Bush Robin[1,4]
Tarsiger chrysaeus	Golden Bush Robin	
Tarsiger indicus	White-browed Bush Robin	
Tarsiger hyperythrus	Rufous-breasted Bush Robin	Rufous-bellied Bush Robin
Irania gutturalis	White-throated Robin*	Irania
*Phoenicurus erythronota**	Eversmann's Redstart*	Rufous-backed Redstart[1]
*Phoenicurus alaschanicus**	Przevalski's Redstart*	Ala Shan Redstart[1]
*Phoenicurus coeruleocephalus**	Blue-capped Redstart*	Blue-headed Redstart
Phoenicurus ochruros	Black Redstart	
Phoenicurus phoenicurus	Common Redstart	Redstart
Phoenicurus hodgsoni	Hodgson's Redstart	
Phoenicurus frontalis	Blue-fronted Redstart	
Phoenicurus schisticeps	White-throated Redstart	
Phoenicurus auroreus	Daurian Redstart	
Phoenicurus moussieri	Moussier's Redstart	
Phoenicurus erythrogaster	Güldenstädt's Redstart*	White-winged Redstart[1]
*Chaimarrornis leucocephalus**	White-capped Redstart*	White-capped Water Redstart[1], River Redstart, River Chat
Rhyacornis fuliginosus	Plumbeous Redstart*	Plumbeous Water Redstart[1]
*Hodgsonius phaenicuroides**	White-bellied Redstart	Hodgson's Shortwing
Cinclidium leucurum	White-tailed Robin	
*Grandala coelicolor**	Grandala	Hodgson's Grandala
Cochoa purpurea	Purple Cochoa	
Cercomela familiaris (V)	Familiar Chat*	Red-tailed Chat
Cercomela melanura	Blackstart	
Saxicola macrorhyncha (V)	Stoliczka's Bushchat*	White-browed Bushchat[1]
Saxicola rubetra	Whinchat	
Saxicola dacotiae	Canary Islands Stonechat*	Canary Islands Chat[1], Fuerteventura Chat[2], Canary Chat
*Saxicola torquata**	Common Stonechat*	Stonechat, Collared Bushchat
incl. *maura*	Siberian Stonechat	
Saxicola insignis	Hodgson's Bushchat*	White-throated Bushchat[1], Hodgson's Stonechat
Saxicola caprata	Pied Bushchat*	Pied Stonechat
Saxicola ferrea	Grey Bushchat	Dark-grey Bushchat
Myrmecocichla aethiops (V)	Northern Anteater Chat	Ant Chat
Oenanthe isabellina	Isabelline Wheatear	
*Oenanthe bottae**	Red-breasted Wheatear*	Botta's Wheatear[1]
*Oenanthe oenanthe**	Northern Wheatear	Wheatear
*Oenanthe pleschanka**	Pied Wheatear	Pleschanka's Wheatear
*Oenanthe cypriaca**	Cyprus Wheatear	Cyprus Pied Wheatear

Oenanthe hispanica	Black-eared Wheatear	
Oenanthe deserti	Desert Wheatear	
Oenanthe finschii	Finsch's Wheatear	
Oenanthe moesta	Red-rumped Wheatear	
*Oenanthe xanthoprymna**	Red-tailed Wheatear*	Rufous-tailed Wheatear[1]
incl. *chrysopygia*	Red-tailed Wheatear	
*Oenanthe picata**	Variable Wheatear*	Eastern Pied Wheatear
*Oenanthe lugens**	Mourning Wheatear	
incl. *lugentoides*	Arabian Wheatear	South Arabian Wheatear
Oenanthe monacha	Hooded Wheatear	
Oenanthe alboniger	Hume's Wheatear	
Oenanthe leucopyga	White-crowned Wheatear*	White-tailed Wheatear[1,2], White-crowned Black Wheatear
Oenanthe leucura	Black Wheatear	
Saxicoloides fulicata	Indian Robin	
Copsychus saularis (A)	Oriental Magpie Robin	Magpie Robin
Monticola rufocinerea	Little Rock Thrush	
Monticola saxatilis	Rufous-tailed Rock Thrush	Chestnut-tailed Rock Thrush, Rock Thrush
*Monticola cinclorhynchus**	Blue-capped Rock Thrush	Blue-headed Rock Thrush
*Monticola gularis**	White-throated Rock Thrush	
*Monticola rufiventris**	Chestnut-bellied Rock Thrush	
*Monticola solitarius**	Blue Rock Thrush	
incl. *philippensis*	Red-bellied Rock Thrush	
*Myophonus caeruleus**	Blue Whistling Thrush	
Zoothera mollissima	Plain-backed Thrush	Plain-backed Mountain Thrush
Zoothera dixoni	Long-tailed Thrush	Long-tailed Mountain Thrush
*Zoothera dauma**	Scaly Thrush*	White's Thrush[3], Golden Mountain Thrush
incl. *aurea*	White's Thrush	
*Zoothera major**	Amami Thrush	
Zoothera monticola	Long-billed Thrush	
Zoothera wardii (A)	Pied Thrush	Pied Ground Thrush
Zoothera sibirica	Siberian Thrush	
*Zoothera naevia** (V)	Varied Thrush	
*Zoothera terrestris** (E)	Bonin Thrush	Bonin Islands Thrush
Hylocichla mustelina *(V)	Wood Thrush	
Catharus guttatus (V)	Hermit Thrush	
*Catharus minimus**	Grey-cheeked Thrush	
incl. *bicknelli*	Bicknell's Thrush	
Catharus ustulatus (V)	Swainson's Thrush	Olive-backed Thrush
Catharus fuscescens (V)	Veery	
*Turdus menachensis**	Yemen Thrush	
Turdus unicolor	Tickell's Thrush*	Indian Grey Thrush
Turdus cardis	Japanese Thrush*	Grey Thrush

Turdus albocinctus	White-collared Blackbird	
Turdus torquatus	Ring Ouzel	
Turdus boulboul	Grey-winged Blackbird	
Turdus merula	Common Blackbird*	Eurasian Blackbird[1], Blackbird
Turdus rubrocanus	Chestnut Thrush	Grey-headed Thrush
Turdus kessleri	Kessler's Thrush*	White-backed Thrush[1]
*Turdus chrysolaus**	Brown-headed Thrush	Brown Thrush
Turdus celaenops	Izu Thrush	Izu Islands Thrush, Seven Islands Thrush
Turdus feae	Grey-sided Thrush	Fea's Thrush
*Turdus hortulorum**	Grey-backed Thrush	
Turdus pallidus	Pale Thrush	
*Turdus obscurus**	Eyebrowed Thrush*	Eye-browed Thrush
*Turdus naumanni**	Dusky Thrush*	Naumann's Thrush, Rufous-tailed Thrush
incl. *eunomus*	Dusky Thrush	
*Turdus ruficollis**	Dark-throated Thrush*	Red-throated Thrush, Black-throated Thrush
incl. *atrogularis*	Black-throated Thrush	
Turdus pilaris	Fieldfare	
Turdus mupinensis	Chinese Thrush*	Chinese Song Thrush, Verreaux's Song Thrush
Turdus philomelos	Song Thrush	
Turdus iliacus	Redwing	
Turdus viscivorus	Mistle Thrush	
Turdus migratorius (V)	American Robin	
Enicurus scouleri	Little Forktail	
Enicurus leschenaulti	White-crowned Forktail	
Enicurus maculatus	Spotted Forktail	

SYLVIIDAE

*Tesia castaneocoronata**	Chestnut-headed Tesia	
*Urosphena squameiceps**	Asian Stubtail Warbler*	Asian Stubtail[1], Stub-tailed Bush Warbler, Short-tailed Bush Warbler
*Cettia diphone**	Japanese Bush Warbler	Bush Warbler
incl. *canturians*	Manchurian Bush Warbler	
*Cettia fortipes**	Brownish-flanked Bush Warbler	Strong-footed Bush Warbler, Brown-flanked Bush Warbler
Cettia major	Chestnut-crowned Bush Warbler	Large Bush Warbler
*Cettia flavolivacea**	Aberrant Bush Warbler	
*Cettia acanthizoides**	Yellowish-bellied Bush Warbler	Verreaux's Bush Warbler
Cettia brunnifrons	Grey-sided Bush Warbler	Rufous-capped Bush Warbler
Cettia cetti	Cetti's Warbler	

*Bradypterus thoracicus**	Spotted Bush Warbler	
incl. *davidi*	Père David's Bush Warbler	
Bradypterus major	Large-billed Bush Warbler*	Long-billed Bush Warbler[1]
*Bradypterus tacsanowskius**	Chinese Bush Warbler	
Bradypterus luteoventris	Brown Bush Warbler	
*Cisticola juncidis**	Zitting Cisticola*	Fan-tailed Cisticola, Fan-tailed Warbler
*Prinia gracilis**	Graceful Prinia*	Graceful Warbler
*Prinia inornata** (V)	Plain Prinia	
*Prinia criniger**	Striated Prinia	Brown Hill Warbler
*Prinia atrogularis**	Hill Prinia	Black-throated Prinia
*Spiloptila clamans**	Cricket Warbler*	Cricket Longtail[1], Scaly-fronted Warbler
*Scotocerca inquieta**	Scrub Warbler*	Streaked Scrub Warbler[1,2]
*Rhopophilus pekinensis**	Chinese Hill Warbler*	White-browed Chinese Warbler[1]
Locustella certhiola	Pallas's Grasshopper Warbler	Pallas's Warbler
*Locustella ochotensis**	Middendorff's Grasshopper Warbler	Middendorff's Warbler
*Locustella pleskei**	Styan's Grasshopper Warbler*	Pleske's Grasshopper Warbler[1]
Locustella lanceolata	Lanceolated Warbler	
Locustella naevia	Common Grasshopper Warbler	Grasshopper Warbler
Locustella fluviatilis	River Warbler*	Eurasian River Warbler[1], European River Warbler
Locustella luscinioides	Savi's Warbler	
*Locustella fasciolata**	Gray's Grasshopper Warbler	Gray's Warbler
incl. *amnicola*	Sakhalin Grasshopper Warbler	
*Locustella pryeri**	Japanese Swamp Warbler*	Marsh Grassbird[1], Japanese Marsh Warbler
*Acrocephalus melanopogon**	Moustached Warbler*	European Moustached Warbler
Acrocephalus paludicola	Aquatic Warbler	
Acrocephalus schoenobaenus	Sedge Warbler*	European Sedge Warbler
*Acrocephalus sorghophilus**	Speckled Reed Warbler*	Streaked Reed Warbler[1]
Acrocephalus bistrigiceps	Black-browed Reed Warbler	
*Acrocephalus concinens**	Blunt-winged Warbler	
*Acrocephalus agricola**	Paddyfield Warbler	
incl. *tangorum*	Manchurian Reed Warbler	
Acrocephalus dumetorum	Blyth's Reed Warbler	
Acrocephalus brevipennis	Cape Verde Warbler*	Cape Verde Swamp Warbler[1], Cape Verde Cane Warbler
Acrocephalus palustris	Marsh Warbler	
*Acrocephalus baeticatus**	African Reed Warbler	African Marsh Warbler
Acrocephalus scirpaceus	European Reed Warbler*	Eurasian Reed Warbler[1,2], Reed Warbler
*Acrocephalus stentoreus**	Clamorous Reed Warbler	
*Acrocephalus arundinaceus**	Great Reed Warbler	
incl. *orientalis*	Oriental Reed Warbler	Eastern Great Reed Warbler
*Acrocephalus griseldis**	Basra Reed Warbler	

*Acrocephalus aedon**	Thick-billed Warbler	Thick-billed Reed Warbler
Hippolais pallida	Olivaceous Warbler	
*Hippolais caligata**	Booted Warbler	
incl. *rama*	Sykes's Warbler	
Hippolais languida	Upcher's Warbler	
Hippolais olivetorum	Olive-tree Warbler	
Hippolais icterina	Icterine Warbler	
Hippolais polyglotta	Melodious Warbler	
*Parisoma buryi**	Yemen Warbler	Arabian Tit Warbler
Sylvia sarda	Marmora's Warbler	
Sylvia undata	Dartford Warbler	
Sylvia deserticola	Tristram's Warbler	
Sylvia conspicillata	Spectacled Warbler	
Sylvia cantillans	Subalpine Warbler	
*Sylvia mystacea**	Ménétries's Warbler*	Menetries's Warbler[1]
Sylvia melanocephala	Sardinian Warbler	
*Sylvia melanothorax**	Cyprus Warbler	
Sylvia rueppelli	Rüppell's Warbler*	Rueppell's Warbler[1]
Sylvia nana	Desert Warbler	
Sylvia leucomelaena	Arabian Warbler*	Red Sea Warbler[1]
Sylvia hortensis	Orphean Warbler	
Sylvia nisoria	Barred Warbler*	European Barred Warbler
*Sylvia curruca**	Lesser Whitethroat	
incl. *althaea*	Hume's Whitethroat	Hume's Lesser Whitethroat
incl. *minula*	Desert Whitethroat*	Small Whitethroat[1], Desert Lesser Whitethroat
Sylvia communis	Common Whitethroat*	Greater Whitethroat[1], Whitethroat
Sylvia borin	Garden Warbler	
Sylvia atricapilla	Blackcap*	European Blackcap
*Seicercus burkii**	Golden-spectacled Warbler	Black-browed Warbler
Seicercus xanthoschistos	Grey-hooded Warbler	
Seicercus poliogenys	Grey-cheeked Warbler	
Seicercus castaniceps (A)	Chestnut-crowned Warbler	
Phylloscopus umbrovirens	Brown Woodland Warbler	
Phylloscopus davisoni	White-tailed Leaf Warbler	
Phylloscopus reguloides	Blyth's Leaf Warbler	
*Phylloscopus coronatus**	Eastern Crowned Warbler	
Phylloscopus occipitalis	Western Crowned Warbler	Large Crowned Leaf Warbler
Phylloscopus tenellipes	Pale-legged Leaf Warbler	
*Phylloscopus borealoides**	Sakhalin Leaf Warbler	
*Phylloscopus ijimae**	Ijima's Leaf Warbler	
Phylloscopus tytleri	Tytler's Leaf Warbler	Slender-billed Warbler
*Phylloscopus trochiloides**	Greenish Warbler	Dull-green Leaf Warbler
incl. *plumbeitarsus*	Two-barred Warbler	Two-barred Greenish Warbler
incl. *nitidus*	Bright-green Warbler*	Yellowish-breasted Warbler[1], Green Warbler

Phylloscopus magnirostris	Large-billed Leaf Warbler	
Phylloscopus borealis	Arctic Warbler	
Phylloscopus pulcher	Buff-barred Warbler	Orange-barred Leaf Warbler
Phylloscopus maculipennis	Ashy-throated Warbler	Grey-faced Leaf Warbler
Phylloscopus proregulus	Pallas's Leaf Warbler*	Lemon-rumped Warbler[1], Pallas's Warbler
*Phylloscopus chloronotus**	Lemon-rumped Warbler*	Pale-rumped Warbler[1]
incl. *kansuensis*	Gansu Leaf Warbler	
*Phylloscopus sichuanensis**	Chinese Leaf Warbler	
Phylloscopus subviridis	Brooks's Leaf Warbler	
Phylloscopus inornatus	Yellow-browed Warbler*	Inornate Warbler[1]
*Phylloscopus humei**	Hume's Leaf Warbler*	Buff-browed Warbler[1], Hume's Yellow-browed Warbler
Phylloscopus schwarzi	Radde's Warbler	
Phylloscopus armandii	Yellow-streaked Warbler	
Phylloscopus fuscatus	Dusky Warbler	
*Phylloscopus fuligiventer**	Smoky Warbler	
Phylloscopus griseolus	Sulphur-bellied Warbler	Olivaceous Leaf Warbler
*Phylloscopus offinis**	Tickell's Leaf Warbler	
*Phylloscopus subaffinis**	Buff-throated Warbler	Buff-bellied Leaf Warbler
*Phylloscopus bonelli**	Bonelli's Warbler*	
incl. *orientalis*	Eastern Bonelli's Warbler	
Phylloscopus sibilatrix	Wood Warbler	
*Phylloscopus neglectus**	Plain Leaf Warbler*	Plain Willow Warbler
*Phylloscopus collybita**	Chiffchaff*	Common Chiffchaff[1,2], Eurasian Chiffchaff
incl. *sindianus*	Mountain Chiffchaff	
incl. *lorenzii*	Caucasian Chiffchaff	
Phylloscopus trochilus	Willow Warbler	
*Regulus calendula** (V)	Ruby-crowned Kinglet	
*Regulus regulus**	Goldcrest*	Common Goldcrest[1]
incl. *teneriffae*	Canary Islands Kinglet*	Tenerife Goldcrest[1]
*Regulus ignicapillus**	Firecrest	
Leptopoecile sophiae	Severtzov's Tit-warbler*	White-browed Tit-warbler[1], Stoliczka's Tit-warbler
*Leptopoecile elegans**	Crested Tit-warbler	

MUSCICAPIDAE

Niltava grandis	Large Niltava	
Niltava sundara	Rufous-bellied Niltava	
Niltava davidi	Fujian Niltava	Fukien Niltava
*Niltava vivida**	Vivid Niltava	
*Cyornis banyumas**	Hill Blue Flycatcher	Large-billed Blue Flycatcher
*Muscicapella hodgsoni**	Pygmy Blue Flycatcher	
*Cyanoptila cyanomelana**	Blue-and-white Flycatcher	

*Eumyias thalassina**	Verditer Flycatcher	
*Muscicapa ferruginea**	Ferruginous Flycatcher	
Muscicapa sibirica	Dark-sided Flycatcher*	Sooty Flycatcher, Siberian Flycatcher
Muscicapa griseisticta	Grey-streaked Flycatcher*	Grey-spotted Flycatcher
Muscicapa ruficauda	Rusty-tailed Flycatcher*	Rufous-tailed Flycatcher
*Muscicapa dauurica**	Asian Brown Flycatcher	Brown Flycatcher
Muscicapa striata	Spotted Flycatcher	
*Muscicapa gambagae**	Gambaga Flycatcher	Gambage Dusky Flycatcher
Ficedula sapphira	Sapphire Flycatcher	Sapphire-headed Flycatcher
Ficedula tricolor	Slaty-blue Flycatcher	
Ficedula superciliaris	Ultramarine Flycatcher	White-browed Blue Flycatcher
Ficedula westermanni	Little Pied Flycatcher	
Ficedula hodgsonii	Slaty-backed Flycatcher	Rusty-breasted Blue Flycatcher
Ficedula hyperythra	Snowy-browed Flycatcher	Rufous-breasted Blue Flycatcher
Ficedula monileger (A)	White-gorgeted Flycatcher	
Ficedula strophiata	Rufous-gorgeted Flycatcher	Orange-gorgeted Flycatcher
*Ficedula parva**	Red-breasted Flycatcher*	Red-throated Flycatcher
incl. *albicilla*	Red-throated Flycatcher	
*Ficedula subrubra**	Kashmir Flycatcher	Kashmir Red-breasted Flycatcher
Ficedula mugimaki	Mugimaki Flycatcher	
*Ficedula zanthopygia**	Yellow-rumped Flycatcher	
*Ficedula narcissina**	Narcissus Flycatcher	
incl. *elisae*	Chinese Flycatcher	Chinese Narcissus Flycatcher
*Ficedula semitorquata**	Semi-collared Flycatcher	
Ficedula albicollis	Collared Flycatcher	
Ficedula hypoleuca	European Pied Flycatcher*	Pied Flycatcher[2]
*Culicicapa ceylonensis**	Grey-headed Flycatcher*	Grey-headed Canary Flycatcher[1]

RHIPIDURIDAE*

Rhipidura hypoxantha	Yellow-bellied Fantail	
Rhipidura albicollis (A)	White-throated Fantail	

MONARCHIDAE*

Terpsiphone viridis	African Paradise Flycatcher	Paradise Flycatcher
Terpsiphone paradisi	Asian Paradise Flycatcher	Paradise Flycatcher
Terpsiphone atrocaudata	Japanese Paradise Flycatcher	Black Paradise Flycatcher

TIMALIIDAE*

Pomatorhinus erythrogenys	Rusty-cheeked Scimitar Babbler	
*Pomatorhinus erythrocnemis**	Spot-breasted Scimitar Babbler	
Pomatorhinus ruficollis	Streak-breasted Scimitar Babbler	Rufous-necked Scimitar Babbler

Pomatorhinus ferruginosus	Coral-billed Scimitar Babbler	
Xiphirhynchus superciliaris	Slender-billed Scimitar Babbler	
Pnoepyga albiventer	Scaly-breasted Wren-babbler	
*Pnoepyga immaculata**	Nepal Wren-babbler	
Pnoepyga pusilla	Pygmy Wren-babbler	Brown Wren-babbler
Spelaeornis caudatus	Rufous-throated Wren-babbler*	Tailed Wren-babbler
Spelaeornis troglodytoides	Bar-winged Wren-babbler	
Stachyris ruficeps	Rufous-capped Babbler	Red-headed Babbler
*Moupinia poecilotis**	Rufous-tailed Babbler	Rufous-tailed Moupinia
*Panurus biarmicus**	Bearded Reedling*	Bearded Parrotbill[1], Bearded Tit[3], Reedling[4]
*Conostoma oemodium**	Great Parrotbill	
*Paradoxornis paradoxus**	Three-toed Parrotbill	
Paradoxornis unicolor	Brown Parrotbill	
*Paradoxornis guttaticollis**	Spot-breasted Parrotbill	Spotted-breasted Parrotbill
*Paradoxornis conspicillatus**	Spectacled Parrotbill	
*Paradoxornis webbianus**	Vinous-throated Parrotbill	
*Paradoxornis brunneus**	Brown-winged Parrotbill	
Paradoxornis zappeyi	Grey-hooded Parrotbill*	Crested Parrotbill, Dusky Parrotbill Zappey's Parrotbill
Paradoxornis przewalskii	Przevalski's Parrotbill*	Rusty-throated Parrotbill[1]
Paradoxornis fulvifrons	Fulvous Parrotbill	Fulvous-fronted Parrotbill
Paradoxornis nipalensis	Black-throated Parrotbill	Nepal Parrotbill, Orange Suthora
*Paradoxornis verreauxi**	Golden Parrotbill	
*Paradoxornis heudei**	Reed Parrotbill*	Chinese Parrotbill, Yangtze Parrotbill
incl. *polivanovi*	Polivanov's Parrotbill	
Turdoides altirostris	Iraq Babbler	
Turdoides caudatus	Common Babbler	
Turdoides squamiceps	Arabian Babbler*	Brown Babbler
Turdoides fulvus	Fulvous Babbler*	Fulvous Chatterer[1]
Babax lanceolatus	Chinese Babax	
Babax waddelli	Giant Babax	
Babax koslowi	Kozlov's Babax*	Tibetan Babax[1]
Garrulax perspicillatus	Masked Laughingthrush	
Garrulax albogularis	White-throated Laughingthrush	
Garrulax striatus	Striated Laughingthrush	
Garrulax variegatus	Variegated Laughingthrush	
Garrulax davidi	Père David's Laughingthrush*	Plain Laughingthrush[1]
Garrulax sukatschewi	Sukatschev's Laughingthrush*	Snowy-cheeked Laughingthrush[1]
Garrulax cineraceus	Moustached Laughingthrush	
Garrulax rufogularis (A)	Rufous-chinned Laughingthrush	
Garrulax lunulatus	Barred Laughingthrush	
*Garrulax bieti**	Biet's Laughingthrush	White-speckled Laughingthrush[1]
*Garrulax maximus**	Giant Laughingthrush	
Garrulax ocellatus	Spotted Laughingthrush	White-spotted Laughingthrush

Garrulax canorus	Hwamei	Hwamey
Garrulax lineatus	Streaked Laughingthrush	
Garrulax squamatus (A)	Blue-winged Laughingthrush	
Garrulax subunicolor	Scaly Laughingthrush	Scaled Laughingthrush, Plain-coloured Laughingthrush
Garrulax elliotii	Elliot's Laughingthrush	
Garrulax henrici	Prince Henri's Laughingthrush*	Brown-cheeked Laughingthrush[1]
Garrulax affinis	Black-faced Laughingthrush	
Garrulax erythrocephalus	Chestnut-crowned Laughingthrush	Red-headed Laughingthrush
Garrulax formosus	Red-winged Laughingthrush	
*Liocichla omeiensis**	Emei Shan Liocichla*	Omei Shan Liocichla[1], Szechwan Liocichla
Leiothrix lutea	Red-billed Leiothrix	Pekin Robin
Myzornis pyrrhoura	Fire-tailed Myzornis	
Pteruthius rufiventer (A)	Black-headed Shrike-babbler	Rufous-bellied Shrike-babbler
*Pteruthius flaviscapis**	White-browed Shrike-babbler	Red-winged Shrike-babbler
*Pteruthius xanthochlorus**	Green Shrike Babbler	
Actinodura nipalensis	Hoary-throated Barwing	Hoary Barwing
*Actinodura waldeni**	Streak-throated Barwing	
Minla strigula	Chestnut-tailed Minla	Chestnut-tailed Siva, Bar-throated Minla
Minla ignotincata	Red-tailed Minla	Red-tailed Siva
Alcippe chrysotis	Golden-breasted Fulvetta	
Alcippe castaneceps	Rufous-winged Fulvetta	Chestnut-headed Tit Babbler
Alcippe vinipectus	White-browed Fulvetta	
Alcippe striaticollis	Chinese Fulvetta	Mountain Tit Babbler
Alcippe ruficapilla	Spectacled Fulvetta	
Alcippe cinereiceps	Streak-throated Fulvetta	
*Alcippe ludlowi**	Ludlow's Fulvetta	Brown-headed Fulvetta
Heterophasia capistrata	Black-capped Sibia*	Rufous Sibia[1]
Heterophasia pulchella	Beautiful Sibia	
Yuhina flavicollis	Whiskered Yuhina	Yellow-naped Yuhina
Yuhina gularis	Stripe-throated Yuhina	
Yuhina diademata	White-collared Yuhina	
*Yuhina occipitales**	Rufous-vented Yuhina	

AEGITHALIDAE

Aegithalos fuliginosus	Sooty Tit*	White-necklaced Tit[1]
*Aegithalos iouschistos**	Black-browed Tit	Rufous-fronted Tit
incl. *bonvaloti*	Black-headed Tit	
*Aegithalos niveogularis**	White-throated Tit	
Aegithalos leucogenys	White-cheeked Tit	
Aegithalos concinnus	Black-throated Tit	Red-headed Tit
Aegithalos caudatus	Long-tailed Tit	

PARIDAE		
Sylviparus modestus	Yellow-browed Tit	
Parus superciliosus	White-browed Tit	
*Parus palustris**	Marsh Tit	
incl. *hypermelaena*	Black-bibbed Tit*	Black-bibbed Marsh Tit[1]
*Parus lugubris**	Sombre Tit	
incl. *hyrcanus*	Caspian Tit*	Hyrcanian Tit[1]
*Parus montanus**	Willow Tit	
incl. *songarus*	Songar Tit	
Parus cinctus	Siberian Tit	Grey-headed Chickadee
Parus dichrous	Grey-crested Tit	Brown Crested Tit
Parus cristatus	Crested Tit	
Parus davidi	Père David's Tit*	Rusty-breasted Tit[1]
Parus venustulus	Yellow-bellied Tit	
Parus varius	Varied Tit	
*Parus rufonuchalis**	Rufous-naped Tit*	Dark-grey Tit[1], Simla Black Tit
*Parus rubidiventris**	Rufous-vented Tit	
incl. *beavani*	Sikkim Tit	Sikkim Black Tit
Parus melanolophus	Spot-winged Tit*	Black-crested Tit[1], Crested Black Tit
Parus ater	Coal Tit	
Parus xanthogenys (A)	Black-lored Tit	Yellow-cheeked Tit
*Parus spilonotus** (A)	Yellow-cheeked Tit	Black-spotted Yellow Tit
Parus caeruleus	Blue Tit	
*Parus cyanus**	Azure Tit	
incl. *flavipectus*	Yellow-breasted Tit	Yellow-breasted Azure Tit
*Parus major**	Great Tit	Grey Tit
incl. *cinereus*	Cinereous Tit*	Grey Tit
incl. *minor*	Japanese Tit	
*Parus bokharensis**	Turkestan Tit	Turkestan Great Tit
Parus monticolus	Green-backed Tit	
SITTIDAE		
Sitta yunnanensis	Yunnan Nuthatch	
*Sitta villosa**	Chinese Nuthatch*	Snowy-browed Nuthatch[1]
*Sitta krueperi**	Krüper's Nuthatch*	Krueper's Nuthatch[1]
*Sitta whiteheadi**	Corsican Nuthatch	
Sitta ledanti	Algerian Nuthatch*	Kabylie Nuthatch[1]
Sitta canadensis (V)	Red-breasted Nuthatch	
Sitta leucopsis	White-cheeked Nuthatch	Przevalski's Nuthatch
Sitta himalayensis	White-tailed Nuthatch	
*Sitta cashmirensis**	Kashmir Nuthatch	

Sitta europaea	Eurasian Nuthatch*	Wood Nuthatch[1,2], Common Nuthatch, Nuthatch
*Sitta nagaensis**	Chestnut-vented Nuthatch	Naga Nuthatch
Sitta tephronota	Eastern Rock Nuthatch*	Great Rock Nuthatch
Sitta neumayer	Western Rock Nuthatch	Rock Nuthatch
TICHODROMADIDAE*		
Tichodroma muraria	Wallcreeper	
CERTHIDAE		
Certhia discolor	Brown-throated Treecreeper	Sikkim Treecreeper
Certhia himalayana	Bar-tailed Treecreeper	Himalayan Treecreeper
*Certhia nipalensis**	Rusty-flanked Treecreeper	Nepal Treecreeper
Certhia familiaris	Eurasian Treecreeper	Common Treecreeper, Treecreeper
Certhia brachydactyla	Short-toed Treecreeper	
REMIZIDAE*		
Cephalopyrus flammiceps	Fire-capped Tit	
*Remiz pendulinus**	Eurasian Penduline Tit*	European Penduline Tit, Penduline Tit
incl. *macronyx*	Black-headed Penduline Tit	
incl. *coronatus*	White-crowned Penduline Tit	
incl. *consobrinus*	Chinese Penduline Tit	
NECTARINIIDAE		
Anthreptes platurus	Pygmy Sunbird	
*Anthreptes metallicus**	Nile Valley Sunbird	
Nectarinia asiatica	Purple Sunbird	
Nectarinia habessinica	Shining Sunbird	
Nectarinia osea	Palestine Sunbird*	Orange-tufted Sunbird
Aethopyga gouldiae	Mrs Gould's Sunbird*	Gould's Sunbird[1]
Aethopyga nipalensis	Green-tailed Sunbird	Nepal Yellow-backed Sunbird
Aethopyga ignicauda	Fire-tailed Sunbird	
DICAEIDAE*		
Dicaeum agile (A)	Thick-billed Flowerpecker	
*Dicaeum melanoxanthum**	Yellow-bellied Flowerpecker	
Dicaeum ignipectus	Buff-bellied Flowerpecker*	Fire-breasted Flowerpecker[1]

ZOSTEROPIDAE

*Zosterops palpebrosus**	Oriental White-eye	
*Zosterops erythropleurus**	Chestnut-flanked White-eye	
*Zosterops japonicus**	Japanese White-eye	
*Zosterops abyssinicus**	Abyssinian White-eye*	White-breasted White-eye[1]

MELIPHAGIDAE

*Apalopteron familiare**	Bonin Honeyeater	Bonin Islands Honeyeater

ORIOLIDAE*

Oriolus chinensis	Black-naped Oriole	
*Oriolus tenuirostris** (A)	Slender-billed Oriole	
Oriolus oriolus	Eurasian Golden Oriole	Golden Oriole

LANIIDAE

*Tchagra senegala**	Black-crowned Tchagra*	Black-headed Bush Shrike
*Rhodophoneus cruentus**	Rosy-patched Bush Shrike*	Rosy-patched Shrike
Lanius tigrinus	Tiger Shrike	Thick-billed Shrike
Lanius bucephalus	Bull-headed Shrike	
*Lanius cristatus**	Brown Shrike	
*Lanius isabellinus**	Isabelline Shrike*	Rufous-tailed Shrike[1]
incl. *phoenicuroides*	Red-tailed Shrike	
*Lanius collurio**	Red-backed Shrike	
Lanius vittatus	Bay-backed Shrike	
Lanius schach	Long-tailed Shrike	Rufous-backed Shrike
*Lanius tephronotus**	Grey-backed Shrike	Tibetan Shrike
Lanius minor	Lesser Grey Shrike	
*Lanius excubitor**	Great Grey Shrike*	Northern Shrike[1]
incl. *meridionalis*	Southern Grey Shrike	
Lanius sphenocercus	Chinese Grey Shrike	
Lanius senator	Woodchat Shrike	
Lanius nubicus	Masked Shrike	

DICRURIDAE*

*Dicrurus macrocercus**	Black Drongo	
Dicrurus leucophaeus	Ashy Drongo	Grey Drongo
Dicrurus hottentottus	Hair-crested Drongo*	Spangled Drongo

ARTAMIDAE*

*Artamus leucorynchus** (V)	White-breasted Woodswallow	White-breasted Swallow Shrike

CORVIDAE

Garrulus glandarius	Eurasian Jay	Jay
Garrulus lanceolatus	Lanceolated Jay*	Black-headed Jay[1], Black-throated Jay
Garrulus lidthi	Lidth's Jay	Ryukyu Jay
Perisoreus infaustus	Siberian Jay	
Perisoreus internigrans	Sichuan Jay	Szechwan Grey Jay
Urocissa flavirostris	Gold-billed Magpie	Yellow-billed Blue Magpie
Urocissa erythrorhyncha	Blue Magpie	Red-billed Blue Magpie
*Cyanopica cyanus**	Azure-winged Magpie	
Pica pica	Common Magpie*	Black-billed Magpie[1,2], Magpie
Podoces hendersoni	Henderson's Ground Jay*	Mongolian Ground Jay[1]
Podoces biddulphi	Biddulph's Ground Jay*	Xinjiang Ground Jay[1]
Podoces panderi	Pander's Ground Jay*	Turkestan Ground Jay[1]
Podoces pleskei	Pleske's Ground Jay*	Iranian Ground Jay[1]
Pseudopodoces humilis	Hume's Ground Jay*	Tibetan Ground Jay[1]
*Nucifraga caryocatactes**	Spotted Nutcracker*	Eurasian Nutcracker, Nutcracker
Pyrrhocorax graculus	Alpine Chough*	Yellow-billed Chough[1,2]
Pyrrhocorax pyrrhocorax	Red-billed Chough	Chough
Corvus monedula	Western Jackdaw*	Eurasian Jackdaw[1,2], Jackdaw
*Corvus dauuricus**	Daurian Jackdaw	
Corvus splendens	House Crow	Indian House Crow
Corvus frugilegus	Rook	
*Corvus corone**	Carrion Crow	Hooded Crow
incl. *cornix*	Hooded Crow	
Corvus macrorhynchos	Large-billed Crow	Jungle Crow
Corvus torquatus	Collared Crow	
*Corvus albus** (V)	Pied Crow	
*Corvus ruficollis**	Brown-necked Raven	
Corvus corax	Common Raven	Northern Raven, Raven
Corvus rhipidurus	Fan-tailed Raven	

STURNIDAE

Onychognathus tristramii	Tristram's Starling*	Tristram's Grackle
Cinnyricinclus leucogaster	Violet-backed Starling	Amethyst Starling
Sturnus pagodarum	Brahminy Starling	Brahminy Myna
Sturnus sericeus (V)	Red-billed Starling	Silky Starling
*Sturnus sturninus**	Purple-backed Starling*	Daurian Starling[2]
*Sturnus philippensis**	Chestnut-cheeked Starling	Red-cheeked Starling
*Sturnus sinensis** (V)	White-shouldered Starling	Chinese Starling
Sturnus vulgaris	Common Starling*	European Starling, Starling
*Sturnus unicolor**	Spotless Starling	
Sturnus roseus	Rose-coloured Starling*	Rosy Starling[1,2]
Sturnus cineraceus	White-cheeked Starling	Grey Starling
*Creatophora cinerea** (V)	Wattled Starling	

Acridotheres tristis	Common Myna	Indian Myna
Acridotheres ginginianus (I/V)	Bank Myna	
Acridotheres cristatellus (I/V)	Crested Myna	Tufted Myna

PASSERIDAE

Passer ammodendri	Saxaul Sparrow	
*Passer domesticus**	House Sparrow	
incl. *italiae*	Italian Sparrow	
incl. *indicus*	Indian Sparrow	
Passer hispaniolensis	Spanish Sparrow	
Passer pyrrhonotus	Sind Jungle Sparrow*	Sind Sparrow[1]
Passer rutilans	Russet Sparrow	Cinnamon Sparrow
Passer moabiticus	Dead Sea Sparrow	
*Passer iagoensis**	Iago Sparrow*	Cape Verde Sparrow[2], Rufous-backed Sparrow
Passer simplex	Desert Sparrow	
Passer montanus	Eurasian Tree Sparrow*	Tree Sparrow
Passer luteus	Sudan Golden Sparrow	Golden Sparrow
*Passer euchlorus**	Arabian Golden Sparrow	
*Carpospiza brachydactyla**	Pale Rockfinch*	Pale Rock Sparrow
Petronia xanthocollis	Chestnut-shouldered Petronia*	Yellow-throated Sparrow
Petronia dentata	Bush Petronia	Lesser Rock Sparrow
Petronia petronia	Rock Sparrow*	Rock Petronia[4]
*Montifringilla theresae**	Theresa's Snowfinch*	Afghan Snowfinch[1]
*Montifringilla blanfordi**	Blanford's Snowfinch*	Plain-backed Snowfinch[1]
*Montifringilla ruficollis**	Rufous-necked Snowfinch	Red-necked Snowfinch
*Montifringilla davidiana**	Père David's Snowfinch*	Small Snowfinch[1]
*Montifringilla taczanowskii**	White-rumped Snowfinch	Taczanowski's Snowfinch
*Montifringilla adamsi**	Adams's Snowfinch*	Black-winged Snowfinch[1], Tibetan Snowfinch
*Montifringilla nivalis**	White-winged Snowfinch*	Eurasian Snowfinch, Snowfinch
incl. *henrici*	Prince Henri's Snowfinch*	Tibetan Snowfinch

PLOCEIDAE*

Ploceus galbula	Rüppell's Weaver*	Rueppell's Weaver[1]
Ploceus manyar (I)	Streaked Weaver	

ESTRILDIDAE*

Lagonosticta senegala	Red-billed Firefinch*	Senegal Firefinch
Estrilda astrild	Common Waxbill	
*Estrilda rufibarba**	Arabian Waxbill	
*Amandava amandava** (I/V)	Red Avadavat	Red Munia, Avadavat
Amandava subflava	Zebra Waxbill	Orange-breasted Waxbill

*Lonchura malabarica**	Indian Silverbill*	White-throated Silverbill[1,4], White-throated Munia
*Lonchura cantans**	African Silverbill	Warbling Silverbill
Lonchura striata (I)	White-rumped Munia	White-backed Munia
Lonchura punctulata (I)	Scaly-breasted Munia	Spotted Munia
Lonchura malacca (I)	Chestnut Munia	Black-headed Munia
Padda oryzivora (I)	Java Sparrow	
Amadina fasciata (V)	Cut-throat*	Cut-throat Finch
VIREONIDAE		
Vireo flavifrons (V)	Yellow-throated Vireo	
Vireo philadelphicus (V)	Philadelphia Vireo	
Vireo olivaceus (V)	Red-eyed Vireo	
FRINGILLIDAE		
Fringilla coelebs	Common Chaffinch*	Chaffinch[1,3]
Fringilla teydea	Blue Chaffinch*	Teydefinch[1], Teydean Finch[3], Canary Islands Chaffinch[4]
Fringilla montifringilla	Brambling	
Serinus pusillus	Red-fronted Serin*	Fire-fronted Serin[1,2]
Serinus serinus	European Serin	Serin
Serinus syriacus	Syrian Serin*	Tristram's Serin
Serinus canaria	Atlantic Canary*	Island Canary[1,2], Canary
*Serinus citrinella**	Citril Finch	Citral Finch
incl. *corsicana*	Corsican Finch	Corsican Citril Finch
*Serinus rothschildi**	Arabian Serin*	Olive-rumped Serin[1], Arabian Canary
Serinus menachensis	Yemen Serin	
Rhynchostruthus socotranus	Golden-winged Grosbeak	
Callacanthis burtoni	Spectacled Finch*	Red-browed Finch
*Carduelis chloris**	European Greenfinch	Greenfinch
*Carduelis sinica**	Grey-capped Greenfinch*	Oriental Greenfinch
*Carduelis ambigua**	Black-headed Greenfinch	
Carduelis spinoides	Yellow-breasted Greenfinch	
*Carduelis carduelis**	European Goldfinch	Goldfinch
incl. *caniceps*	Grey-crowned Goldfinch	Grey-headed Goldfinch
*Carduelis spinus**	Eurasian Siskin	Siskin
*Carduelis thibetana**	Tibetan Siskin*	Tibetan Serin[1]
*Carduelis cannabina**	Common Linnet*	Eurasian Linnet[1], Linnet
Carduelis yemenensis	Yemen Linnet	
*Carduelis flavirostris**	Twite	
*Carduelis flammea**	Common Redpoll	Mealy Redpoll, Redpoll
*Carduelis hornemanni**	Arctic Redpoll*	Hoary Redpoll[1]

Loxia leucoptera	Two-barred Crossbill*	White-winged Crossbill[1]
Loxia curvirostra	Common Crossbill*	Red Crossbill[1], Crossbill
*Loxia scotica**	Scottish Crossbill	
Loxia pytyopsittacus	Parrot Crossbill	
Leucosticte nemoricola	Plain Mountain Finch	Hodgson's Mountain Finch
Leucosticte brandti	Brandt's Mountain Finch*	Black-headed Mountain Finch[1]
*Leucosticte sillemi**	Sillem's Mountain Finch	
Leucosticte arctoa	Asian Rosy Finch*	Rosy Mountain Finch, Rosy Finch
*Leucosticte tephrocotis**	Grey-crowned Rosy Finch	
Rhodopechys sanguinea	Crimson-winged Finch	
*Rhodospiza obsoleta**	Desert Finch	
*Bucanetes mongolicus**	Mongolian Finch	Mongolian Trumpeter Finch
*Bucanetes githagineus**	Trumpeter Finch	
Carpodacus rubescens	Blanford's Rosefinch*	Crimson Rosefinch[1]
Carpodacus nipalensis	Dark-breasted Rosefinch	Nepal Rosefinch
Carpodacus erythrinus	Common Rosefinch*	Scarlet Rosefinch, Scarlet Grosbeak
Carpodacus pulcherrimus	Beautiful Rosefinch	
*Carpodacus eos**	Pink-rumped Rosefinch	
*Carpodacus rodochrous**	Pink-browed Rosefinch	
Carpodacus vinaceus	Vinaceous Rosefinch	
Carpodacus edwardsii	Dark-rumped Rosefinch	Large Rosefinch
Carpodacus synoicus	Sinai Rosefinch*	Pale Rosefinch[1]
Carpodacus roseus	Pallas's Rosefinch	
Carpodacus trifasciatus	Three-banded Rosefinch	
*Carpodacus rodopeplus**	Spot-winged Rosefinch	
Carpodacus thura	White-browed Rosefinch	
*Carpodacus rhodochlamys**	Red-mantled Rosefinch	
incl. *grandis*	Blyth's Rosefinch	Himalayan Rosefinch
Carpodacus rubicilloides	Streaked Rosefinch	Eastern Great Rosefinch
Carpodacus rubicilla	Great Rosefinch	
*Carpodacus puniceus**	Red-breasted Rosefinch*	Red-fronted Rosefinch[1]
*Kozlowia roborowskii**	Roborovski's Rosefinch*	Tibetan Rosefinch[1]
Pinicola enucleator	Pine Grosbeak	
*Pinicola subhimachalus**	Crimson-browed Finch	Red-headed Finch
Chaunoproctus ferreorostris (E)	Bonin Grosbeak	Bonin Islands Grosbeak
Haematospiza sipahi	Scarlet Finch	
Pyrrhoplectes epauletta	Gold-naped Finch	Gold-crowned Black Finch
Uragus sibiricus	Long-tailed Rosefinch	
*Urocynchramus pylzowi**	Przevalski's Rosefinch*	Pink-tailed Bunting[1], Pink-tailed Rosefinch
Pyrrhula nipalensis	Brown Bullfinch	
Pyrrhula aurantiaca	Orange Bullfinch	
Pyrrhula erythrocephala	Red-headed Bullfinch	
Pyrrhula erythaca	Grey-headed Bullfinch	Beavan's Bullfinch

*Pyrrhula pyrrhula**	Eurasian Bullfinch*	Common Bullfinch[2], Bullfinch
incl. *murina*	Azores Bullfinch	
incl. *griseiventris*	Grey-bellied Bullfinch*	Japanese Bullfinch
incl. *cineracea*	Grey Bullfinch*	Baikal Bullfinch[1]
		Grey-breasted Bullfinch
Mycerobas icterioides	Black-and-yellow Grosbeak	
Mycerobas affinis	Collared Grosbeak	Allied Grosbeak
Mycerobas melanozanthos	Spot-winged Grosbeak	
Mycerobas carnipes	White-winged Grosbeak	
Eophona migratoria	Yellow-billed Grosbeak	Yellow-billed Hawfinch
Eophona personata	Japanese Grosbeak	Japanese Hawfinch
Coccothraustes coccothraustes	Hawfinch	
Hesperiphona vespertina (V)	Evening Grosbeak	

PARULIDAE*

Mniotilta varia (V)	Black-and-white Warbler	
Vermivora chrysoptera (V)	Golden-winged Warbler	
Vermivora peregrina (V)	Tennessee Warbler	
Parula americana (V)	Northern Parula	Parula Warbler
*Dendroica petechia** (V)	Yellow Warbler	
Dendroica pensylvanica (V)	Chestnut-sided Warbler	
Dendroica caerulescens (V)	Black-throated Blue Warbler	
Dendroica virens (V)	Black-throated Green Warbler	
Dendroica fusca (V)	Blackburnian Warbler	
Dendroica tigrina (V)	Cape May Warbler	
Dendroica magnolia (V)	Magnolia Warbler	
Dendroica coronata (V)	Yellow-rumped Warbler	Myrtle Warbler
Dendroica palmarum (V)	Palm Warbler	
Dendroica striata (V)	Blackpoll Warbler	
Setophaga ruticilla (V)	American Redstart	
Seiurus aurocapillus (V)	Ovenbird	
Seiurus noveboracensis (V)	Northern Waterthrush	
Geothlypis trichas (V)	Common Yellowthroat	Yellowthroat
Wilsonia citrina (V)	Hooded Warbler	
Wilsonia pusilla (V)	Wilson's Warbler	
Wilsonia canadensis (V)	Canada Warbler	

THRAUPIDAE*

Piranga rubra (V)	Summer Tanager	
Piranga olivacea (V)	Scarlet Tanager	

EMBERIZIDAE*

Pipilo erythrophthalmus (V)	Rufous-sided Towhee	
Spizella arborea (V)	American Tree Sparrow	Tree Sparrow
Chondestes grammacus (V)	Lark Sparrow	
Passerculus sandwichensis *(V)	Savannah Sparrow	
incl. *princeps* (V)	Ipswich Sparrow	
*Passerella iliaca** (V)	Fox Sparrow	
*Melospiza melodia** (V)	Song Sparrow	
Zonotrichia leucophrys (V)	White-crowned Sparrow	
Zonotrichia albicollis (V)	White-throated Sparrow	
Zonotrichia atricapilla (V)	Golden-crowned Sparrow	
Junco hyemalis (V)	Dark-eyed Junco	Slate-coloured Junco
Calcarius lapponicus	Lapland Longspur*	Lapland Bunting
Plectrophenax nivalis	Snow Bunting	
*Latoucheornis siemsseni**	Slaty Bunting*	Fukien Slaty Bunting, Chinese Blue Bunting
Emberiza variabilis	Grey Bunting	
Emberiza spodocephala	Black-faced Bunting	
Emberiza sulphurata	Japanese Yellow Bunting*	Yellow Bunting[1]
Emberiza koslowi	Kozlov's Bunting*	Tibetan Bunting[1]
*Emberiza leucocephalos**	Pine Bunting	
Emberiza citrinella	Yellowhammer	Yellow Bunting
Emberiza cirlus	Cirl Bunting	
Emberiza stewarti	White-capped Bunting*	Chestnut-breasted Bunting[1]
Emberiza cia	Rock Bunting	Eurasian Rock Bunting
*Emberiza godlewskii**	Godlewski's Bunting	Eastern Rock Bunting
Emberiza cioides	Meadow Bunting	
Emberiza jankowskii	Jankowski's Bunting*	Rufous-backed Bunting[1]
Emberiza striolata	House Bunting	
Emberiza tahapisi	Cinnamon-breasted Bunting	Cinnamon-breasted Rock Bunting
Emberiza cineracea	Cinereous Bunting	
Emberiza hortulana	Ortolan Bunting	
Emberiza buchanani	Grey-necked Bunting	
Emberiza caesia	Cretzschmar's Bunting	
Emberiza fucata	Chestnut-eared Bunting	Grey-headed Bunting
Emberiza elegans	Yellow-throated Bunting	
Emberiza chrysophrys	Yellow-browed Bunting	
Emberiza tristrami	Tristram's Bunting	
Emberiza rustica	Rustic Bunting	
Emberiza pusilla	Little Bunting	
Emberiza rutila	Chestnut Bunting	
Emberiza aureola	Yellow-breasted Bunting	
Emberiza schoeniclus	Common Reed Bunting*	Reed Bunting[1,2]
Emberiza pallasi	Pallas's Reed Bunting*	Pallas's Bunting[1,2]
Emberiza yessoensis	Japanese Reed Bunting*	Ochre-rumped Bunting[1]

*Emberiza bruniceps**	Red-headed Bunting	
Emberiza melanocephala	Black-headed Bunting	
*Miliaria calandra**	Corn Bunting	
Spiza americana (V)	Dickcissel	
Pheucticus ludovicianus (V)	Rose-breasted Grosbeak	
Guiraca caerulea (V)	Blue Grosbeak	
Passerina cyanea (V)	Indigo Bunting	
Passerina amoena (V)	Lazuli Bunting	

ICTERIDAE*

Dolichonyx oryzivorus (V)	Bobolink	
Molothrus ater (V)	Brown-headed Cowbird	
Euphagus carolinensis (V)	Rusty Blackbird	
Quiscalus quiscula (V)	Common Grackle	
Xanthocephalus xanthocephalus (V)	Yellow-headed Blackbird	
Icterus galbula (V)	Northern Oriole	Baltimore Oriole

TAXONOMIC NOTES

GAVIIDAE

Gavia arctica Black-throated Loon: includes *viridigularis* Green-throated Loon (or Green-throated Diver), formerly occasionally treated as specifically distinct, but it intergrades with nominate *arctica* in northern Siberia (Vaurie 1965a).

Gavia pacifica Pacific Loon: formerly usually (including by Voous 1977 and Cheng 1987) treated as conspecific with *G. arctica* Black-throated Loon, but found not to interbreed in wide zone of overlap in NE Siberia (Kistchinski 1980, Kistchinski & Flint 1983).

Gavia adamsii Yellow-billed Loon: formerly sometimes (including by Cheng 1987) treated as conspecific with *G. immer* Great Northern Loon.

PODICIPEDIDAE

Tachybaptus ruficollis Little Grebe: alternatively (as in Cheng 1987 and Stepanyan 1990) *Podiceps ruficollis*.

DIOMEDEIDAE

(merged in Procellariidae by Sibley & Monroe 1990)

PROCELLARIIDAE

Pterodroma feae Fea's Petrel: until recently (including by Voous 1977) treated as conspecific with *P. mollis* Soft plumaged Petrel, but see Bourne (1983) and Zino & Zino (1986).

Pterodroma madeira Zino's Petrel: until recently usually (including by Voous 1977) treated as conspecific with *P. mollis* Soft plumaged Petrel, but see Bourne (1983) and Zino & Zino (1986).

Pterodroma phaeopygia Dark-rumped Petrel: includes *sandwichensis* Hawaiian Petrel, the sole form to have occurred in the Palearctic (as a vagrant), sometimes (including by Sibley & Monroe 1993, but not 1990) treated as specifically distinct. Sibley & Monroe (1993) quoted the work of Tomkins & Milne (1991) in support of specific status, although the latter authors only tentatively suggest this course of action.

Pterodroma cervicalis White-necked Petrel: often treated as conspecific with *P. externa* Juan Fernandez Petrel, but Imber (1985) pointed out the obvious differences between the two and suggested that these taxa are not even closely related.

Bulweria fallax Jouanin's Petrel: formerly sometimes treated as conspecific with *B. bulwerii* Bulwer's Petrel.

Calonectris diomedea Cory's Shearwater: alternatively *Procellaria diomedea*. Includes *edwardsii* Cape Verde Shearwater, perhaps worthy of specific rank. For details of some of the fairly marked morphological differences shown by this form, see Granadeiro (1993).

Calonectris leucomelas Streaked Shearwater: alternatively *Procellaria leucomelas* or (as in Cheng 1987) *Puffinus leucomelas*.

Puffinus yelkouan Mediterranean Shearwater: usually (including by Voous 1977 and Stepanyan 1990) treated as conspecific with *P. puffinus* Manx Shearwater, but see Bourne *et al.* (1988). Includes *mauretanicus* Balearic Shearwater, which is morphologically very distinct and may be worthy of specific rank.

Puffinus lherminieri Audubon's Shearwater: sometimes treated as conspecific with *P. assimilis* Little Shearwater, but they are usually treated as allospecies (e.g. Sibley & Monroe 1990). Includes *persicus* Persian Shearwater and *bannermani* Bannerman's Shearwater, either or both of which are sometimes (including by Sibley & Monroe 1990) treated as specifically distinct. The former is sometimes treated as conspecific with *P. assimilis* Little Shearwater. Detailed studies of these little known forms that could provide support for specific status are lacking.

HYDROBATIDAE

(merged in Procellariidae by Sibley & Monroe 1990)

Oceanodroma monorhis Swinhoe's Storm-petrel: sometimes treated as conspecific with *O. leucorhoa* Leach's Storm-petrel. Arguments in favour of this treatment are put by Bretagnolle *et al.* (1991), but Dawson (1992) presented DNA data that suggest that *monorhis* should be treated as a distinct species.

Oceanodroma tristrami Tristram's Storm-petrel: formerly sometimes treated as conspecific with *O. markhami* Markham's Storm-petrel.

SULIDAE

Morus capensis Cape Gannet: alternatively (as in Dowsett & Forbes-Watson 1993) *Sula capensis*. Formerly sometimes treated as conspecific with *M. bassanus* Northern Gannet.

Morus bassanus Northern Gannet: alternatively (as in Voous 1977, Stepanyan 1990 and Dowsett & Forbes-Watson 1993) *Sula bassana*.

PHALACROCORACIDAE

Phalacrocorax carbo Great Cormorant: includes *lucidus* White-breasted Cormorant, sometimes (including by Sibley & Monroe 1990, but not 1993) treated as specifically distinct. Both morphology and behaviour point towards it being conspecific (Urban & Jefford 1974, Snow 1978).

Phalacrocorax pygmeus Pygmy Cormorant: sometimes (as in Stepanyan 1990 and Sibley & Monroe 1990, but not 1993) spelt *P. pygmaeus*.

ANHINGIDAE

Anhinga rufa African Darter: sometimes (including by Voous 1977 and Brown *et al.* 1982) treated as conspecific with *A. melanogaster* Oriental Darter. They are equally often treated as allospecies based on morphological differences (e.g. Vaurie 1965a, Sibley & Monroe 1990, Dowsett & Forbes-Watson 1993), but they are fairly close to each other (and to Australian Darter *A. novaehollandiae*) and so the decision is essentially arbitrary.

PELECANIDAE

Pelecanus crispus Dalmatian Pelican: formerly sometimes (including by Cheng 1987) treated as conspecific with *P. philippensis* Spot-billed Pelican.

ARDEIDAE

Ixobrychus sturmii Dwarf Bittern: alternatively (as in Voous 1977) *Ardeirallus sturmii*.

Dupetor flavicollis Black Bittern: alternatively (as in Sibley & Monroe 1990, but not 1993) *Ixobrychus flavicollis*.

Butorides virescens Green Heron: often (including by Voous 1977) treated as conspecific with *B. striatus* Striated Heron following Payne (1974). There is, however, only a small percentage of possible intermediates in the zone of overlap, or close approach, in the southern Caribbean (Voous 1986) and for this and other reasons Sibley & Monroe (1990) decided to treat these taxa as allospecies.

Bubulcus ibis Cattle Egret: Sheldon (1987) suggests this species is closer to *Ardea* than to *Egretta* based on DNA hybridization data. Includes *coromanda* Eastern Cattle Egret, occasionally treated as specifically distinct (e.g. McAllan & Bruce 1988), but see Payne & Risley (1976) who point out that further studies are necessary, and White & Bruce (1986).

Egretta caerulea Little Blue Heron: alternatively (as in Voous 1977) *Hydranassa caerulea*.

Egretta tricolor Tricolored Heron: alternatively (as in Voous 1977) *Hydranassa tricolor*.

Egretta ardesiaca Black Heron: alternatively *Hydranassa ardesiaca*.

Egretta gularis Western Reef Egret: sometimes treated as conspecific with *E. garzetta* Little Egret. The two occur in close proximity, yet reports of interbreeding (e.g. Hancock & Kushlan 1984) are rare and disputed (see, for example, Sibley & Monroe 1990). Note: Hancock & Kushlan quote Naik & Parasharya (1984, in error for 1983) as offering further evidence of interbreeding, but this paper does not report such an occurrence.

Egretta intermedia Intermediate Egret: alternatively (as in Sibley & Monroe 1990) *Mesophoyx intermedia*. Sheldon (1987) suggests this species is closer to *Ardea* than to *Egretta*, based on DNA hybridization data.

Egretta alba Great Egret: alternatively (as in Sibley & Monroe 1990) *Casmerodius albus*. Sheldon (1987) suggests this species is closer to *Ardea* than to *Egretta*, based on DNA hybridization data.

Ardea cinerea Grey Heron: includes *monicae* Mauritanian Heron, which may possibly be specifically distinct, although the behavioural differences described by Mahe (1985) could be just a localized response to the atypical nature of the coastal habitat frequented at the Banc d'Arguin. Erard *et al.* (1989) recognized *monicae* as a species because of morphological differences and a lack of interbreeding with *cinerea*, but the latter is only a winter visitor at the Banc d'Arguin (the nearest breeding area being in the Iberian peninsula). Geographical isolation is a rather weak basis for species recognition.

Ardea herodias Great Blue Heron: formerly sometimes treated as conspecific with *A. cinerea* Grey Heron.

Ardea purpurea Purple Heron: includes *bournei* Bourne's Heron, which de Naurois (1988) suggests may be specifically distinct.

CICONIIDAE

Ciconia boyciana Oriental Stork: often (including by Voous 1977 and Cheng 1987) treated as conspecific with *C. ciconia* White Stork. Now frequently treated as specifically distinct (e.g. Sibley & Monroe 1990, Stepanyan 1990) due to significant morphological differences (including black bill coloration).

THRESKIORNITHIDAE

Threskiornis melanocephalus Black-headed Ibis: sometimes (including by Cheng 1987) treated as conspecific with *T. aethiopicus* Sacred Ibis, but see Snow (1978) who treated them, along with *molucca* Australian Ibis, as members of a superspecies.

PHOENICOPTERIDAE

Phoenicopterus ruber Greater Flamingo: Includes *roseus* Greater Flamingo of the Old World, occasionally (including by Stepanyan 1990) treated as specifically distinct. (*P. ruber* then takes the English name 'American Flamingo'.)

Phoenicopterus minor Lesser Flamingo: alternatively (as in Dowsett & Forbes-Watson 1993) *Phoeniconaias minor*.

ANATIDAE

Dendrocygna species are treated as part of a separate family, Dendrocygnidae, by Sibley & Monroe (1990).

Cygnus columbianus Tundra Swan: includes *bewickii* Bewick's Swan, sometimes (including by Stepanyan 1990) treated as specifically distinct, but is reported to freely interbreed with *columbianus* in the zone of contact in the Chukotka peninsula, NE Siberia (e.g. Stepanyan 1990). How extensive this hybridization really is remains to be demonstrated.

Cygnus buccinator Trumpeter Swan: occasionally treated as conspecific with *C. cygnus* Whooper Swan.

Anser cygnoides Swan Goose: alternatively (as in Stepanyan 1990) *Cygnopsis cygnoides*.

Anser brachyrhynchus Pink-footed Goose: formerly sometimes treated as conspecific with *A. fabalis* Bean Goose, but kept separate because of differences in behaviour, proportions and plumage coloration (see C. S. Roselaar in Cramp & Simmons 1977).

Anser indicus Bar-headed Goose: alternatively (as in Stepanyan 1990) *Eulabeia indica*.

Anser caerulescens Snow Goose: alternatively (as in Stepanyan 1990) *Chen caerulescens*. Includes '*hyperboreus*' Snow Goose, the white morph of *A. caerulescens* which was formerly (but erroneously) treated as specifically distinct.

Anser rossii Ross's Goose: alternatively (as in Stepanyan 1990) *Chen rossii*.

Anser canagica Emperor Goose: Sometimes (as in Voous 1977) spelt *A. canagicus*. Alternatively *Chen canagica* or (as in Stepanyan 1990) *Philacte canagica*.

Branta canadensis Canada Goose: includes *hutchinsii* Hutchins's Goose, which may have occurred as a vagrant in the Palearctic (Cramp & Simmons 1977) and which is sometimes, as with other members of the Canada Goose complex, treated as specifically distinct. Mitochondrial DNA studies (Quinn *et al.* 1991) suggest the *canadensis* complex probably consists of at least two species, a large *B. canadensis* and a small *B. hutchinsii* which includes the other three subspecies groups.

Branta bernicla Brent Goose: includes *nigricans* Black Brant, sometimes treated as specifically distinct. Mixed pairs and intermediates have been reported from the Canadian Arctic (Delacour & Zimmer 1952), but the extent of interbreeding is uncertain (American Ornithologists' Union 1983).

Branta ruficollis Red-breasted Goose: alternatively (as in Stepanyan 1990) *Rufibrenta ruficollis*.

Anas crecca Common Teal: includes *carolinensis* Green-winged Teal, a vagrant to the Palearctic, sometimes treated as specifically distinct. Livezey (1991) treated *carolinensis* as a species based on differences in morphology.

Anas rubripes American Black Duck: sometimes treated as conspecific with *A. platyrhynchos* Mallard due to hybridization in extensive zone of overlap in North America, but an assessment of the nature of this hybridization favours specific status for *rubripes* (Hepp *et al.* 1988).

Anas poecilorhyncha Spot-billed Duck: includes *zonorhyncha* Eastern Spot-billed Duck, the only form occurring in the Palearctic, which was given specific status by Livezey (1991) based on differences in bill and tertial patterns.

Marmaronetta angustirostris Marbled Duck: alternatively (as in Stepanyan 1990) *Anas angustirostris*.

Melanitta nigra Common Scoter: includes *americana* Black Scoter, sometimes (including by Stepanyan 1990) treated as specifically distinct. Differs in morphology and no certain intergrades known, but also uncertain if ranges come into contact in N Siberia (C. S. Roselaar in Cramp & Simmons 1977).

Melanitta fusca Velvet Scoter: includes *deglandi* White-winged Scoter, sometimes (including by Stepanyan 1990) treated as specifically distinct due mainly to differences in bill structure and coloration (see C. S. Roselaar in Cramp & Simmons 1977). Also includes *stejnegeri* Asian Scoter (or Asiatic Scoter[1]) which is usually treated as a race of *deglandi* if this is given specific rank, but which is occasionally treated as a full species. The ranges of *stejnegeri* and nominate *fusca* may not come into contact (Vaurie 1965a), so *deglandi* (together with *stejnegeri*) mostly treated as conspecific pending further data.

Lophodytes cucullatus Hooded Merganser: alternatively (as in Voous 1977) *Mergus cucullatus*.

Mergellus albellus Smew: alternatively (as in Voous 1977, Cheng 1987 and Stepanyan 1990) *Mergus albellus*.

ACCIPITRIDAE

Pernis ptilorhyncus Crested Honey Buzzard: sometimes (as in Cheng 1987) spelt *P. ptilorhynchus*. Formerly sometimes treated as conspecific with *P. apivorus* European Honey Buzzard. Although some intermediates have been reported in the area of contact in western Siberia (Vaurie 1965a), treated as allospecies by Amadon & Bull (1988).

Milvus migrans Black Kite: synonym (as in Cheng 1987) *M. korschun*. Includes *lineatus* Black-eared Kite, sometimes (including by Sibley & Monroe 1990) treated as specifically distinct. Also includes *aegyptius* Yellow-billed Kite, likewise sometimes treated as specifically distinct. Supporting evidence for specific status for either seems to be weak. In the case of *lineatus*, there is extensive hybridization in the broad zone of contact (Vaurie 1965a).

Milvus milvus Red Kite: includes *fasciicauda* Cape Verde Kite, a variable form showing characters intermediate between *M. milvus* and *M. m. migrans* (but averaging closer to the former). It may be a hybrid population (de Naurois 1972).

Haliaeetus pelagicus Steller's Sea Eagle: includes *niger*, sometimes (including tentatively by Stepanyan 1990) treated as specifically distinct, but most likely a dark morph or subspecies of *H. pelagicus* (Vaurie 1965a).

Gyps bengalensis Indian White-backed Vulture: alternatively (as in Stepanyan 1990) *Pseudogyps bengalensis*.

Gyps himalayensis Himalayan Griffon Vulture: formerly sometimes treated as conspecific with *G. fulvus* Eurasian Griffon Vulture. They are sympatric over wide areas of Central Asia (see Vaurie 1965a), although *himalayensis* breeds at higher altitudes.

Circaetus gallicus Short-toed Eagle: synonym (as in Cheng 1987) *C. ferox*.

Spilornis cheela Crested Serpent Eagle: includes *perplexus* Ryukyu Serpent Eagle, sometimes treated as specifically distinct (e.g. Brazil 1991). Amadon (1974) discussed the problems involved in determining the taxonomic status of the island forms.

Circus spilonotus Eastern Marsh Harrier: sometimes (including by Voous 1977 and Stepanyan 1990) treated as conspecific with *C. aeruginosus* Western Marsh Harrier. Although there is some hybridization where the ranges meet in Central Siberia (Vaurie 1965a, pers. obs. in Transbaikal), this morphologically highly distinct form was separated by Amadon (1978). Further studies in the area of contact are needed.

Circus melanoleucos Pied Harrier: sometimes (as in Voous 1977) spelt *C. melanoleucus*.

Micronisus gabar Gabar Goshawk: alternatively (as in Sibley & Monroe 1990, but not 1993) *Melierax gabar*.

Accipiter gularis Japanese Sparrowhawk: sometimes (including by Voous 1977 and Cheng 1987) treated as conspecific with *A. virgatus* Besra. Morphologically very distinct (Vaurie 1965a), but contrary to Vaurie, the breeding ranges do not overlap in Taiwan and eastern China (Wattel 1973). The latter author treated *gularis* as conspecific with *virgatus*, but they are mostly separated due to differences in morphology and vocalizations (see Mees 1981).

Accipiter brevipes Levant Sparrowhawk: formerly sometimes treated as conspecific with *A. badius* Shikra.

Buteo rufinus Long-legged Buzzard: includes *cirtensis* of North Africa and probably parts of the Middle East, which is much smaller than nominate *rufinus* and differs also in plumage to some extent. May possibly deserve specific status. Research is needed.

Buteo hemilasius Upland Buzzard: sometimes treated as conspecific with *B. rufinus* Long-legged Buzzard, but the breeding ranges overlap in Central Asia and Mongolia (Vaurie 1965a)

Aquila nipalensis Steppe Eagle: often (including by Voous 1977, Cheng 1987 and Stepanyan 1990) treated as conspecific with *A. rapax* Tawny Eagle. The morphological, ecological and ethological differences are so extensive, however, that *nipalensis* should be treated as specifically distinct (Clark 1992). (The western form *orientalis* was included in *A. vindhiana* Asian Tawny Eagle in Sibley & Monroe 1990, but this was an error that was corrected in Sibley & Monroe 1993.)

Aquila rapax Tawny Eagle: includes *vindhiana* Asian Tawny Eagle, treated as specifically distinct by Sibley & Monroe (1990) based on a pers. comm. from A. C. Kemp pointing out differences in morphology, habitat and feeding behaviour, but later treated as conspecific by Sibley & Monroe (1993) following a further pers. comm. from W. S. Clark stating that the morphological and habitat differences were too slight, and the behaviour too little studied, to warrant specific status. Note: the breeding distribution for *vindhiana* given in Sibley & Monroe (1990) is greatly exaggerated due to the erroneous inclusion of *orientalis* in this species rather than *A. nipalensis*.

Aquila heliaca Imperial Eagle: includes *adalberti* Spanish Imperial Eagle, sometimes (including by Sibley & Monroe 1990) treated as specifically distinct, but in spite of significant indications such as a distinct juvenile plumage, the case put forward by Hiraldo *et al.* (1976) and Gonzalez *et al.* (1989) has not been widely accepted so far.

Hieraaetus pennatus Booted Eagle: alternatively (as in Cheng 1987) *Aquila pennata.*

Hieraaetus fasciatus Bonelli's Eagle: alternatively (as in Cheng 1987) *Aquila fasciata.*

PANDIONIDAE

(merged in Accipitridae by Sibley & Monroe 1990)

FALCONIDAE

Falco amurensis Amur Falcon: sometimes (including by Cheng 1987) treated as conspecific with *F. vespertinus* Red-footed Falcon, but usually given specific status owing to morphological differences (which are especially marked in the female).

Falco jugger Laggar Falcon: formerly sometimes treated as conspecific with *F. biarmicus* Lanner Falcon.

Falco cherrug Saker Falcon: includes *altaicus* Altai Falcon, sometimes (including by Sibley & Monroe 1990, but not 1993, and tentatively by Cheng 1987) treated as specifically distinct, or treated as conspecific with *F. rusticolus* Gyr Falcon. It was not recognized as being distinct from *F. cherrug milvipes* by Stepanyan (1990), however, and this is now a widespread view. Amadon & Bull (1988) treated it as colour morph of *F. cherrug*, but specimens at Leningrad, including the type, do not differ noticeably from other *F. cherrug* (U. Olsson *in litt.*).

Falco pelegrinoides Barbary Falcon: sometimes (including by Cheng 1987) treated as conspecific with *F. peregrinus* Peregrine Falcon, but separated by Vaurie (1961) on the basis of morphological differences and an apparent absence of interbreeding in the areas of contact (with one possible exception). The case for separating the two forms is not particularly strong and further studies are needed.

TETRAONIDAE

(merged in Phasianidae by Sibley & Monroe 1990)

Dendragapus falcipennis Siberian Grouse: alternatively (as in Cheng 1987) *Falcipennis falcipennis.*

Bonasa bonasia Hazel Grouse: alternatively (as in Cheng 1987) *Tetrastes bonasia.*

Bonasa sewerzowi Severtzov's Grouse: alternatively (as in Cheng 1987) *Tetrastes sewerzowi.*

Lagopus lagopus Willow Ptarmigan: includes *scoticus* Red Grouse, formerly treated as specifically distinct. An apparently intermediate population, *variegatus*, inhabits islands off the western coast of Norway, but this population, although not adopting a completely white winter plumage, is closer to nominate *lagopus* (Vaurie 1965a). Höhn (1969) regarded *scoticus* as a form half way to the status of a distinct species, but in view of the pronounced morphological differences, the debatable significance of *variegatus* and the differences in behavioural ecology (see Cramp & Simmons 1980) the taxonomic status of *scoticus* deserves reconsideration.

Tetrao tetrix Black Grouse: alternatively (as in Cheng 1987) *Lyrurus tetrix.*

Tetrao mlokosiewiczi Caucasian Grouse: alternatively *Lyrurus mlokosiewiczi.*

PHASIANIDAE

Callipepla californica California Quail: treated as part of a separate family, Odontophoridae, by Sibley & Monroe 1990.

Colinus virginianus Northern Bobwhite: treated as part of a separate family, Odontophoridae, by Sibley & Monroe 1990.

Tetraophasis szechenyii Széchenyi's Monal Partridge: sometimes (including by Cheng 1987) treated as conspecific with *T. obscurus* Verreaux's Monal Partridge. Only weakly distinguished from *T. obscurus* according to Johnsgard (1988).

Alectoris chukar Chukar: formerly sometimes treated as conspecific with *A. graeca* Rock Partridge, but is sympatric with it without interbreeding (Vaurie 1965a) and the proteins of *graeca* are closer to those of *A. rufa* Red-legged Partridge (Randi *et al.* 1992).

Alectoris magna Przevalski's Partridge: formerly sometimes treated as conspecific with *A. chukar* Chukar, but is sympatric with the latter in China (Vaurie 1965a).

Alectoris philbyi Philby's Partridge: formerly sometimes treated as conspecific with *A. chukar* Chukar, but is morphologically distinct.

Perdix dauurica Daurian Partridge: often (as in Voous 1977, Cheng 1987 and Sibley & Monroe 1990) spelt *P. dauuricae* (but see Sibley & Monroe 1993).

Coturnix japonica Japanese Quail: sometimes (including by Cheng 1987) treated as conspecific with *C. coturnix* Common Quail. Sympatric with the latter in Mongolia and differs in morphology and vocalizations (Vaurie 1965a). Although morphological differences are comparatively small, the advertising call is completely different.

Lophura leucomelanos Kalij Pheasant: often (as in Voous 1977 and Cheng 1987) spelt *L. leucomelana* (but see Sibley & Monroe 1990).

Crossoptilon harmani Tibetan Eared Pheasant: sometimes (including by Voous 1977 and Cheng 1987) treated as conspecific with *C. crossoptilon* White Eared Pheasant. Differs in morphology and size and only shows any variation where it meets *C. crossoptilon* according to Ludlow (1951), the ranges of the two being connected by a broad zone occupied by the highly variable '*drouynii*' (Vaurie 1965a)

Phasianus colchicus Common Pheasant: includes *versicolor* Green Pheasant, sometimes (including by Voous 1977) treated as specifically distinct. Hybridization between introduced *versicolor* and *colchicus* in Hawaii is sufficiently extensive to support them being treated as conspecific (Schwartz & Schwartz 1951, Goodwin 1982). Goodwin (1982) also pointed out the morphological similarities between *versicolor* and adjacent mainland populations of *P. colchicus*. Nonetheless, hybrids between native *versicolor* and introduced *colchicus* in Japan have apparently shown low fertility (Brazil 1991).

MELEAGRIDIDAE

(merged in Phasianidae by Sibley & Monroe 1990)

RALLIDAE

Gallirallus okinawae Okinawa Rail: alternatively *Rallus okinawae*. First discovered only in 1981 (Yamashina & Mano 1981).

Gallirallus striatus Slaty-breasted Rail: alternatively (as in Cheng 1987) *Rallus striatus*.

Porzana bicolor Black-tailed Crake: alternatively (as in Sibley & Monroe 1990) *Amaurornis bicolor* (but see Inskipp & Round 1989).

Aenigmatolimnas marginalis Striped Crake: alternatively (as in Voous 1977) *Porzana marginalis*. This species was placed after *P. pusilla* by Voous (1977). Retained in *Aenigmatolimnas* by Dowsett & Dowsett-Lemaire (1980) and most subsequent authors.

Coturnicops exquisitus Swinhoe's Rail: sometimes (as in Voous 1977) spelt *C. exquisita*. Alternatively (as in Cheng 1987 and Stepanyan 1990) *Porzana exquisita*. Sometimes treated as conspecific with *C. noveboracensis* Yellow Rail and does not differ greatly in morphology (see Ripley 1977), but usually treated as an allospecies.

Amaurornis flavirostra Black Crake: sometimes (as in Dowsett & Forbes-Watson 1993) spelt *A. flavirostris*. Alternatively (as in Voous 1977) *Limnocorax flavirostra*. This species was placed after *Crex crex* by Voous (1977). Placed in *Amaurornis* by Dowsett & Dowsett-Lemaire (1980) and most subsequent authors.

Porphyrula alleni Allen's Gallinule: alternatively (as in Sibley & Monroe 1990) *Porphyrio alleni*.

Porphyrula martinica Purple Gallinule: alternatively (as in Sibley & Monroe 1990) *Porphyrio martinica*.

Porphyrio porphyrio Purple Swamp-hen: includes *poliocephalus* Indian Swamp-hen (or Indian Purple Gallinule) and *madagascariensis* African Swamp-hen (or African Purple Gallinule), either or both of which were formerly sometimes treated as specifically distinct (but see Mayr 1938).

GRUIDAE

Anthropoides virgo Demoiselle Crane: alternatively (as in Sibley & Monroe 1990) *Grus virgo*.

OTIDIDAE

Tetrax tetrax Little Bustard: alternatively *Otis tetrax*.

HAEMATOPODIDAE

(merged in Charadriidae by Sibley & Monroe 1990)

Haematopus meadewaldoi Canary Islands Oystercatcher: often (including by Voous 1977) treated as conspecific with *H. moquini* African Oystercatcher (or African Black Oystercatcher), or occasionally as conspecific with *H. ostralegus* Eurasian Oystercatcher, but see Hockey (1982).

IBIDORHYNCHIDAE

(merged in Charadriidae by Sibley & Monroe 1990)

RECURVIROSTRIDAE

(merged in Charadriidae by Sibley & Monroe 1990)

Himantopus himantopus Black-winged Stilt: includes *leucocephalus* White-headed Stilt, a vagrant to the Palearctic, sometimes (including by Sibley & Monroe 1990) treated as specifically distinct. Sibley & Monroe (1990) point out that it may be conspecific, however, and this is the view of most recent authors. See C. S. Roselaar in Cramp & Simmons (1993) for support for inclusion of the various related forms in *H. himantopus* and Mayr & Short (1970) for the opposing view.

DROMADIDAE

(merged in Glareolidae by Sibley & Monroe 1990)

BURHINIDAE

Esacus recurvirostris Great Thick-knee: alternatively (as in Sibley & Monroe 1990) *Burhinus recurvirostris*. Synonym (as in Cheng 1987) *E. magnirostris*.

GLAREOLIDAE

Glareola maldivarum Oriental Pratincole: sometimes treated as conspecific with *G. pratincola* Collared Pratincole, but differs morphologically and the two forms have bred sympatrically in Pakistan (Roberts 1991).

Glareola nordmanni Black-winged Pratincole: formerly sometimes treated as conspecific with *G. pratincola* Collared Pratincole, but the breeding ranges overlap (Vaurie 1965a, Cramp & Simmons 1983).

CHARADRIIDAE

Charadrius semipalmatus Semipalmated Plover: sometimes treated as conspecific with *C. hiaticula* Common Ringed Plover, but usually regarded as members of a superspecies. Mixed pairs were reported on Baffin Island by Smith (1969), who considered the two forms to be largely allopatric morphs of a single polymorphic species. Occur alongside each other on Baffin Island and on St Lawrence Island in the Bering Sea (Sibley & Monroe 1990).

Charadrius placidus Long-billed Plover: formerly sometimes (including by Cheng 1987) treated as conspecific with *C. hiaticula* Common Ringed Plover (but see Vaurie 1965a).

Charadrius veredus Oriental Plover: formerly sometimes (including by Cheng 1987) treated as conspecific with *C. asiaticus* Caspian Plover (but see Vaurie 1965a).

Charadrius morinellus Eurasian Dotterel: alternatively (as in Sibley & Monroe 1990 and Stepanyan 1990) *Eudromias morinellus*.

Pluvialis dominica American Golden Plover: formerly sometimes treated as conspecific with *P. apricaria* European Golden Plover.

Pluvialis fulva Pacific Golden Plover: formerly (including by Voous 1977 and Cheng 1987) treated as conspecific with *P. dominica* American Golden Plover, but they are sympatric and reproductively isolated (Connors 1983, Knox 1987, Connors *et al.* 1993).

Vanellus spinosus Spur-winged Lapwing: alternatively (as in Voous 1977 and Stepanyan 1990) *Hoplopterus spinosus*.

Vanellus tectus Black-headed Lapwing: alternatively (as in Voous 1977) *Hoplopterus tectus*.

Vanellus cinereus Grey-headed Lapwing: alternatively (as in Voous 1977) *Hoplopterus cinereus* or (as in Stepanyan 1990) *Microsarcops cinereus*.

Vanellus indicus Red-wattled Lapwing: alternatively (as in Voous 1977) *Hoplopterus indicus* or (as in Stepanyan 1990) *Lobivanellus indicus*.

Vanellus gregarius Sociable Lapwing: alternatively (as in Voous 1977 and Stepanyan 1990) *Chettusia gregaria*.

Vanellus leucurus White-tailed Lapwing: alternatively (as in Voous 1977) *Chettusia leucura* or (as in Stepanyan 1990) *Vanellochettusia leucura*.

SCOLOPACIDAE

Calidris alba Sanderling: alternatively (as in Cheng 1987) *Crocethia alba*.

Calidris subminuta Long-toed Stint: formerly sometimes treated as conspecific with *C. minutilla* Least Sandpiper, but they differ in plumage, wing formula and structure (especially toe proportions): see J. Wattel in Cramp & Simmons (1983).

Calidris ptilocnemis Rock Sandpiper: sometimes treated as conspecific with *C. maritima* Purple Sandpiper, but they are usually regarded as members of a superspecies (e.g. American Ornithologists' Union 1983, Cramp & Simmons 1983).

Gallinago gallinago Common Snipe: alternatively (as in Cheng 1987) *Capella gallinago*.

Gallinago stenura Pintail Snipe: alternatively (as in Cheng 1987) *Capella stenura*.

Gallinago megala Swinhoe's Snipe: alternatively (as in Cheng 1987) *Capella megala*.

Gallinago hardwickii Latham's Snipe: alternatively (as in Cheng 1987) *Capella hardwickii*.

Gallinago solitaria Solitary Snipe: alternatively (as in Cheng 1987) *Capella solitaria*.

Gallinago nemoricola Wood Snipe: alternatively (as in Cheng 1987) *Capella nemoricola.*

Limnodromus scolopaceus Long-billed Dowitcher: formerly treated as conspecific with *L. griseus* Short-billed Dowitcher (but see Pitelka 1950).

Scolopax mira Amami Woodcock: formerly treated as conspecific with *S. rusticola* Eurasian Woodcock (but see Vaurie 1965a and Brazil & Ikenaga 1987 for details of the many differences).

Numenius minutus Little Curlew: sometimes (including by Cheng 1987) treated as conspecific with *N. borealis* Eskimo Curlew, but it differs in morphology (see, for example, Cramp & Simmons 1983).

Xenus cinereus Terek Sandpiper: alternatively (as in Sibley & Monroe 1990) *Tringa cinerea.*

Actitis hypoleucos Common Sandpiper: alternatively (as in Cheng 1987 and Sibley & Monroe 1990) *Tringa hypoleucos.*

Actitis macularia Spotted Sandpiper: alternatively (as in Sibley & Monroe 1990) *Tringa macularia.*

Heteroscelus brevipes Grey-tailed Tattler: alternatively (as in Sibley & Monroe 1990) *Tringa brevipes.* Formerly sometimes treated as conspecific with *H. incanus* Wandering Tattler, but they are usually considered to be members of a superspecies (e.g. American Ornithologists' Union 1983).

Heteroscelus incanus Wandering Tattler: alternatively (as in Cheng 1987 and Sibley & Monroe 1990) *Tringa incana.*

Steganopus tricolor Wilson's Phalarope: alternatively (as in Voous 1977 and Stepanyan 1990) *Phalaropus tricolor.* Biochemical studies indicate that this species is closer to the tringines than the other phalaropes (Dittmann *et al.* 1989).

Phalaropus fulicaria Red Phalarope: often (as in Voous 1977, Cheng 1987 and Stepanyan 1990) spelt *P. fulicarius* (but see Parkes 1982).

STERCORARIIDAE

(merged in Laridae by Sibley & Monroe 1990)

Catharacta skua Great Skua: alternatively (as in Voous 1977 and Stepanyan 1990) *Stercorarius skua.*

Catharacta antarctica Southern Skua: alternatively *Stercorarius antarcticus.* Sometimes (including by Voous 1977) treated as conspecific with *C. skua* Great Skua. Includes *lonnbergi* (sometimes spelt *loennbergi* or *lönnbergi*) Brown Skua, the sole form presumed to have been recorded from the Palearctic (as a vagrant: see Oman Bird Record Committee 1994), which is sometimes (including by Sibley & Monroe 1990) treated as specifically distinct. While often considered conspecific with *C. skua* (e.g. Devillers 1978), the morphological differences between *antarctica* and *skua* are comparable to those between *C. a. lonnbergi* and *C. maccormicki* which breed sympatrically, with only limited hybridization, in the South Shetland Islands (Parmalee 1988). Allospecies treatment (as adopted by Sibley & Monroe 1990) is therefore appropriate, but *lonnbergi* is here treated as conspecific with *antarctica,* contra Sibley & Monroe.

Catharacta maccormicki South Polar Skua: alternatively (as in Voous 1977) *Stercorarius maccormicki.* Sometimes (including by Stepanyan 1990) treated as conspecific with *C. skua* Great Skua. See also *C. antarctica.*

LARIDAE

Larus relictus Relict Gull: originally thought to be a subspecies of *L. melanocephalus* Mediterranean Gull or *L. brunnicephalus* Brown-headed Gull, or even a hybrid, but later demonstrated to be a distinct species (Auezov 1971).

Larus sabini Sabine's Gull: alternatively (as in Sibley & Monroe 1990 and Stepanyan 1990) *Xema sabini.*

Larus canus Mew Gull: includes *kamtschatschensis* Kamchatka Gull, sometimes treated as specifically distinct on the basis of morphological differences (see Johansen 1961) but it intergrades with the form *heinei* in northern Siberia (see C. S. Roselaar in Cramp & Simmons 1983). Also includes the North American race *brachyrhynchus,* which has occurred as a vagrant in the Komandor Islands (Stepanyan 1990), and which may possibly merit specific status.

Larus fuscus Lesser Black-backed Gull: formerly sometimes treated as conspecific with *L. argentatus* Herring Gull, but the breeding ranges extensively overlap with little or no hybridization in most areas (Vaurie 1965a, Barth 1975).

Larus cachinnans Yellow-legged Gull: often (including by Voous 1977 and Cheng 1987) treated as conspecific with *L. argentatus* Herring Gull, but shown to breed sympatrically with the latter without interbreeding (Marion *et al.* 1985, Yésou 1991). Formerly sometimes treated as conspecific with *L. fuscus* Lesser Black-backed Gull. Its relationship with *L. fuscus* may be closer than its relationship with *argentatus* (Yésou 1991). Includes *atlantis*, which possibly also represents a distinct species (Yésou 1991).

Larus armenicus Armenian Gull: usually (including by Voous 1977) treated as conspecific with *L. argentatus* Herring Gull, or else (including by Stepanyan 1990) treated as conspecific with L. *cachinnans* Yellow-legged Gull when the latter is given specific rank. Morphological differences combined with geographic isolation have led some authors to propose specific rank for this form (Devillers & Potvliege 1981, J. Haffer in Glutz von Blotzheim & Bauer 1982, Dubois 1985), but Bourne (1989) and Filchagov (1993) have pointed out the plumage similarity to *barabensis* and thus to *heuglini*, while Filchagov (1993) has shown that the black bill band (prominent in almost all winter adults: see Satat & Laird 1992), a character used to support specific status, varies seasonally in some individuals. A dark bill band can also be a winter feature of the *heuglini-taimyrensis-barabensis* group and some members of this group still show small dark markings in the breeding season (Hirschfeld 1992, Filchagov 1993). Likewise iris colour in *armenicus* has also been found to vary seasonally to some extent (Filchagov 1993). Filchagov concludes that, based on present knowledge, the only basis for the promotion of *armenicus* to a full species appears to be its geographical isolation, a rather weak basis for species recognition in systematics. Nonetheless, this conclusion is somewhat contradicted by his own evidence which makes it clear that the black bill band is still fully developed in two-thirds of breeding *armenicus* and only reduced or absent in one third, so this unique feature, not seen (to anything like this degree) in any other member of the *argentatus/fuscus* complex, is found in the majority of the breeding population. Likewise most individuals still showed a dark iris in summer. Kept separate here pending further studies.

Larus heuglini Heuglin's Gull: usually (including by Voous 1987 and Sibley & Monroe 1990) treated as conspecific with *L. argentatus* Herring Gull, or (as in Cramp & Simmons 1983) with *L. fuscus* Lesser Black-backed Gull. The systematics of the large gulls in the *argentatus/fuscus* complex remains contentious. Apparent absence of interbreeding with *argentatus* or *fuscus* in the Kola region of northwestern Russia, where all three occur in close proximity but where *heuglini* appears to be reproductively isolated from both (Filchagov & Semashko 1987), militates against treating *heuglini* as conspecific with either, so kept separate here pending further studies. P. Yésou (*in litt.*) points out that the relationships between *cachinnans* and *barabensis* (which appears closer to *L. heuglini taimyrensis*) are not yet fully understood and that there is a possibility that the *heuglini* group will prove to be conspecific with *L. cachinnans*. In the meantime it seems preferable to keep *heuglini* separate pending further studies. Includes *vegae* Vega Gull, often (including by Voous 1977, Cheng 1987 and Sibley & Monroe 1990) treated as part of the *heuglini* group and thereby considered conspecific with *L. argentatus* (or sometimes *L. fuscus*), but occasionally treated as specifically distinct. There is, however, a continuum from *heuglini* through *taimyrensis* to *vegae* (Filchagov *et al.* 1992), so *vegae* is best grouped with *heuglini*.

Larus schistisagus Slaty-backed Gull: sometimes treated as conspecific with *L. argentatus* Herring Gull, as some hybridization reported (see Vaurie 1965a). The hybridization is with the form *vegae*, however, which is here included in *L. heuglini* Heuglin's Gull rather than *L. argentatus*. See also *L. heuglini*.

Larus glaucescens Glaucous-winged Gull: formerly sometimes treated as conspecific with *L. argentatus* Herring Gull (with which there is at least limited hybridization), but may be conspecific with *L. occidentalis* Western Gull with which it hybridizes extensively (American Ornithologists' Union 1983).

Larus glaucoides Iceland Gull: includes *kumlieni* Kumlien's Gull, a vagrant to the Palearctic, which may (with *thayeri* treated as a subspecies) be worthy of specific status. Also includes *thayeri* Thayer's Gull, a vagrant to the Palearctic (Japan: see Brazil 1991), sometimes (mostly formerly, and including by Voous 1977) treated as specifically distinct, but see Snell (1989) who refuted the earlier findings of Smith (1966).

STERNIDAE

(merged in Laridae by Sibley & Monroe 1990)

Sterna nilotica Gull-billed Tern: alternatively (as in Voous 1977, Cheng 1987 and Stepanyan 1990) *Gelochelidon nilotica*.

Sterna caspia Caspian Tern: alternatively (as in Cheng 1987 and Stepanyan 1990) *Hydroprogne caspia*. Synonym *H. tschegrava*.

Sterna bergii Greater Crested Tern: alternatively (as in Cheng 1987) *Thalasseus bergii*.

Sterna bengalensis Lesser Crested Tern: alternatively (as in Cheng 1987) *Thalasseus bengalensis*.

Sterna bernsteini Chinese Crested Tern: synonyms (as in Voous 1977) *S. zimmermanni* and (as in Cheng 1987) *Thalasseus zimmermanni*, but see Sibley & Monroe (1990).

Sterna sandvicensis Sandwich Tern: alternatively (as in Stepanyan 1990) *Thalasseus sandvicensis*.

Sterna albifrons Little Tern: includes *saundersi* Saunders's Tern, often (including by Voous 1977 and Sibley & Monroe 1990) treated as specifically distinct. Sibley & Monroe (1990) note that it may be conspecific, however, and with the increased level of information now available there seems to be insufficient justification for specific status for *saundersi*. C. S. Roselaar (in Cramp 1985) has convincingly demonstrated that none of the supposed differences in structure, plumage, moult or habitat used to justify specific status in the past are exclusive to this form: all are shared to some extent by nominate *albifrons* from adjacent areas. Vaurie (1965a) thought that it was probably sympatric with *albifrons* in the Persian Gulf, but this has never been confirmed. Instead, all the evidence points towards extensive intergradation in the Persian Gulf and Iraq.

Anous minutus Black Noddy: sometimes (including by Voous 1977) treated as conspecific with *A. tenuirostris* Lesser Noddy, but the variable populations of *minutus* can be separated as a group from the unvarying *tenuirostris* (Serventy *et al.* 1971) and the two forms have recently been found breeding sympatrically in the eastern Indian Ocean (Stokes & Hinchey 1992).

RYNCHOPIDAE

(merged in Laridae by Sibley & Monroe 1990)

ALCIDAE

(merged in Laridae by Sibley & Monroe 1990)

Cepphus columba Pigeon Guillemot: formerly sometimes treated as conspecific with *C. grylle* Black Guillemot, but they are now usually regarded as members of a superspecies (e.g. American Ornithologists' Union 1983).

Brachyramphus marmoratus Marbled Murrelet: includes *perdix* Long-billed Murrelet, the only form found in the Palearctic, which may well be worthy of specific rank. It shows considerable differences in both morphology and genetics (Piatt 1994).

Alle alle Little Auk: alternatively *Plotus alle*.

Lunda cirrhata Tufted Puffin: alternatively (as in Sibley & Monroe 1990) *Fratercula cirrhata*.

PTEROCLIDAE

(= Pteroclididae in Voous 1977)

Pterocles lichtensteinii Lichtenstein's Sandgrouse: formerly sometimes treated as conspecific with *P. indicus* Painted Sandgrouse.

COLUMBIDAE

Columba bollii Bolle's Pigeon: formerly sometimes treated as conspecific with *C. trocaz* Trocaz Pigeon, but *bollii* is as close to *C. junoniae* Laurel Pigeon, with which it is sympatric, as it is to *trocaz* (see C. S. Roselaar in Cramp 1985) and so now usually kept separate.

Streptopelia roseogrisea African Collared Dove: formerly sometimes treated as conspecific with *S. decaocto* Eurasian Collared Dove, but they are now usually regarded as members of a superspecies (see Goodwin 1970, Snow 1978). Includes '*risoria*', the domesticated 'Ringed Turtle Dove' (or 'Barbary Dove').

Streptopelia tranquebarica Red Turtle Dove: alternatively (as in Cheng 1987) *Oenopopelia tranquebarica*.

Streptopelia chinensis Spotted Dove: includes *suratensis*, which differs markedly in morphology (see Vaurie 1965a). Intermediates are found in Burma and SW China (Goodwin 1970).

PSITTACIDAE

Psittacula finschii Grey-headed Parakeet: sometimes (including by Voous 1977 and Cheng 1987) treated as conspecific with *P. himalayana* Slaty-headed Parakeet, but the two are sympatric in NE India (Husain 1959) and different enough to warrant allospecies treatment according to Sibley & Monroe (1990).

CUCULIDAE

Clamator jacobinus Jacobin Cuckoo: alternatively (as in Sibley & Monroe 1990) *Oxylophus jacobinus*.

Hierococcyx fugax Hodgson's Hawk Cuckoo: alternatively (as in Cheng 1987 and Sibley & Monroe 1990) *Cuculus fugax*. Includes *hyperythrus* Northern Hawk Cuckoo, the sole form recorded from the Palearctic (breeding in NE Asia), which may possibly be worthy of specific status, but no evidence has yet been presented in support of this treatment.

Hierococcyx varius Common Hawk Cuckoo: alternatively (as in Sibley & Monroe 1990) *Cuculus varius*.

Hierococcyx sparverioides Large Hawk Cuckoo: alternatively (as in Cheng 1987 and Sibley & Monroe 1990) *Cuculus sparverioides*.

Coccyzus species are treated as part of a separate family, Coccyzidae, by Sibley & Monroe 1990.

Centropus species are treated as a separate family, Centropodidae, by Sibley & Monroe 1990.

TYTONIDAE

Tyto capensis Grass Owl: Includes *longimembris* Eastern Grass Owl, the form recorded from the Palearctic (as a vagrant to Japan: see Brazil 1991), which is sometimes (including by Sibley & Monroe 1990) treated as specifically distinct. In spite of the wide geographic separation, morphological differences are not significant (Amadon & Jewett 1946), and there appears to be no justification, as yet, for treating them as separate species.

STRIGIDAE

Otus bakkamoena Collared Scops Owl: includes *lempiji* Collared Scops Owl, sometimes (including by Sibley & Monroe 1990, but not 1993) treated as specifically distinct. Roberts & King (1986) separated the two forms on vocal differences, but Voous (1988) considered these differences to be intraspecific. (If *lempiji* is split off, *O. bakkamoena* is renamed 'Indian Scops Owl'.)

Otus brucei Pallid Scops Owl: formerly sometimes treated as conspecific with *O. scops* European Scops Owl or with *O. sunia* Oriental Scops Owl, but is sympatric with the former in Pakistan (Roberts & King 1986) and elsewhere in W Asia (Vaurie 1965a).

Otus senegalensis African Scops Owl: sometimes (including by Sibley & Monroe 1993, but not 1990) treated as conspecific with *O. scops* European Scops Owl, but it differs in vocalizations (see Dowsett & Dowsett-Lemaire 1993).

Otus sunia Oriental Scops Owl: sometimes (including by Cheng 1987 and Sibley & Monroe 1993, but not 1990) treated as conspecific with *O. scops* European Scops Owl. The status of this closely related form has oscillated back and forth but it is morphologically and vocally distinct (Marshall 1978, Roberts & King 1986). This species was placed after *O. bakkamoena* by Voous (1977), but is usually placed near to *O. scops* to reflect the close relationship.

Otus elegans Ryukyu Scops Owl: sometimes (including by Voous 1977) treated as conspecific with *O. sunia* Oriental Scops Owl or (including by Cheng 1987) as conspecific with *O. scops* European Scops Owl when *sunia* is included in that species. Occasionally treated as conspecific with *O. manadensis* Sulawesi Scops Owl. It is morphologically and vocally distinct, however (Marshall 1978). Now considered to be part of the *O. magicus* Moluccan Scops Owl superspecies (see Sibley & Monroe 1993).

Bubo bubo Eurasian Eagle Owl: includes *ascalaphus* Pharaoh Eagle Owl and *bengalensis* Rock Eagle Owl, either of which are sometimes (including by Sibley & Monroe 1990) treated as specifically distinct. However, *ascalaphus* intergrades with *Bubo bubo interpositus* in the Middle East while *bengalensis* has the same plumage pattern as *B. bubo*, differing only in size (Vaurie 1965a).

Strix uralensis Ural Owl: includes *davidi* Père David's Owl, occasionally (including by Sibley & Monroe 1990) treated as specifically distinct. Although there are morphological differences, little is known about this form. Information about behaviour and vocalizations is largely lacking. May well be worthy of specific status, but retained in *S. uralensis* pending further data.

APODIDAE

Apus alexandri Cape Verde Swift: sometimes treated as conspecific with either *A. unicolor* Plain Swift or *A. apus* Common Swift, but Brooke (1971a) considered it had no close relatives.

Apus unicolor Plain Swift: sometimes treated as conspecific with *A. apus* Common Swift, a view supported by Brooke (1971a), but more usually kept separate because of smaller size, more deeply forked tail and plumage differences (see C. S. Roselaar in Cramp *et al.* 1985).

Apus melba Alpine Swift: alternatively (as in Sibley & Monroe 1990) *Tachymarptis melba*.

Apus affinis Little Swift: includes *nipalensis* House Swift, sometimes (including by Sibley & Monroe 1990) treated as specifically distinct. The two forms were separated by Snow (1978) on the basis of rather slight morphological differences and apparent contact without intergradation in the Indian subcontinent, but the supposed sympatry in Nepal (Brooke 1971b) has not been confirmed (see Inskipp & Inskipp 1991).

ALCEDINIDAE

Halcyon species were treated as part of a separate family, Dacelonidae, by Sibley & Monroe (1990), but this was corrected to Halcyonidae in Sibley & Monroe (1993).

Halcyon chloris Collared Kingfisher: alternatively (as in Sibley & Monroe 1990) *Todirhamphus chloris*.

Halcyon cinnamomina Micronesian Kingfisher: alternatively (as in Sibley & Monroe 1990) *Todirhamphus cinnamominus*. Includes *miyakoensis* Miyako Kingfisher, the sole Palearctic form and known only from a single specimen, which is sometimes(including by Voous 1977) treated as specifically distinct. See Vaurie (1965a), Sibley & Monroe (1990) and Fry & Fry (1992) regarding its probable affinities with *H. cinnamomina* and the uncertain origin of the specimen.

Ceryle rudis Pied Kingfisher: this species is treated as part of a separate family, Cerylidae, by Sibley & Monroe (1990).

Ceryle alcyon Belted Kingfisher: alternatively (as in Sibley & Monroe 1990) *Megaceryle alcyon*. This species is treated as part of a separate family, Cerylidae, by Sibley & Monroe (1990).

Ceryle lugubris Crested Kingfisher: alternatively (as in Sibley & Monroe 1990) *Megaceryle lugubris*. This species is treated as part of a separate family, Cerylidae, by Sibley & Monroe (1990).

MEROPIDAE

Merops persicus Blue-cheeked Bee-eater: sometimes (including by Voous 1977) treated as conspecific with *M. superciliosus* Madagascar Bee-eater (with the English name 'Blue-cheeked Bee-eater' being applied to the enlarged species). *M. p. chrysocercus* appears to intergrade with *M. s. superciliosus* and *M. s. alternans* in subsaharan Africa according to C. S. Roselaar (in Cramp 1985), but their breeding distributions are allopatric (Dowsett & Dowsett-Lemaire 1993). There are also close morphological similarities between *M. persicus* and the Asian *M. philippinus* and between the latter and *M. superciliosus*. Fry (1984) considered that there was no persuasive argument for uniting any particular two (see also discussion in Dowsett & Dowsett-Lemaire 1993).

CORACIIDAE

Coracias noevia Rufous-crowned Roller: often (as in Fry *et al.* 1988 and Dowsett & Forbes-Watson 1993) spelt *C. naevia.*

UPUPIDAE

Upupa epops Eurasian Hoopoe: the populations in subsaharan African and the southern Sahara are sometimes (as in Sibley & Monroe 1990) all included in the *africana* African Hoopoe group, which is sometimes treated as specifically distinct due to morphological differences and apparent sympatry in eastern Africa. At other times (as in Sibley & Monroe 1993, following a pers. comm. by R. Liversidge) *africana* is restricted to the southern half of the continent, making it extralimital to the Palearctic, and this is the treatment followed here. Note: the apparently intermediate specimens referred to by Vaurie (1959b) do not relate to *africana* as restrictively defined here, but only to the populations further north in Africa and which are here included in *U. epops*.

CAPITONIDAE

Megalaima species and other Asian barbets are treated as a separate family, Megalaimidae, by Sibley & Monroe (1990).

PICIDAE

Picus viridis European Green Woodpecker: includes *sharpei* Iberian Green Woodpecker (or Iberian Woodpecker[1]), which is morphologically distinct and may possibly be worthy of specific status.

Picus vaillantii Levaillant's Green Woodpecker: sometimes (including by Sibley & Monroe 1990, but not 1993) treated as conspecific with *P. viridis* European Green Woodpecker. Now often treated as specifically distinct as it not only shows similarities with *viridis* but also has characters that link it with *P. canus* Grey-headed Woodpecker, *P. squamatus* Scaly-bellied Woodpecker and *P. awokera* Japanese Green Woodpecker, so is perhaps an offshoot of a common ancestor (C. S. Roselaar in Cramp *et al.* 1985).

Dendrocopos species are alternatively placed in *Picoides*.

Dendrocopos leucopterus White-winged Woodpecker: sometimes treated as conspecific with *D. major* Great Spotted Woodpecker. Often regarded as members of a superspecies, but they occasionally hybridize and may be conspecific (C. S. Roselaar in Cramp et al. 1985).

Dendrocopos leucotos White-backed Woodpecker: includes *lilfordi* Lilford's Woodpecker, sometimes treated as specifically distinct. Haffer (1989) states that they differ in ecology and are altitudinally separated in eastern Yugoslavia, and that there is little evidence of hybridization.

Dendrocopos canicapillus Grey-capped Woodpecker: formerly sometimes treated as conspecific with *D. nanus* Brown-capped Woodpecker.

PITTIDAE

Pitta nympha Fairy Pitta: sometimes (including by Voous 1977) treated as conspecific with *P. brachyura* Indian Pitta. Now generally treated as members of a superspecies (e.g. Sibley & Monroe 1990). (Note: *P. brachyura* is often renamed 'Blue-winged Pitta' when *nympha, moluccensis* Blue-winged Pitta and *megarhyncha* Mangrove Pitta are treated as conspecific.)

ALAUDIDAE

Mirafra cantillans Singing Bush Lark: sometimes treated as conspecific with *M. javanica* Eastern Bush Lark (or Eastern Singing Bush Lark, or Australasian Lark[1]), with the English name 'Singing Bush Lark' being applied to the enlarged species. Regarded as members of a superspecies by Hall & Moreau (1970) and most subsequent authors.

Ammomanes cincturus Bar-tailed Lark: formerly sometimes treated as conspecific with *A. phoenicurus* Rufous-tailed Lark.

Calandrella cinerea Red-capped Lark: includes *blanfordi* Blanford's Lark, the sole Palearctic form, which is occasionally (including by Sibley & Monroe 1990) treated as specifically distinct, but see Dowsett & Dowsett-Lemaire (1993).

Calandrella brachydactyla Greater Short-toed Lark: sometimes (including by Cheng 1987 and Stepanyan 1990) treated as conspecific with *C. cinerea* Red-capped Lark, but they differ morphologically and are now usually treated as members of a superspecies (see Hall & Moreau 1970).

Calandrella rufescens Lesser Short-toed Lark: synonym *C. pispoletta*. Includes *cheleensis* (synonym *leucophaea*) Asian Short-toed Lark, sometimes (including by Sibley & Monroe 1990 and Stepanyan 1990) treated as specifically distinct. According to K. Mild (*in litt.*) none of the ten criteria used to separate *leucophaea* from *C. rufescens heinei* by Stepanyan (1967) are correct or else possible to check. Differences in measurements and morphological characters are insufficient to separate the taxa, the song appears to be identical to the human ear and no behavioural or ecological differences appear to exist. The supposed sympatry appears to be based on old literature and cannot be reliably checked from museum skins. This form is included in *C. rufescens* in the forthcoming *Larks, pipits and wagtails: an identification guide* by P. Alström and K. Mild.

Galerida theklae Thekla Lark: formerly sometimes treated as conspecific with *G. malabarica* Malabar Lark (or Malabar Crested Lark).

Alauda arvensis Eurasian Skylark: includes *japonica* Japanese Skylark, sometimes treated as conspecific with *A. gulgula* Oriental Skylark, or (including by Sibley & Monroe 1990 and Stepanyan 1990) treated as specifically distinct. Published evidence that supports specific status is largely lacking, however. The statement by Udagawa (1953) that *japonica* breeds sympatrically with *A. a. lonnbergi* on the small island of Yagishiri off NW Hokkaido, which was also mentioned by Vaurie (1959a), has never been confirmed. Included in *A. arvensis* in the forthcoming *Larks, pipits and wagtails: an identification guide* by P. Alström and K. Mild.

HIRUNDINIDAE

Riparia riparia Sand Martin: includes *diluta* Pale Sand Martin, which Goroshko (1993) treated as specifically distinct due to differences in morphology and reproductive isolation in the areas of overlap. Apparently intermediate populations are known from several different areas in Asia (Vaurie 1959a), so retained here in *R. riparia* pending further studies.

Hirundo fuligula Rock Martin: alternatively (as in Voous 1977) *Ptyonoprogne fuligula*. Includes *obsoleta* Pale Crag Martin, sometimes (including by Sibley & Monroe 1990) treated as specifically distinct (but see Hall & Moreau 1970 and Dowsett & Dowsett-Lemaire 1993). Occasionally treated as conspecific with *H.*

rupestris Eurasian Crag Martin, but it comes into contact with, or even overlaps with, the latter in western Asia and few intermediates have been reported (see Vaurie 1959a, C. S. Roselaar in Cramp 1988).

Hirundo rupestris Eurasian Crag Martin: alternatively (as in Voous 1977, Cheng 1987 and Stepanyan 1990) *Ptyonoprogne rupestris*.

Hirundo pyrrhonota American Cliff Swallow: alternatively (as in Stepanyan 1990) *Petrochelidon pyrrhonota*.

Delichon dasypus Asian House Martin: sometimes (including by Cheng 1987) treated as conspecific with *D. urbica* Common House Martin, but they overlap without interbreeding (Vaurie 1954d) and there are also differences in their biology including nest shape (Dyrnev *et al.* 1983).

MOTACILLIDAE

(merged in Passeridae by Sibley & Monroe 1990)

Anthus richardi Richard's Pipit: sometimes (including by Voous 1977 and Cheng 1987) treated as conspecific with *A. novaeseelandiae* Australasian Pipit (with the English name 'Richard's Pipit' also being applied to the enlarged species). There is an increasing tendency to treat *richardi*, as well as *rufulus* Paddyfield Pipit and extralimital forms in subsaharan Africa, as allospecies, but further studies of the *novaeseelandiae* complex are clearly desirable.

Anthus rufulus Paddyfield Pipit: sometimes (including by Voous 1977 and Cheng 1987) treated as conspecific with *A. novaeseelandiae* Australasian Pipit, or occasionally grouped separately with *A. richardi* Richard's Pipit. There is an increasing tendency to treat the *novaeseelandiae* complex as a series of allospecies (e.g. Sibley & Monroe 1990). The various populations of the south Asian *rufulus* group often show quite marked morphological differences compared to *A. richardi*, but whether or not *rufulus* should be treated as distinct from *A. novaeseelandiae* is debatable.

Anthus godlewskii Blyth's Pipit: formerly sometimes (including by Cheng 1987) treated as conspecific with *A. campestris* Tawny Pipit, but the breeding ranges overlap in Mongolia (Piechocki & Bolod 1972) and it shows differences in morphology (C. S. Roselaar in Cramp 1988). The song also differs from those of *A. campestris* and *A. richardi* (pers. obs. in Mongolia).

Anthus sylvanus Upland Pipit: this species was placed after *A. novaeseelandiae* by Voous (1977), following suggestions by R. K. Murton in Gooders (1970) that this species was a montane, non-migratory derivative of the latter, but T. P. Inskipp (*in. litt.*) points out that the author's photographs used to illustrate the article are not of this species but of some form of *A. novaeseelandiae*!

Anthus gustavi Pechora Pipit: includes *menzbieri* Menzbier's Pipit, which has a highly disjunct breeding distribution and shows some morphological differences (C. S. Roselaar in Cramp 1988) and a rather different song (pers. obs. at Lake Khanka, Ussuriland). Further studies may show this form to be worthy of specific rank.

Anthus petrosus Rock Pipit: sometimes (including by Voous 1977) treated as conspecific with *A. spinoletta* Water Pipit, but see Alström & Mild (1987) and Knox (1988a).

Anthus rubescens Buff-bellied Pipit: formerly (including by Voous 1977 and Cheng 1987) treated as conspecific with *A. spinoletta* Water Pipit, but the ranges overlap without hybridization (Nazarenko 1978, Alström & Mild 1987, Knox 1988a). The original study was limited in time and scope, so more extensive studies in the area of overlap are desirable.

Motacilla flava Yellow Wagtail: includes a series of more or less distinct groups, some of which, especially *feldegg* Black-headed Wagtail, *lutea* Yellow-headed Wagtail and *taivana* Green-headed Wagtail, are sometimes (including by Stepanyan 1990) treated as specifically distinct. The form *taivana*, sometimes together with *flavissima* British Yellow Wagtail (or Yellowish-crowned Wagtail[1]), has frequently been included with *lutea* in a separate *M. lutea*. See the discussion of this complex situation by C. S. Roselaar in Cramp (1988).

Motacilla alba White Wagtail: includes *lugens* Black-backed Wagtail, sometimes (including by Sibley & Monroe 1990 and Stepanyan 1990) treated as specifically distinct. Although *lugens* and *M. a. ocularis* are apparently sympatric in Kamchatka and southern Ussuriland, some hybridization occurs in the zone of overlap according to Kistchinski & Lobkov (1979). This is said to be restricted, but more detailed studies, which might throw further light on the situation, have not so far been forthcoming. P. Alström and K. Mild (*in litt.*) state that examination of large numbers of museum skins indicates that *lugens* and *ocularis* intergrade and that they regard specific status for *lugens* as premature. These authors include *lugens* in *M. alba* in their forthcoming *Larks, pipits and wagtails: an identification guide* and I prefer to follow this more cautious approach here. Note: Sibley & Monroe (1990) erroneously include in *M. lugens* the forms *leucopsis* and *alboides*. In fact *M. lugens* includes only the form *lugens* of northeastern Asia (see Morlan 1981). Also includes *personata* Masked Wagtail, sometimes (including by Stepanyan 1990) treated as specifically distinct. While it apparently behaves as a good species where it comes into contact with *M. a. dukhunensis* in the former USSR, it hybridizes extensively with it elsewhere (C. S. Roselaar in Cramp 1988). Other members of the *alba* complex, including *yarrellii* British Pied Wagtail (or Pied Wagtail) and *subpersonata* Moroccan Pied Wagtail (or Moroccan Wagtail[1]), may possibly deserve specific status also.

Motacilla grandis Japanese Wagtail: sometimes (including by Cheng 1987) treated as conspecific with *M. alba* Eurasian Pied Wagtail, but they are sympatric in Japan (Brazil 1991).

Motacilla aguimp African Pied Wagtail: formerly sometimes treated as conspecific with *M. alba* Eurasian Pied Wagtail, but now usually treated as a member of a superspecies (e.g. Hall & Moreau 1970).

CAMPEPHAGIDAE

(merged in Corvidae by Sibley & Monroe 1990)

Pericrocotus tegimae Ryukyu Minivet: sometimes treated as conspecific with *P. divaricatus* Ashy Minivet, but differs in morphology, moult and vocalizations (Stresemann & Stresemann 1972, Brazil 1991).

PYCNONOTIDAE

Pycnonotus leucotis White-eared Bulbul: sometimes (including by Voous 1977) treated as conspecific with *P. leucogenys* Himalayan Bulbul, but see Vaurie (1959a) and Sibley & Monroe (1990). The relationship between the two forms is clouded by the uncertain status of the apparently intermediate form *humii*, which may or may not represent a hybrid population (Vaurie 1959a).

Pycnonotus xanthopygos White-spectacled Bulbul: formerly sometimes treated as conspecific with *P. barbatus* Common Bulbul, but they are now usually regarded as members of a superspecies (e.g. Hall & Moreau 1970).

Hypsipetes amaurotis Brown-eared Bulbul: alternatively (as in Sibley & Monroe 1990) *Ixos amaurotis* or (as in Stepanyan 1990) *Microscelis amaurotis*.

Hypsipetes leucocephalus Black Bulbul: formerly usually (including by Voous 1977 and Cheng 1987) treated as conspecific with *H. madagascariensis* (alternatively *Microscelis madagascariensis*) Madagascar Bulbul (with the English name 'Black Bulbul' being applied to the enlarged species). Following the discovery of two sympatric forms in the Comoros (Louette & Herremans 1985), the tendency has been to treat the widely scattered members of the *madagascariensis* complex as distinct species (e.g. A. S. Cheke in Diamond 1987). Sibley & Monroe (1990) treat them as allospecies.

BOMBYCILLIDAE

Hypocolius ampelinus Grey Hypocolius: treated as the sole member of a separate family, Hypocolidae, by Sibley & Monroe (1990).

TROGLODYTIDAE
(merged in Certhidae by Sibley & Monroe 1990)

PRUNELLIDAE
(merged in Passeridae by Sibley & Monroe 1990)

Prunella ocularis Radde's Accentor: formerly sometimes treated as conspecific with *P. fulvescens* Brown Accentor, but considered to be more closely related to *P. atrogularis* Black-throated Accentor by Marien (1951) and treated as a separate species by Vaurie (1955a, 1959a) and most subsequent authors.

Prunella fagani Arabian Accentor: formerly sometimes treated as conspecific with *P. ocularis* Radde's Accentor, but appears as closely related to *P. atrogularis* Black-throated Accentor or *P. fulvescens* Brown Accentor, so treated as a distinct species by Vaurie (1955a) and most subsequent authors.

TURDIDAE
(merged in Muscicapidae by Sibley & Monroe 1990)

Cercotrichas galactotes Rufous-tailed Scrub Robin: alternatively (as in Dowsett & Forbes-Watson 1993) *Erythropygia galactotes*.

Luscinia sibilans Rufous-tailed Robin: alternatively *Pseudaedon sibilans*.

Luscinia obscura Blackthroat: in the past has sometimes been considered a dark morph of *L. pectardens* Firethroat (Goodwin & Vaurie 1956, Vaurie 1959a), but this theory was challenged by Ripley (1958) and since more information has emerged about its morphology (see Ripley & King 1966) and its breeding distribution, which lies to the north of that of *L. pectardens* in southern Gansu, southern Shaanxi (Cheng 1987) and northernmost Sichuan (H. Buck pers. comm., pers. obs.), it has generally been treated as a distinct species. Studies of this little known form are badly needed.

Phoenicurus erythronota Eversmann's Redstart: often (as in Voous 1977, Cheng 1987 and Stepanyan 1990) spelt *P. erythronotus* (but see Sibley & Monroe 1990).

Phoenicurus alaschanicus Przevalski's Redstart: formerly sometimes treated as conspecific with *P. erythronota* Eversmann's Redstart. Vaurie (1959a) tentatively included this form with *erythronota*, but the males differ markedly in morphology and the breeding ranges are widely allopatric, so now usually treated as a full species.

Phoenicurus coeruleocephalus Blue-capped Redstart: often (as in Voous 1977, Cheng 1987, Sibley & Monroe 1990 and Stepanyan 1990) spelt *P. caeruleocephalus*, but the original spelling (*Phoenicura coeruleocephala*) was not validly emended and under current ICZN rules must stand.

Chaimarrornis leucocephalus White-capped Redstart: alternatively *Thamnolaea leucocephala*. This unusual species was placed after *Oenanthe leucura* by Voous (1977), following Goodwin (1957), but more recently Orenstein (1979) proposed that it should be included in *Phoenicurus*. Sibley & Monroe (1990) retained it in its own genus, however, but placed it immediately after *Phoenicurus*, which is the treatment followed here.

Hodgsonius phaenicuroides White-bellied Redstart: often (as in Voous 1977 and Cheng 1987) spelt *H. phoenicuroides*.

Grandala coelicolar Grandala: often (as in Voous 1977, Cheng 1987 and Sibley & Monroe 1990) spelt *G. coelicolor*, but the original spelling was not validly emended and under current ICZN rules must stand.

Saxicola torquata Common Stonechat: includes *maura* Siberian Stonechat, sometimes (including by Sibley & Monroe 1990, but not 1993) treated as specifically distinct. Separation rests on morphological differences combined with a supposed lack of intergradation in the Caucasus region (see Vaurie 1959a), but apparent intermediates between *armenica* (a member of the *maura* group) and *S. t. rubicola* are encountered in NE Turkey and the Transcaucasus region (pers. obs.). The degree of intergradation in the area of contact requires further investigation.

Oenanthe bottae Red-breasted Wheatear: formerly sometimes treated as conspecific with *O. isabellina* Isabelline Wheatear, but they are now usually regarded as members of a superspecies (see Hall & Moreau 1970).

Oenanthe oenanthe Northern Wheatear: includes *seebohmi* Seebohm's Wheatear (or Black-throated Wheatear), formerly sometimes treated as specifically distinct.

Oenanthe pleschanka Pied Wheatear: sometimes (including by Cheng 1987) treated as conspecific with *O. hispanica* Black-eared Wheatear. The degree and effects of hybridization in the zones of overlap are complex (Panov 1986), but the areas of overlap have proved to be narrow and the two forms are usually treated as a superspecies (see C. S. Roselaar in Cramp 1988).

Oenanthe cypriaca Cyprus Wheatear: sometimes (including by Voous 1977) treated as conspecific with *O. pleschanka* Pied Wheatear, but differs in morphology (showing almost no sexual dimorphism), vocalizations, behaviour and habitat (see Christensen 1974, Sluys & van den Berg 1982).

Oenanthe xanthoprymna Red-tailed Wheatear: includes *chrysopygia* Rufous-tailed Wheatear, occasionally treated as specifically distinct. Morphological differences are marked, but some intergradation occurs (Vaurie 1949c, 1959a). The extent of hybridization is, however, largely unknown and the two forms may merit treatment as distinct species.

Oenanthe picata Variable Wheatear: the origins of polymorphism in the *O. picata* complex have been discussed in detail by Panov (1992).

Oenanthe lugens Mourning Wheatear: includes *lugentoides* Arabian Wheatear, sometimes (including by Sibley & Monroe 1990) treated as specifically distinct, but the published supporting evidence appears to be very limited. Sibley & Monroe (1990) refer only to Hollom *et al.* (1988) in support of specific status, but while treating *lugentoides* as specifically distinct the latter do not give their reasons for doing so. There are, however, some modest morphological differences and possibly some differences in vocalizations compared to nominate *lugens*.

Monticola cinclorhynchus Blue-capped Rock Thrush: sometimes (as in Voous 1977) spelt *M. cinclorhyncha*.

Monticola gularis White-throated Rock Thrush: alternatively (as in Stepanyan 1990) *Petrophila gularis*. Formerly sometimes (including by Cheng 1987) treated as conspecific with *M. cinclorhynchus* Blue-capped Rock Thrush, but morphological differences are pronounced.

Monticola rufiventris Chestnut-bellied Rock Thrush: formerly sometimes treated as conspecific with *M. solitarius* Blue Rock Thrush, but is morphologically distinct.

Monticola solitarius Blue Rock Thrush: includes *philippensis* Red-bellied Rock Thrush, sometimes treated as specifically distinct. Stepanyan (1990) only tentatively included *philippensis* in *M. solitarius*. Although *philippensis* is morphologically distinct, many intermediates have been recorded (Vaurie 1959a).

Myophonus caeruleus Blue Whistling Thrush: often (as in Voous 1977 and Cheng 1987) spelt *Myiophoneus caeruleus* or (as in Sibley & Monroe 1990, who misquote their references) *Myiophonus caeruleus*.

Zoothera dauma Scaly Thrush: includes *aurea* White's Thrush, which may merit specific status. Little attention has been payed to the *dauma* complex in mainland Asia, but with so many forms being split in Australasia and the Asian islands (see Sibley & Monroe 1990), more attention should be given to the mainland forms. The drawn out, haunting whistles of the migratory *aurea* (and the partly migratory *toratugumi*) are so different from the much more typical, thrush-type songs of nominate *dauma* of the Himalayas and the other south Asian forms (see Ali & Ripley 1973, M. G. Wilson in Cramp 1988) that it is hard to imagine that they would not be reproductively isolated if they were to come into contact with each other. Sonagraphic analysis of the vocalizations of the two Australian forms of the *dauma* complex has been used to support recognition of these forms as distinct species (Ford 1983), and studies in Asia may lead to similar conclusions.

Zoothera major Amami Thrush: sometimes (including by Voous 1977) treated as conspecific with *Z. dauma* White's Thrush, but differs in size, number of retrices and vocalizations (Ishihara 1986, Brazil 1991).

Zoothera naevia Varied Thrush: alternatively (as in Stepanyan 1990) *Ixoreus naevius*.

Zoothera terrestris Bonin Thrush: alternatively (as in Voous 1977) *Cichlopasser terrestris*.

Hylocichla mustelina Wood Thrush: alternatively (as in Sibley & Monroe 1990) *Catharus mustelinus*.

Catharus minimus Grey-cheeked Thrush: includes *bicknelli* Bicknell's Thrush, which has occurred as a vagrant in the Palearctic. Ouellet (1993) argues in favour of specific status for this form, based on differences in morphology, ecology, vocalizations and genetics.

Turdus menachensis Yemen Thrush: sometimes (including by Dowsett & Forbes-Watson 1993, following Dowsett & Dowsett-Lemaire 1993) treated as conspecific with *T. olivaceus* Olive Thrush.

Turdus chrysolaus Brown-headed Thrush: formerly sometimes (including by Cheng 1987) treated as conspecific with *T. pallidus* Pale Thrush. Regarded as members of a superspecies (together with *T. eunomus*) by Stepanyan (1983).

Turdus hortulorum Grey-backed Thrush: formerly sometimes treated as conspecific with *T. dissimilis* Black-breasted Thrush, but they are morphologically very dissimilar.

Turdus obscurus Eyebrowed Thrush: formerly sometimes (including by Cheng 1987) treated as conspecific with *T. pallidus* Pale Thrush, but the breeding ranges overlap (Vaurie 1959a). Regarded as members of a superspecies (together with *T. chrysolaus*) by Stepanyan (1983).

Turdus naumanni Dusky Thrush: includes *eunomus* Dusky Thrush, sometimes treated as specifically distinct. The breeding ranges overlap in the west and intermediates are common there, but apparent intermediates also occur in areas such as the Anadyr river, far from the range of *T. n. naumanni*, where there is no chance of hybridization (Dementiev & Gladkov 1954b).

Turdus ruficollis Dark-throated Thrush: includes *atrogularis* Black-throated Thrush, sometimes treated as specifically distinct, but they hybridize freely in the zone of contact in the Altai region and the Lower Tunguska river according to Vaurie (1959a).

SYLVIIDAE

Tesia castaneocoronata Chestnut-headed Tesia: alternatively *Oligura castaneocoronata*.

Urosphena squameiceps Asian Stubtail Warbler: alternatively (as in Voous 1977 and Cheng 1987) *Cettia squameiceps*. Placing this species in *Urosphena* rather than *Cettia* is appropriate as it is most unlike a typical *Cettia* in both morphology and vocalizations (King 1989).

Cettia diphone Japanese Bush Warbler: alternatively (as in Stepanyan 1990) *Horeites diphone*. Includes *canturians* Manchurian Bush Warbler, occasionally (including by Sibley & Monroe 1990) treated as specifically distinct, but published evidence in support of this treatment is largely lacking.

Cettia fortipes Brownish-flanked Bush Warbler: formerly sometimes treated as conspecific with *C. vulcania* (synonym *C. montana*) Sunda Bush Warbler (or Mountain Bush Warbler), but see Wells (1982).

Cettia flavolivacea Aberrant Bush Warbler: sometimes (as in Cheng 1987) spelt *C. flavolivaceus*.

Cettia acanthizoides Yellowish-bellied Bush Warbler: Sibley & Monroe (1990) used *C. robustipes* for this species, but this was in error (see Sibley & Monroe 1993).

Bradypterus thoracicus Spotted Bush Warbler: includes *davidi* Père David's Bush Warbler, which may be worthy of specific status (see Round, P. D. & Loskot, V. M. A reappraisal of the taxonomy of the Spotted Bush Warbler *Bradypterus thoracicus*. *Forktail* in press.)

Bradypterus tacsanowskius Chinese Bush Warbler: sometimes (as in Voous 1977) spelt *B. taczanowskius*.

Cisticola species are treated as part of a separate family, Cisticolidae, by Sibley & Monroe 1990.

Prinia species are treated as part of a separate family, Cisticolidae, by Sibley & Monroe 1990.

Prinia inornata Plain Prinia: sometimes (including by Cheng 1987) treated as conspecific with *P. subflava* Tawny-flanked Prinia (but see Hall & Moreau 1970).

Prinia criniger Striated Prinia: includes *catharia* of west-central China, sometimes (including by Cheng 1987) treated (together with other extralimital forms) as conspecific with *P. polychroa* Brown Prinia. Some of these populations overlap with *polychroa*, however, without interbreeding (Deignan 1957).

Spiloptila clamans Cricket Warbler: alternatively *Prinia clamans*. Treated as part of a separate family, Cisticolidae, by Sibley & Monroe (1990).

Scotocerca inquieta Scrub Warbler: treated as part of a separate family, Cisticolidae, by Sibley & Monroe (1990).

Rhopophilus pekinensis Chinese Hill Warbler: treated as part of a separate family, Cisticolidae, by Sibley & Monroe (1990). This unusual bird is of uncertain affinities and may be more closely related to the babblers (see Sibley & Monroe 1990).

Locustella ochotensis Middendorff's Grasshopper Warbler: sometimes treated as conspecific with *L. certhiola* Pallas's Grasshopper Warbler. Although Sibley & Monroe (1990) state that *L. certhiola* and *L. ochotensis* are marginally sympatric in eastern Siberia with little or no interbreeding, apparently intermediate individuals are frequently met with in the Magadan area on the north coast of the Sea of Okhotsk (A. V. Andreev pers. comm., pers. obs.). To my ear, the vocalizations seem rather similar also. Further studies are needed.

Locustella pleskei Styan's Grasshopper Warbler: sometimes (including by Voous 1977 and Cheng 1987) treated as conspecific with *L. ochotensis* Middendorff's Grasshopper Warbler, or sometimes (when *ochotensis* is also treated as conspecific) with *L. certhiola* Pallas's Grasshopper Warbler. Nazarov & Shibaev (1983) treated *pleskei* as distinct based on differences in morphology, vocalizations and ecology. However, the differences in time of arrival, habitat and behaviour on the breeding grounds in Japan reported by Kennerley & Leader (1993) may simply reflect the very considerable differences in latitude (and thus habitat and climate) between the almost subtropical Izu islands and the northern island of Hokkaido. In the Russian Far East *pleskei* arrives on the small islands in the Vladivostok area only in the last half of May while the first *ochotensis* reach southern Sakhalin at the very end of May. In both areas the birds often nest in damp, grassy places with rich herbage and low bushes close to the sea (S. Surmach and S. C. Madge pers. comm., pers. obs.). If *ochotensis* merits specific status, then *pleskei* is different enough again to be treated separately. Further studies are needed: in particular the extent of the differences in the vocalizations needs to be established.

Locustella fasciolata Gray's Grasshopper Warbler: includes *amnicola* Sakhalin Grasshopper Warbler, sometimes (including by Stepanyan 1990 and Sibley & Monroe 1990, but not 1993). Reported to be more rufescent, differ in wing formula and be sympatric with *L. fasciolata* in Sakhalin (see Stepanyan 1972, 1990; Mayr & Vuilleumier 1983), but differences thought to be too slight to warrant separation by Neufeldt & Netschajew (1977). Believed to refer to first autumn individuals of *fasciolata* by L. Svensson (*in. litt.*). See also Sibley & Monroe !993).

Locustella pryeri Japanese Swamp Warbler: alternatively *Megalurus pryeri*. Morioka & Shigeta (1993) have argued convincingly that, because of differences in structure (i.e. bill, legs and feet), wing formula, tail length, length of undertail coverts and the characteristics of the rictal bristles, this species should not be placed in the otherwise purely Oriental and Australasian genus *Megalurus*. Instead, because of many similarities, they recommend it should be placed in *Locustella*, which is the treatment followed here. These authors indicate that further studies could result in this unusual species, which is unique among the Sylviidae in having a vestigial wing claw, being placed in its own genus.

Acrocephalus melanopogon Moustached Warbler: alternatively (as in Stepanyan 1990) *Lusciniola melanopogon*.

Acrocephalus sorghophilus Speckled Reed Warbler: sometimes (as in Voous 1977) spelt *A. sorgophilus*.

Acrocephalus concinens Blunt-winged Warbler: sometimes (including by Cheng 1987) treated as conspecific with *A. agricola* Paddyfield Warbler, but considered specifically distinct by Alström *et al.* (1991) on the basis of differences in both morphological and vocalizations.

Acrocephalus agricola Paddyfield Warbler: includes *tangorum* Manchurian Reed Warbler, sometimes (including by Sibley & Monroe 1990, but not 1993) treated as specifically distinct, or as conspecific with *A. bistrigiceps* Black-browed Reed Warbler. The taxonomic status of this form is disputed, with conspecificity with *agricola* supported by Alström *et al.* (1991 and, more tentatively, 1994) and specific status by Kennerley & Leader (1992). Further studies are needed.

Acrocephalus baeticatus African Reed Warbler: sometimes treated as conspecific with *A. scirpaceus* European Reed Warbler, or occasionally with *A. dumetorum* Blyth's Reed Warbler, but see Ash *et al.* (1989). Note: Sibley & Monroe (1990) state that Ash *et al.* (1989) treat *baeticatus* as a race of *A. cinnamomeus* Cinnamon Reed Warbler, but in fact the reverse is true.

Acrocephalus stentoreus Clamorous Reed Warbler: formerly sometimes treated as conspecific with *A. arundinaceus* Great Reed Warbler, but the breeding ranges overlap with no sign of interbreeding (see Stresemann & Arnold 1949).

Acrocephalus arundinaceus Great Reed Warbler: includes *orientalis* Oriental Reed Warbler, sometimes (including by Sibley & Monroe 1990, but not 1993) treated as specifically distinct (but see Sibley & Monroe 1993). Although some support for specific status is provided by the different juvenile plumage and, to some degree, by the different moult strategy, the vocalizations appear to be fairly similar. Further studies are needed.

Acrocephalus griseldis Basra Reed Warbler: sometimes (including by Voous 1977) treated as conspecific with *A. arundinaceus*. Sibley & Monroe (1993) note that this species may be conspecific with *A. stentoreus* Clamorous Reed Warbler, but give no explanation for this statement. This form is morphologically very different from either, has different vocalizations and is now increasingly treated as specifically distinct (see Pearson & Backhurst 1988).

Acrocephalus aedon Thick-billed Warbler: alternatively (as in Cheng 1987 and Stepanyan 1990) *Phragmaticola aedon* (but spelt *aeedon* in Stepanyan).

Hippolais caligata Booted Warbler: includes *rama* Sykes's Warbler, sometimes (including by Stepanyan 1990 and Sibley & Monroe 1993, but not 1990) treated as specifically distinct. Morphological differences are, however, not particularly marked and there appear to be no significant differences in vocalizations, while many intermediates are known to occur (Svensson 1994). K. Mild (*in litt.*) states that playback studies support conspecificity.

Parisoma buryi Yemen Warbler: alternatively (as in Sibley & Monroe 1990 and Dowsett & Forbes-Watson 1993) *Sylvia buryi*. This unusual species is of uncertain affinities and, while retained here in *Parisoma* pending further developments, is placed close to *Sylvia* in view of the close relationship between the two genera (see Dowsett & Dowsett-Lemaire 1993). Placed after *Bradypterus luteoventris* by Voous (1977).

Sylvia mystacea Ménétries's Warbler: formerly sometimes treated as conspecific with *S. melanocephala* Sardinian Warbler or occasionally as conspecific with *S. cantillans* Subalpine Warbler. Although very different from nominate *melanocephala*, is quite close in coloration and structure to *S. m. momus* (and also *S. m. norrisae*) of the Middle East (C. S. Roselaar in Cramp 1992, Svensson 1992). *S. mystacea* exhibits some differences in vocalizations and there is no evidence of hybridization in the possible area of contact with *momus* in the Levant (see E. K. Dunn and C. S. Roselaar in Cramp 1992) so best kept separate.

Sylvia melanothorax Cyprus Warbler: formerly sometimes treated as conspecific with *S. melanocephala* Sardinian Warbler, but they show considerable differences in morphology and are now usually regarded as members of a superspecies (see C. S. Roselaar in Cramp 1992).

Sylvia curruca Lesser Whitethroat: includes *althaea* Hume's Whitethroat, sometimes (including by Stepanyan 1990 and by Sibley & Monroe 1993, but not 1990) treated as specifically distinct. Also includes *minula* Desert Whitethroat, sometimes (including by Cheng 1987 and by Sibley & Monroe 1993, but not 1990) treated as specifically distinct. In spite of the arguments of Haffer (1989) in favour of treating the *curruca*, *althaea* and *minula* groups as three separate species, there is such a high level of intergradation between the different populations that it seems prudent to treat them as conspecific until such time as further studies suggest otherwise (see C. S. Roselaar in Cramp 1992, Svennson 1992).

Seicercus burkii Golden-spectacled Warbler: According to P. Alström (*in litt.*), three distinct forms resembling *burkii* occur together on Emei Shan in central Sichuan and probably merit treatment as separate species. Two of these forms (one of which is *S. burkii sensu stricto*) occur above 2000m on Emei Shan in central Sichuan and thus reach our limits.

Phylloscopus coronatus Eastern Crowned Warbler: formerly sometimes treated as conspecific with *P. occipitalis* Western Crowned Warbler, but DNA studies indicate that the relationship is not very close (Richman & Price 1992).

Phylloscopus borealoides Sakhalin Leaf Warbler: sometimes (including by Voous 1977, by Sibley & Monroe 1990, but not 1993, and tentatively by Stepanyan 1990) treated as conspecific with *P. tenellipes* Pale-legged Leaf Warbler, but separated by Martens (1988) on the basis of completely different vocalizations as well as some morphological differences. (See also Weprincew *et al.* 1989, 1990.)

Phylloscopus ijimae Ijima's Leaf Warbler: formerly sometimes treated as conspecific with *P. coronatus* Eastern Crowned Warbler or as conspecific with *P. tenellipes* Pale-legged Leaf Warbler (but see Martens 1980). Recent DNA studies indicate that its relationships with these species are not very close (Richman & Price 1992).

Phylloscopus trochiloides Greenish Warbler: includes *plumbeitarsus* Two-barred Warbler, sometimes (including by Voous 1977 and by Sibley & Monroe 1990, but not 1993) treated as specifically distinct. Differences in morphology are slight and reports that the ranges overlap without any interbreeding in south-central Siberia (Vaurie 1959a, Williamson 1967) are disputed (Svensson 1992). Vocalizations, behaviour and habitat are all very similar (Svensson 1992) and play-back experiments strongly support conspecificity (K. Mild *in litt.*). (See also K. M. Bauer & J. Haffer in Glutz von Blotzheim 1991). Also includes *nitidus* Bright-green Warbler, usually (including by Voous 1977, by Stepanyan 1990 and by Sibley & Monroe 1990, but not 1993) treated as specifically distinct. In spite of the greater degree of morphological distinctness of *nitidus*, vocalizations, behaviour and habitat are virtually identical (Svensson 1992) and playback studies in Turkey strongly support conspecificity (K. Mild *in litt.*). Contrary to Albrecht (1984), there is virtually no evidence of intergradation in museum skins (Svensson 1992), but in any event the evidence suggests that there is a substantial gap between the breeding distributions of *nitidus* and *P. t. viridanus*. The latter is found breeding in the southern Tien Shan (Dementiev & Gladkov 1954b, Vaurie 1959a) but is thought only to be a passage migrant in eastern Afghanistan (Paludan 1959), an area where Vaurie (1959a) thought it probably bred. Similarly no breeding *nitidus* were found in western Afghanistan by Paludan (1959). The nearest confirmed breeding areas for *nitidus* being in the Kopet Dagh in Iran and adjacent Turkmenistan (Dementiev & Gladkov 1954b, Vaurie 1959a). A record in May from the Kugitang (or Kuh i Tang) range in southernmost Uzbekistan, where breeding has not been confirmed (Dementiev & Gladkov 1954b), may well relate to passage migrants.

Phylloscopus chloronotus Lemon-rumped Warbler: sometimes (including by Voous 1977, Cheng 1987 and Sibley & Monroe 1990, but not 1993) treated as conspecific with *P. proregulus* Pallas's Leaf Warbler, but considered specifically distinct by Alström & Olsson (1990) on the basis of marked differences in vocalizations and some differences in morphology. Includes *kansuensis* Gansu Leaf Warbler, which has a very different song and which may well be worthy of specific status. A forthcoming paper (provisionally entitled 'Re-evaluation of the taxonomic status of *Phylloscopus proregulus kansuensis* Meise') by P. Alström & U. Olsson will argue in favour of specific status for this form.

Phylloscopus sichuanensis Chinese Leaf Warbler: a newly described species from west-central and north-central China. Morphologically quite similar to *P. chloronotus*, but is sympatric with it in west-central China and has strikingly different vocalizations as well as some differences in habitat and breeding biology (Alström *et al.* 1992).

Phylloscopus humei Hume's Leaf Warbler: usually (including by Voous 1977, Cheng 1987, Sibley & Monroe 1990 and, tentatively, by Stepanyan 1990) treated as conspecific with *P. inornatus* Yellow-browed Warbler. Although the morphological differences are modest, the vocalizations of *humei* differ very greatly from *inornatus* (Madge 1985, Svensson 1987, Alström & Olsson 1988, E. K. Dunn in Cramp 1992). Profound differences in vocalizations have recently been used to separate other allopatric *Phylloscopus* species showing only moderate morphological differences, notably *chloronotus* from *proregulus* and *borealoides* from *tenellipes*, and *humei* must surely qualify for specific status on the same basis. It is possible *humei* may prove to be sympatric with *inornatus* in the Tuva region of southern Siberia (Svensson 1992). Note: the form *mandelli* of the eastern Himalayas and W China is included with *humei*. Although at one time there was some suggestion that the vocalizations of this form were intermediate between *humei* and nominate *inornatus*, the song has since been shown to be effectively identical to that of *humei*, as is one of the usual calls, while another call differs from both forms (Alström & Olsson 1988). Interestingly, while *mandelli* always reacts strongly to play-back experiments with the song of *humei*, *inornatus* sometimes reacts to the song of *humei/mandelli*, and vice versa (Alström & Olsson 1988).

Phylloscopus fuligiventer Smoky Warbler: sometimes (including by Cheng 1987) treated as conspecific with *P. fuscatus*. Vaurie (1954c) treated *fuligiventer* as conspecific, but this approach was disputed by Ripley (1961), who followed Ludlow (1951) in treating them separately, and by Williamson (1967) who pointed out that treating them as conspecific would result in an irregular cline in coloration. Includes *tibetanus* Sikang Warbler (or Sikang Smoky Warbler), formerly occasionally treated as specifically distinct.

Phylloscopus offinis Tickell's Leaf Warbler: often (as in Voous 1977, Cheng 1987 and Sibley & Monroe 1990) spelt *P. affinis*, but the original spelling (*Motacilla offinis*) was not validly emended and under current ICZN rules must stand. (Note: this revision has no effect on the spelling of *P. subaffinis*.)

Phylloscopus subaffinis Buff-throated Warbler: sometimes (including by Voous 1977) treated as conspecific with *P. offinis* (= *affinis*) Tickell's Leaf Warbler. The two forms are widely sympatric (Cheng 1987) and Alström & Olsson (1992) treated them as distinct due to differences in morphology and vocalizations. Note: '*arcanus*', which was thought to be an intermediate form between *offinis* and *subaffinis*, has subsequently been shown to be misidentified *Cettia. f. flavolivacea* (Alström *et al.* 1993).

Phylloscopus bonelli Bonelli's Warbler: includes *orientalis* Eastern Bonelli's Warbler, which may possibly deserve specific status. Playback experiments support this hypothesis (Helb *et al.* 1982).

Phylloscopus neglectus Plain Leaf Warbler: formerly sometimes treated as conspecific with *P. collybita* Chiffchaff, but only until the extent of the sympatry with the latter became apparent (see Vaurie 1959a).

Phylloscopus collybita Chiffchaff: includes *sindianus* Mountain Chiffchaff, sometimes (including by Voous 1977 and Sibley & Monroe 1990, but not 1993) treated as specifically distinct. Also includes *lorenzii* Caucasian Chiffchaff, sometimes (including by Stepanyan 1990 and Sibley & Monroe 1993, but not 1990) treated as specifically distinct, or (including by Voous 1977) treated as conspecific with *sindianus*. Both forms show marked morphological differences compared with the western populations of *P. collybita*, being grey-brown rather than greenish above and with no yellow in the plumage, but both are close to *tristis* ('Siberian Chiffchaff') in appearance. The form *lorenzii* is considered to be an isolated population of the eastern group of 'brown chiffchaffs' which has secondarily come into contact with *P. c. abietinus*, a representative of the western group of 'green chiffchaffs' (see Vaurie 1959a). The case for treating *lorenzii* (sometimes in combination with the morphologically very similar *sindianus*) as a distinct species depends on *lorenzii* being reproductively isolated in spite of the apparent sympatry with *P. c. abietinus*. Some apparent intermediates between *P. c. abietinus* and *lorenzii* were reported by Vaurie (1954c), and such specimens may equate with '*caucasica*', recently separated from *abietinus* by Loskot (1991). This population is said to exhibit plumage characters which are intermediate between *abietinus* and *lorenzii*, being browner and less green than the former on the upperparts and having little or no yellow below. According to Loskot (*in. litt.* to K. Mild) it breeds in a lower zone in the Caucasus, being altitudinally separated from *lorenzii* in most areas by a dense band of coniferous forest and only coming into contact with it where this band is broken or absent. As well as occupying a different habitat (mainly lower and middle altitude oak forest), timing of reproduction is another isolating mechanism since '*caucasica*' mostly breeds earlier, but this difference in timing is said to be less pronounced or even non-existent in those areas where the two forms come into contact. The extent to which '*caucasica*' and *lorenzii* behave as good species where they come into contact has not yet been studied. A series of skins of '*caucasica*' examined by K. Mild (*in litt.*) did not appear to be safely separable from *abietinus* or from '*brevirostris*' of NW Turkey, or even from '*menzbieri*' of NE Iran and Turkmenistan. (The latter is sometimes included in *tristis*: see A. van Loon in Cramp *et al.* 1992.) The population '*brevirostris*' of NW Turkey also shows intermediate characters between *abietinus* and *lorenzii*, but it is considered closer to the former (Watson (1962). Breeding chiffchaffs in the mountains of NE Turkey show the characters of *lorenzii* (K. Mild *in litt.*) and, as chiffchaffs of some form or another are now known to be distributed across much of northern Turkey (see Beaman 1978), *lorenzii* may come into contact with '*brevirostris*' somewhere in the Pontic Mountains. Whether or not the two forms behave as separate species if they do come into contact is unknown. The songs of both *sindianus* and *lorenzii* differ from typical *collybita* less than those of *brehmii* ('Iberian Chiffchaff'), *canariensis* ('Canary Islands Chiffchaff'), or *tristis*(see M. G. Wilson in Cramp *et al.* 1992), but play-back experiments with *lorenzii* in NE Turkey failed to elicit strong reactions to the songs of nominate *collybita, abietinus* or '*brevirostris*', or to the songs of *tristis* or *brehmii* (K. Mild *in litt.*) This may be significant, but experiments have also shown that other populations of chiffchaffs fail to react to the played-back songs of different forms. The island form *canariensis* does not react to the song of nominate *collybita* (Thielcke *et al.* 1978). Male *brehmii* usually react strongly to the songs of both nominate *collybita* and *canariensis*, but the reverse is not true (Thielcke *et al.* 1978, Salomon 1987). The Siberian form *tristis* does not respond to the songs of either nominate *collybita* or *brehmii*, and *collybita* in turn does not react to *tristis*(Schubert 1982, Martens & Meincke 1989). The song of *sindianus* is very similar to that of *lorenzii* (Martens 1982), but the song also includes units with a rising pitch that are shared only with *tristis* (Martens & Meincke 1989). Interestingly '*brevirostris*', which is generally considered to be a representative of the western group of 'green chiffchaffs', has a distinctive contact call which sounds very similar to that of both *lorenzii* and *tristis* (pers. obs.). Faced with such a complex situation, and pending detailed studies that investigate the degree of reproductive isolation in the areas of contact in the Caucasus (and potentially N Turkey), I prefer not to single out *lorenzii* for specific status. Further studies, and perhaps genetic comparisons, should help to throw further light on the situation. If *lorenzii* deserves specific status then so may *canariensis* (together with *exsul*), *tristis*, *sindianus* and possibly *brehmii*.

Regulus species are treated as a separate family, Regulidae, by Sibley & Monroe 1990.

Regulus regulus Goldcrest: includes *teneriffae* Canary Islands Kinglet, sometimes (including by Sibley & Monroe 1990) treated as specifically distinct, or as conspecific with *R. ignicapillus* Firecrest. The most frequently held view has been to treat this interesting form as a subspecies of *R. regulus* as it is very similar to the latter in morphology, vocalizations and behaviour (see Lörhl & Thaler 1980). Only the black frontal band is a feature found in *R. ignicapillus* rather than *R. regulus*, but *teneriffae* lacks the prominent white supercilium, black eye-stripe and bronze patch on the 'shoulder' that are such significant features of the latter. This form exhibits much less divergence from typical *R. regulus* than the distinctive *R. goodfellowi* Flamecrest (or Taiwan Firecrest) and so, pending more convincing arguments for full specific status, it seems preferable to retain it in *R. regulus*. Nonetheless, as an unresolved trichotomy, a case can also be made for treating *teneriffae* as specifically distinct.

Leptopoecile elegans Crested Tit Warbler: alternatively (as in Cheng 1987) *Lophobasileus elegans*.

MUSCICAPIDAE

Niltava vivida Vivid Niltava: alternatively (as in Voous 1977) *Cyornis vivida*.

Cyornis banyumas Hill Blue Flycatcher: alternatively (as in Cheng 1987) *Niltava banyumas*.

Muscicapella hodgsoni Pygmy Blue Flycatcher: alternatively (as in Cheng 1987) *Niltava hodgsoni*.

Cyanoptila cyanomelana Blue-and-white Flycatcher: alternatively (as in Voous 1977) *Muscicapa cyanomelana* or (as in Cheng 1987) *Ficedula cyanomelana*.

Eumyias thalassina Verditer Flycatcher: alternatively (as in Voous 1977 and Cheng 1987) *Muscicapa thalassina*.

Muscicapa ferruginea Ferruginous Flycatcher: synonym (as in Voous 1977) *M. rufilata*.

Muscicapa dauurica Asian Brown Flycatcher: synonym (as in Voous 1977, Cheng 1987 and Stepanyan 1990) *M. latirostris* (but see E. Mayr *et al.* in Mayr & Cottrell 1986).

Muscicapa gambagae Gambaga Flycatcher: formerly sometimes treated as conspecific with *M. striata* Spotted Flycatcher.

Ficedula parva Red-breasted Flycatcher: includes *albicilla* Red-throated Flycatcher, which may be worthy of specific status. Differs in vocalizations and morphology, and overlaps with *parva* in European Russia, although some hybridization has been reported (G. Mauersberger and B. Stephan in Stresemann *et al.* 1967, Svensson 1992).

Ficedula subrubra Kashmir Flycatcher: sometimes (including by Voous 1977) treated as conspecific with *F. parva* Red-breasted Flycatcher. Now more often treated as specifically distinct, due to significant morphological differences (see Vaurie 1959a, Ali & Ripley 1972).

Ficedula zanthopygia Yellow-rumped Flycatcher: formerly sometimes treated as conspecific with *F. narcissina* Narcissus Flycatcher, but is morphologically distinct and has a very different song (pers. obs.).

Ficedula narcissina Narcissus Flycatcher: includes *elisae* Chinese Flycatcher, which is morphologically distinct and may be worthy of specific status. Published studies are still lacking.

Ficedula semitorquata Semi-collared Flycatcher: sometimes (including by Stepanyan 1990) treated as conspecific with *F. albicollis* Collared Flycatcher, or sometimes with *F. hypoleuca* European Pied Flycatcher. Now generally treated as specifically distinct due to differences in morphology, vocalizations and behaviour (see Cramp & Perrins 1993, Mild 1993).

Culicicapa ceylonensis Grey-headed Flycatcher: placed in Eopsaltriidae by Sibley & Monroe (1990) but later (1993) returned to Muscicapidae.

RHIPIDURIDAE

(merged in Corvidae by Sibley & Monroe 1990)

MONARCHIDAE

(merged in Corvidae by Sibley & Monroe 1990)

TIMALIIDAE

(merged in Sylviidae by Sibley & Monroe 1990)

Pomatorhinus erythrocnemis Spot-breasted Scimitar Babbler: sometimes (including by Voous 1977 and Cheng 1987) treated as conspecific with *P. erythrogenys* Rusty-cheeked Scimitar Babbler, but is morphologically distinct and the two forms overlap without any sign of hybridization according to Vaurie (1954b). Note: the distributions given for *P. erythrocnemis* and *P. erythrogenys* by Sibley & Monroe (1990) are incorrect. The former reaches no further west than the easternmost Himalayas (see Vaurie 1959a) while the latter is not restricted to Burma and Thailand but also occurs almost throughout the Himalayas (indeed nominate *erythrogenys* occupies the western Himalayas: see Ripley 1982).

Pnoepyga immaculata Nepal Wren-babbler: a newly described species from Nepal, differing in morphology and vocalizations from the other *Pnoepyga* species (Martens & Eck 1991).

Moupinia poecilotis Rufous-tailed Babbler: alternatively (as in Sibley & Monroe 1990) *Chrysomma poecilotis*.

Panurus biarmicus Bearded Reedling: the affinities of this species are uncertain, but it is now usually considered to be closely related to the parrotbills (e.g. Voous 1977, Sibley & Monroe 1990).

Conostoma oemodium Great Parrotbill: often (as in Voous 1977 and Cheng 1987) spelt *C. aemodium*.

Paradoxornis paradoxus Three-toed Parrotbill: sometimes spelt *P. paradoxa*.

Paradoxornis guttaticollis Spot-breasted Parrotbill: sometimes (including by Voous 1977 and Cheng 1987) treated as conspecific with *P. flavirostris* Black-breasted Parrotbill. They are morphologically distinct and the ranges overlap in NE India, with *guttaticollis* tending to replace *flavirostris* at higher altitudes, with no evidence of hybridization (Ali & Ripley 1971).

Paradoxornis conspicillatus Spectacled Parrotbill: sometimes spelt *P. conspicillata*.

Paradoxornis webbianus Vinous-throated Parrotbill: sometimes spelt *P. webbiana*. Alternatively (as in Stepanyan 1990) *Suthora webbiana*.

Paradoxornis brunneus Brown-winged Parrotbill: sometimes spelt *P. brunnea*. Sometimes (including by Voous 1977 and Cheng 1987) treated as conspecific with *P. webbianus* Vinous-throated Parrotbill, but overlaps with *alphonsianus* Ashy-throated Parrotbill (itself often treated as specifically distinct: see 'Omitted species') without any sign of hybridization (Traylor 1967). The comment in Sibley & Monroe (1990) that *brunneus* and *webbianus* hybridize and may be conspecific (attributed to H. G. Deignan *et al.* in Mayr & Paynter 1964 and to Vaurie 1959a) is in error and presumably relates to a misreading of the statement by Deignan *et al.* that hybrids have been reported between *P. b. brunneus* (which Deignan *et al.* treat as a race of *P. webbianus*) and *P. b. ricketti* (which they treat as a full species).

Paradoxornis verreauxi Golden Parrotbill: sometimes (including by Cheng 1987) treated as conspecific with *P. nipalensis* Black-throated Parrotbill, but morphologically very distinct and most often treated as an allospecies (e.g. Sibley & Monroe 1990).

Paradoxornis heudei Reed Parrotbill: includes *polivanovi* Polivanov's Parrotbill, treated as specifically distinct by Stepanyan (1990) although the justification for this approach seems very weak.

Garrulax bieti Biet's Laughingthrush: sometimes (including by Voous 1977 and Cheng 1987) treated as conspecific with *G. lunulatus* Barred Laughingthrush. The status of this poorly known form is uncertain (see Vaurie 1965b), but in view of the marked morphological differences compared to both *G. ocellatus* and *G. maximus* it is probably best treated as specifically distinct.

Garrulax maximus Giant Laughingthrush: formerly sometimes treated as conspecific with *G. ocellatus* Spotted Laughingthrush, but they are sympatric over a wide region of SW China (Cheng 1987, Eck 1987).

Liocichla omeiensis Emei Shan Liocichla: sometimes (including by Voous 1977) treated as conspecific with *L. steerii* Steere's Liocichla. Now generally treated as specifically distinct (e.g. Cheng 1987, Sibley & Monroe 1990) owing to the marked morphological differences.

Pteruthius flaviscapis White-browed Shrike-babbler: synonym *P. erythropterus*.

Pteruthius xanthochlorus Green Shrike-babbler: sometimes (as in Voous 1977) spelt *P. xanthochloris*.

Actinodura waldeni Streak-throated Barwing: sometimes treated as conspecific with *A. nipalensis* Hoary-throated Barwing. They differ in morphology but the potential zone of contact in easternmost Bhutan or western Arunachal Pradesh is ornithologically little-known.

Alcippe ludlowi Ludlow's Fulvetta: usually (including by Voous 1977, Cheng 1987 and Sibley & Monroe 1990, but not 1993) treated as conspecific with *A. cinereiceps* Streak-throated Fulvetta. It is rather surprising that this highly distinctive taxon, which was originally described as a separate species, should ever have been lumped with *A. cinereiceps* when it differs so markedly in morphology. Recently found to be sympatric with *A. c. manipurensis* in eastern Arunachal Pradesh and so considered to merit full species status by Ripley *et al.* (1991).

Yuhina occipitales Rufous-vented Yuhina: often (as in Voous 1977, Cheng 1987 and Sibley & Monroe 1990) spelt *Y. occipitalis*, but the original spelling was not validly emended and under current ICZN rules must stand.

AEGITHALIDAE

Aegithalos iouschistos Black-browed Tit: includes *bonvaloti* Black-headed Tit, which Wunderlich (1991) treated as specifically distinct because of differences in morphology and an apparent lack of hybridization where the ranges meet. Reports on distribution are conflicting: Vaurie (1959a) reported a small gap in the range between *bonvaloti* and *iouschistos*. Interestingly Wunderlich included the form *obscuratus* of central Sichuan with *iouschistos* even though its morphology is closer to that of *bonvaloti* according to Vaurie (1959a). Further studies in the possible areas of contact are desirable.

Aegithalos niveogularis White-throated Tit: formerly sometimes treated as conspecific with *A. iouschistos* Black-browed Tit, but the ranges overlap in Nepal (Inskipp & Inskipp 1991) and no interbreeding has been reported.

PARIDAE

Parus palustris Marsh Tit: includes *hypermelaena* (synonym *hypermelas*), which is probably worthy of specific status as it differs quite sharply in morphology from all other forms of *P. palustris* (see Vaurie 1959a) and shows some differences in vocalizations (pers. obs. in SW China). Its distribution is still poorly known, so uncertain if *hypermelaena* comes into contact with *P. p. dejeani* in north-central China (S. C. Harrap *in litt.*). Retained here in *P. palustris* pending further studies.

Parus lugubris Sombre Tit: includes *hyrcanus* Caspian Tit, which recently has sometimes (including by Stepanyan 1990) been treated as specifically distinct. This form routinely excavates its own nest hole (behaviour thought to be rare or lacking in other forms of *P. lugubris*) and is said to exhibit differences in vocalizations (Loskot 1982, V. M. Loskot in Dathe & Neufeldt 1987), although the voice was thought to be similar by Eck (1980). Retained in *P. lugubris* pending further studies.

Parus montanus Willow Tit: Sometimes treated as conspecific with *P. atricapillus* Black-capped Chickadee, but appears not to be closely related genetically (Gill *et al.* 1989). Includes *songarus* Songar Tit, sometimes (including by Stepanyan 1990) treated as specifically distinct. Although the *songarus* group taken as a whole is distinct from the *montanus* group, there is considerable variation between its members, some of which are widely allopatric. The cap colour varies from brown to black and upperpart colour ranges from grey-brown to warm brown or ochre. Although most members of the group have darker underparts than the *montanus* group, *stötzneri* of SW Manchuria is paler than the others both above and below, differing from *P. m. baicalensis* (from which it is separated by a small gap in distribution) chiefly in its brown rather than black cap. As pointed out by Vaurie (1959a), variation in cap colour by itself is not held to be significant in the case of *P. lugubris* Sombre Tit, so *stötzneri* presents a conundrum for anyone suggesting specific status for the *songarus* group. Vocalizations do not seem to have been studied in any detail, but there are some similarities to my ear. Retained here in *P. montanus* (contra Cramp & Perrins 1993) pending further data.

Parus rufonuchalis Rufous-naped Tit: sometimes treated as conspecific with *P. rubidiventris* Rufous-vented Tit, but it is morphologically and vocally distinct (Martens 1975) and breeds sympatrically with *P. rubidiventris* in the western Himalayas (Jamdar & Price 1990, Gaston *et al.* 1993).

Parus rubidiventris Rufous-vented Tit: includes *beavani* Sikkim Tit, sometimes treated as specifically distinct, or as a race of *P. rufonuchalis* Rufous-naped Tit. The range of this morphologically very distinct form meets or possibly overlaps with that of *P. r. rubidiventris* in Nepal (Inskipp & Inskipp 1991) and no intergradation has been reported, so it may not be conspecific.

Parus spilonotus Yellow-cheeked Tit: formerly sometimes treated as conspecific with *P. xanthogenys* Black-lored Tit, but they overlap in eastern Nepal and the Darjeeling area without evidence of interbreeding (Paynter 1963, Ali & Ripley 1973b, Inskipp & Inskipp 1991).

Parus cyanus Azure Tit: formerly sometimes treated as conspecific with *P. caeruleus* Blue Tit. Includes *flavipectus* Yellow-breasted Tit, sometimes (including by Stepanyan 1990 and Sibley & Monroe 1990) treated as specifically distinct. Hybridization is sometimes said to be limited (e.g. Vaurie 1957a), but actually appears to be frequent in Kirghizstan, judging by the number of intermediates and mixed pairs that are encountered (pers. obs.). Playback studies also strongly support conspecificity (K. Mild *in litt.*). Further studies are needed.

Parus major Great Tit: includes *cinereus* Cinereous Tit and *minor* Japanese Tit, either or both of which are sometimes treated as specifically distinct. Stepanyan (1990) recognized both forms as separate species. Vaurie (1959a) considered that the *cinereus* group intergraded with the *major* group, but reported that there was only limited hybridization between the *minor* and *major* groups.

Parus bokharensis Turkestan Tit: sometimes treated as conspecific with *P. major* Great Tit, but differs in morphology and proportions (Vaurie 1950a, C. S. Roselaar in Cramp & Perrins 1993). Some limited hybridization occurs in Central Asia and Mongolia (Eck 1988).

SITTIDAE

Sitta villosa Chinese Nuthatch: formerly occasionally treated as conspecific with *S. canadensis* Red-breasted Nuthatch.

Sitta krueperi Krüper's Nuthatch: formerly occasionally treated as conspecific with *S. canadensis* Red-breasted Nuthatch.

Sitta whiteheadi Corsican Nuthatch: formerly occasionally treated as conspecific with either *S. canadensis* Red-breasted Nuthatch or *S. villosa* Chinese Nuthatch.

Sitta cashmirensis Kashmir Nuthatch: sometimes (including by Voous 1977) treated as conspecific with *S. castanea* Chestnut-bellied Nuthatch, or with *S. europaea* Eurasian Nuthatch. This form is morphologically closer to *europaea* than *castanea* (which is a lowland and foothills species in the Himalayas), but shows more marked sexual dimorphism than *europaea* and differs from both in having uniform undertail coverts (Vaurie 1950b, 1959a). Allospecies treatment (as adopted by Sibley & Monroe 1990) seems appropriate.

Sitta nagaensis Chestnut-vented Nuthatch: often (including by Voous 1977 and Cheng 1987) treated as conspecific with *S. europaea* Eurasian Nuthatch. *S. n. montium* overlaps range of *S. e. sinensis* in Fujian in eastern China, but is found at higher altitudes (Meyer de Schauensee 1984). The two forms are reported to intergrade in central Sichuan (Voous & van Marle 1953, Vaurie 1959a). However, Traylor (1967) did not report any intergrades in a collection of birds from the same area and simply stated that at Guan Xian (north of Chengdu) the 'lowland' *sinensis* meets the 'highland' *montium*. May be conspecific, but treated here as specifically distinct pending further studies in the zone of overlap. Note: some confusion exists as to the composition and distribution of *S. nagaensis*, and thus the possible area of overlap with *S. europaea*. When *nagaensis* is treated as a full species it does not include all four members of the *sinensis* subspecies group that are often included in *S. europaea* (e.g. Vaurie 1959a). The form *sinensis*, found from Fujian to Sichuan and north to Hebei, is excluded as it differs somewhat in morphology. Hence the overlap that occurs in Fujian and Sichuan (and probably elsewhere in central China) between *S. nagaensis* and *S. europaea* involves *S. n. montium* and *S. e. sinensis*.

TICHODROMADIDAE

(merged in Sittidae by Sibley & Monroe 1990)

CERTHIDAE

Certhia nipalensis Rusty-flanked Treecreeper: treated as conspecific with *C. familiaris* Eurasian Treecreeper by Dementiev & Gladkov (1954a). Mead (1975) concluded that further work might support such an approach, but they are sympatric in a large part of the Himalayas and have quite different vocalizations (Martens 1981).

REMIZIDAE

(merged in Paridae by Sibley & Monroe 1990)

Remiz pendulinus Eurasian Penduline Tit: includes *macronyx* Black-headed Penduline Tit, sometimes (including by Stepanyan 1990) treated as specifically distinct. Also includes *coronatus* White-crowned Penduline Tit, sometimes (including by Sibley & Monroe 1990) treated as specifically distinct. In addition includes *consobrinus* Chinese Penduline Tit, also sometimes (including by Sibley & Monroe 1990) treated as specifically distinct, but at other times included with *coronatus*. Assessment of the taxonomic status of the four subspecies groups within *R. pendulinus* recognized by Vaurie (1959a) or the three groups recognized by C. S. Roselaar (in Cramp & Perrins 1993) is made more difficult by a lack of precise information on breeding ranges, habitat differences, movements and the extent of hybridization or lack of it. The very distinctive *macronyx* group differs markedly in both plumage and structure from the *pendulinus* and *coronatus* groups, but members of the *macronyx* group intergrade extensively with members of the *pendulinus* group where they come into contact in the Ural Delta and in Transcaucasia (Vaurie 1957b, 1959a; Dolgushin *et al.* 1972), supporting the thesis that these two forms are conspecific. On the other hand *macronyx* extensively overlaps with *coronatus* in Turkestan (where it breeds in reedbed habitat and is thus ecologically separated from the mainly willow-haunting *coronatus*) without any sign of interbreeding (see Dolgushin et al. 1972, C. F. Roselaar in Cramp & Perrins 1993). Further, no sign of intergradation has been reported where the breeding range of the *coronatus* group approaches that of *jaxarticus* of the *pendulinus* group, although the latter shows some structural similarities with the *coronatus* group, having small, slender legs and feet and a fine bill. However, the apparent overlap in breeding distribution between *jaxarticus* and *coronatus* at the Aral Sea mentioned by Vaurie (1959a), which provided additional support for specific status for *coronatus*, has now been shown to be spurious. Records of *jaxarticus* from the area relate to migrants and there is no overlap of breeding populations (Dolgushin *et al.* 1972). The propensity of *coronatus* to nest in willows and birches has been presented as a significant ecological difference (Vaurie 1959a), but some members of the the *pendulinus* group mainly nest in willows (Cramp & Perrins 1993) and at least one of these, *menzbieri*, reaches high altitudes in E Turkey (Beaman *et al.* 1975, Beaman 1978) in the same way that the *coronatus* group do in Central Asia. The form *consobrinus* of east Asia shows some similarities in plumage pattern with the *coronatus* group and especially *stoliczkae*, its nearest neighbour, which shows a parallel reduction in the size and intensity of the black frontal band, but there are also some differences (see Vaurie 1959a, C. S. Roselaar in Cramp & Perrins 1993). The breeding ranges of *consobrinus* and the *coronatus* group do not appear to come into contact (see Vaurie 1959a) and structurally it is close to *stoliczkae* (see C. S. Roselaar in Cramp & Perrins 1993), so it may be best included in the *coronatus* group. I prefer to retain all these forms in *R. pendulinus* for the time being pending further studies, but this is an arbitrary decision and a good case can be made for treating *coronatus* (perhaps together with *consobrinus*) and, in spite of the intergradation with the *pendulinus* group, *macronyx* as full species.

NECTARINIIDAE

Anthreptes metallicus Nile Valley Sunbird: sometimes treated as conspecific with *A. platurus* Pygmy Sunbird, but they are usually regarded as members of a superspecies. Morphological differences are rather limited, but there is no sign of interbreeding where the ranges come into contact. The precise limits of the breeding distributions are obscured, however, by seasonal movements (Hall & Moreau 1970, C. S. Roselaar in Cramp & Perrins 1993).

DICAEIDAE

(merged in Nectariniidae by Sibley & Monroe 1990)

Dicaeum melanoxanthum Yellow-bellied Flowerpecker: sometimes (as in Cheng 1987) spelt *D. melanozanthum*.

ZOSTEROPIDAE

Zosterops palpebrosus Oriental White-eye: former spelling (as in Voous 1977 and Cheng 1987) *Z. palpebrosa*. The genus *Zosterops* has been designated as masculine, hence the need for revised spellings for the specific names (see Sibley & Monroe 1990).

Zosterops erythropleurus Chestnut-flanked White-eye: former spelling (as in Voous 1977 and Cheng 1987) *Z. erythropleura*. See *Z. palpebrosus*.

Zosterops japonicus Japanese White-eye: former spelling (as in Voous 1977, Cheng 1987 and Stepanyan 1990) *Z. japonica*. See *Z. palpebrosus*.

Zosterops abyssinicus Abyssinian White-eye: former spelling (as in Voous 1977) *Z. abyssinica*. See *Z. palpebrosus*.

MELIPHAGIDAE

Apalopteron familiare Bonin Honeyeater: sometimes spelt *A. familiaris*.

ORIOLIDAE

(merged in Corvidae by Sibley & Monroe 1990)

Oriolus tenuirostris Slender-billed Oriole: sometimes (including by Voous 1977 and Cheng 1987) treated as conspecific with *O. chinensis* Black-naped Oriole, but they are sympatric in southwestern China (see Vaurie 1959a, Cheng 1987), where *tenuirostris* is apparently restricted to pine forest (C Robson *in litt.*).

LANIIDAE

Tchagra senegala Black-crowned Tchagra: placed with other bush shrikes amongst the Corvidae by Sibley & Monroe 1990. Bush shrikes are sometimes (as in Dowsett & Forbes-Watson 1993) placed in their own family, Malaconotidae.

Rhodophoneus cruentus Rosy-patched Bush Shrike: placed with other bush shrikes amongst the Corvidae by Sibley & Monroe 1990. Bush shrikes are sometimes (as in Dowsett & Forbes-Watson 1993) placed in their own family, Malaconotidae.

Lanius cristatus Brown Shrike: includes *superciliosus*, included only tentatively in *L. cristatus* by Stepanyan (1990), but published evidence in support of specific status for this form is lacking.

Lanius isabellinus Isabelline Shrike: sometimes treated as conspecific with *L. cristatus* Brown Shrike or (as in Cheng 1987) with *L. collurio* Red-backed Shrike. *L. i. speculigerus* overlaps with *L. cristatus* without interbreeding (G. Mauersberger and L. A. Portenko in Stresemann *et. al.* 1971) while *L. i. phoenicuroides* has only a narrow zone of contact with *L. collurio* and fully intermediate populations occur in only a few areas (see C. S. Roselaar in Cramp & Perrins 1993). Includes *phoenicuroides* Red-tailed Shrike, sometimes (together with *speculigerus*) treated as specifically distinct (e.g. Panov 1983) or sometimes (as in Cheng 1987) treated as conspecific with *L. collurio* Red-backed Shrike. Specimens collected in parts of N China are intermediate between *speculigerus* and *isabellinus* (Vaurie 1959a).

Lanius collurio Red-backed Shrike: sometimes (together with *isabellinus*) treated as conspecific with *L. cristatus* Brown Shrike, but see *L. isabellinus*.

Lanius tephronotus Grey-backed Shrike: formerly sometimes treated as conspecific with *L. schach* Long-tailed Shrike. The two forms overlap locally without interbreeding (Biswas 1950), although *L. t. lahulensis* is apparently a stabilized hybrid population (Panov 1983).

Lanius excubitor Great Grey Shrike: includes *meridionalis* Southern Grey Shrike, which is sometimes treated as specifically distinct. Differs in plumage coloration, moult and strength of leg and foot and may well deserve full species status (see Panov 1983, Isenmann & Bouchet 1993).

DICRURIDAE

(merged in Corvidae by Sibley & Monroe 1990)

Dicrurus macrocercus Black Drongo: sometimes treated as conspecific with *D. adsimilis* Fork-tailed Drongo (or African Drongo), but see Vaurie (1949a) and Hall & Moreau (1970), who treat them as members of a superspecies.

ARTAMIDAE

(merged in Corvidae by Sibley & Monroe 1990)

Artamus leucorynchus White-breasted Wood Swallow: often spelt *A. leucorhynchus* (but see Sibley & Monroe 1990).

CORVIDAE

Cyanopica cyanus Azure-winged Magpie: often (including by Voous 1977, Cheng 1987, Stepanyan 1990 and Sibley & Monroe 1990) spelt *C. cyana*, but see C. S. Roselaar in Cramp & Perrins (1994a).

Nucifraga caryocatactes Spotted Nutcracker: includes *multipunctata* Indian Nutcracker (or Larger Spotted Nutcracker), which Madge & Burn (1993) suggest may be a separate species, although it intergrades with *N. c. hemispila* in the Himalayas (Vaurie 1954a, 1965a).

Corvus dauuricus Daurian Jackdaw: sometimes (including by Cheng 1987) treated as conspecific with *C. monedula* Western Jackdaw. Shows marked differences in morphology, including iris colour, and unique plumage sequence (pied juvenile to black 1st-year to pied adult), while hybridization in narrow zone of overlap is rare (see Nechaev 1975, C. S. Roselaar in Cramp & Perrins 1994a).

Corvus corone Carrion Crow: includes *cornix* Hooded Crow, sometimes (including by Stepanyan 1990) treated as specifically distinct. Most often treated as a single species, but extensive hybridization occurs in only a relatively narrow zone and further studies may favour dividing the *corone* complex into two or more species, perhaps including *capellanus* Mesopotamian Crow and *orientalis* Eastern Carrion Crow as well as *corone* and *cornix* (see C. S. Roselaar in Cramp & Perrins 1994a).

Corvus albus Pied Crow: formerly sometimes treated as conspecific with *C. ruficollis* Brown-necked Raven because of hybridization in NE Africa, but this is limited and the two are usually regarded as members of a superspecies (see Hall & Moreau 1970).

Corvus ruficollis Brown-necked Raven: formerly sometimes treated as conspecific with *C. corax* Common Raven, but the breeding ranges overlap in some regions and touch elsewhere without clear evidence of hybridization (see Vaurie 1954a, C. S. Roselaar in Cramp & Perrins 1994a).

STURNIDAE

Sturnus sturninus Purple-backed Starling: alternatively (as in Stepanyan 1990) *Sturnia sturnina*.

Sturnus philippensis Chestnut-cheeked Starling: alternatively (as in Stepanyan 1990) *Sturnia philippensis*.

Sturnus sinensis White-shouldered Starling: alternatively (as in Stepanyan 1990) *Sturnia sinensis*.

Sturnus unicolor Spotless Starling: sometimes treated as conspecific with *S. vulgaris* Common Starling, but differs from nominate *vulgaris* more than any race of that species and breeding ranges now overlap without any sign of interbreeding (C. S. Roselaar in Cramp & Perrins 1994a).

Creatophora cinerea Wattled Starling: sometimes (as in Voous 1977) spelt *C. cineracea*.

PASSERIDAE

Passer domesticus House Sparrow: includes *italiae* Italian Sparrow, which is occasionally treated as specifically distinct but which is usually regarded as a stabilized hybrid population between *P. domesticus* and *P. hispaniolensis* Spanish Sparrow (see discussion by C. S. Roselaar in Cramp & Perrins 1994a). Also includes *indicus* Indian Sparrow, which is sometimes (including by Stepanyan 1990) treated as specifically distinct. Although the *indicus* group is morphologically distinct and the migratory race *bactrianus* overlaps with *domesticus* in Central Asia with only negligible hybridization (Gavrilov 1965), members of the two groups are known to interbreed extensively in other areas (see Summers-Smith 1988).

Passer iagoensis Iago Sparrow: formerly included *motitensis* Rufous Sparrow (or Great Sparrow, or Southern Rufous-backed Sparrow[1]) and other forms of mainland Africa, but these are now often treated as allospecies (see Summers-Smith 1984, 1988).

Passer euchlorus Arabian Golden Sparrow: formerly sometimes treated as conspecific with *P. luteus* Sudan Golden Sparrow (with the English name 'Golden Sparrow' being used for the enlarged species). Now usually regarded as members of a superspecies (e.g. Hall & Moreau 1970).

Carpospiza brachydactyla Pale Rockfinch: alternatively (as in Voous 1977) *Petronia brachydactyla*. The taxonomic position of this species is uncertain and it differs in a number of significant respects from typical *Petronia*. Sometimes thought to be more closely related to the Fringillidae, but its skull structure is not cardueline (Zusi 1978). Placing it in its own genus (see Sibley & Monroe 1990, C. S. Roselaar in Cramp & Perrins 1994a) seems appropriate.

Montifringilla theresae Theresa's Snowfinch: alternatively (as in Stepanyan 1990) *Pyrgilauda theresae*. Gebauer & Kaiser (1994) have presented ecological and behavioural evidence in support of placing this species in *Pyrgilauda* as opposed to *Montifringilla*.

Montifringilla blanfordi Blanford's Snowfinch: alternatively *Pyrgilauda blanfordi*. Gebauer & Kaiser (1994) have presented ecological and behavioural evidence in support of placing this species in *Pyrgilauda* as opposed to *Montifringilla*.

Montifringilla ruficollis Rufous-necked Snowfinch: alternatively *Pyrgilauda ruficollis*. Gebauer & Kaiser (1994) have presented ecological and behavioural evidence in support of placing this species in *Pyrgilauda* as opposed to *Montifringilla*.

Montifringilla davidiana Père David's Snowfinch: alternatively (as in Stepanyan 1990) *Pyrgilauda davidiana*. Gebauer & Kaiser (1994) have presented ecological and behavioural evidence in support of placing this species in *Pyrgilauda* as opposed to *Montifringilla*.

Montifringilla taczanowskii White-rumped Snowfinch: alternatively *Pyrgilauda taczanowskii*. Gebauer & Kaiser (1994) have presented ecological and behavioural evidence in support of placing this species in *Pyrgilauda* as opposed to *Montifringilla*.

Montifringilla adamsi Adams's Snowfinch: C. S. Roselaar (in Cramp & Perrins 1994a) treats *adamsi* as conspecific with *M. nivalis* White-winged Snowfinch as he considers that the characters of the two seem to merge in central Asia. The biology of *M. adamsi* is poorly known, however, and pending field studies (or DNA data) that would support conspecificity, I prefer to retain *adamsi* as specifically distinct.

Montifringilla nivalis White-winged Snowfinch: includes *henrici* Prince Henri's Snowfinch, which is occasionally treated as specifically distinct (Portenko & Vietinghoff-Scheel in Stresemann *et al.* 1974, Cramp & Perrins 1994a). Shows some morphological differences, but, as with *M. adamsi*, field studies of *henrici* are lacking and so I prefer to retain it in *M. nivalis* for the time being.

PLOCEIDAE

(merged in Passeridae by Sibley & Monroe 1990)

ESTRILDIDAE

(merged in Passeridae by Sibley & Monroe 1990)

Estrilda rufibarba Arabian Waxbill: sometimes treated as conspecific with *E. astrild* Common Waxbill, or occasionally as conspecific with *E. troglodytes* Black-rumped Waxbill, but usually regarded as specifically distinct. Hall & Moreau (1970) concluded that there was no justification for combining it with any one mainland African species rather than another. Elzen & Wolters (1978) speculated that it might possibly be a stabilized hybrid between *E. troglodytes* and *E. rhodopyga* Crimson-rumped Waxbill.

Amandava amandava Red Avadavat: alternatively (as in Cheng 1987) *Estrilda amandava*.

Lonchura malabarica Indian Silverbill: alternatively (as in Voous 1977) *Euodice malabarica*.

Lonchura cantans African Silverbill: alternatively (as in Voous 1977) *Euodice cantans*. Sometimes treated as conspecific with *L. malabarica* Indian Silverbill, but they differ greatly in plumage and vocalizations (Harrison 1964) and are usually regarded as members of a superspecies.

FRINGILLIDAE

Serinus citrinella Citril Finch: includes *corsicana* Corsican Finch, occasionally treated as specifically distinct (e.g. Thibault 1983). Differs in morphology, voice and especially habitat, being found in lowland areas and not just high in the mountains (see C. S. Roselaar in Cramp & Perrins 1994a), but retained here in *S. citrinella* pending further studies.

Serinus rothschildi Arabian Serin: sometimes treated as conspecific with *S. atrogularis* Yellow-rumped Seedeater (itself divided into a superspecies by Sibley & Monroe 1990), but usually treated as specifically distinct. May be closer to *S. sulphurata* Brimstone Canary (Hall & Moreau 1970).

Carduelis chloris European Greenfinch: alternatively (as in Stepanyan 1990) *Chloris chloris*.

Carduelis sinica Grey-capped Greenfinch: alternatively (as in Stepanyan 1990) *Chloris sinica*.

Carduelis ambigua Black-headed Greenfinch: formerly sometimes treated as conspecific with *C. spinoides* Yellow-breasted Greenfinch, but they differ greatly in morphology and are sympatric in SE Tibet (see Vaurie 1972, Cheng 1987).

Carduelis carduelis European Goldfinch: includes *caniceps* Grey-crowned Goldfinch, sometimes (including by Stepanyan 1990) treated as specifically distinct, but it intergrades extensively with the *carduelis* group in Siberia (Johansen 1944) and also in Iran (Vaurie 1959a).

Carduelis spinus Eurasian Siskin: alternatively (as in Stepanyan 1990) *Spinus spinus*.

Carduelis thibetana Tibetan Siskin: alternatively (as in Voous 1977, Cheng 1987 and Sibley & Monroe 1990) *Serinus thibetanus*. Placed after *S. canaria* by Voous (1977). Wolters (1967) argued in favour of placing this species in *Serinus* rather than *Carduelis*, and since then it has generally been so treated, but anyone who has studied this bird in the field finds this highly unsatisfactory. There are no other *Serinus* species anywhere in eastern Asia and the vocalizations, behaviour and habitat of this species are very reminiscent of a Eurasian Siskin *Carduelis spinus*. This bird makes continuous nasal buzzings and twitterings as it feeds high in the treetops, typically hanging upside down at the very extremity of the branches while feeding on the seeds or flowers of alders and birches (pers. obs.). Pending further studies, I prefer to retain it in *Carduelis*, the same treatment followed by Vaurie (1959a).

Carduelis cannabina Common Linnet: alternatively (as in Stepanyan 1990) *Acanthis cannabina*.

Carduelis flavirostris Twite: alternatively (as in Stepanyan 1990) *Acanthis flavirostris*.

Carduelis flammea Common Redpoll: alternatively (as in Stepanyan 1990) *Acanthis flammea*.

Carduelis hornemanni Arctic Redpoll: alternatively (as in Stepanyan 1990) *Acanthis hornemanni*. Sometimes treated as conspecific with *C. flammea* Common Redpoll, but they overlap extensively without any (or with only very occasional) hybridization (Molau 1985, Knox 1988b). It is not certain that nominate *hornemanni* and *exilipes* are any more closely related to each other than they are to *C. flammea*, and so the *flammea* complex may comprise three or even more species (Herremans 1990).

Loxia scotica Scottish Crossbill: sometimes treated as conspecific with *L. curvirostra* Common Crossbill, or as conspecific with *L. pytyopsittacus* Parrot Crossbill (but see Knox 1990).

Leucosticte sillemi Sillem's Mountain Finch: a newly described species from western Tibet, differing significantly in morphology from *L. brandti* Brandt's Mountain Finch (see Roselaar 1992, 1994).

Leucosticte tephrocotis Grey-crowned Rosy Finch: sometimes treated as conspecific with *L. arctoa* Asian Rosy Finch, but genetic, biochemical and morphological evidence suggests allospecies treatment for the four forms in the *arctoa* complex is appropriate (see Sibley & Monroe 1990).

Rhodospiza obsoleta Desert Finch: alternatively (as in Cheng 1987 and Sibley & Monroe 1990) *Rhodopechys obsoleta*.

Bucanetes mongolicus Mongolian Finch: alternatively (as in Sibley & Monroe 1990) *Rhodopechys mongolica*. Sometimes (including by Cheng 1987) treated as conspecific with *B. githagineus* Trumpeter Finch, but the breeding ranges widely overlap in Asia (Vaurie 1949b, Stepanyan 1983) and the two are separated by habitat, behaviour, bill size, plumage and vocalizations (Vaurie 1949b, Panov 1989, C. S. Roselaar in Cramp & Perrins 1994a).

Bucanetes githagineus Trumpeter Finch: alternatively (as in Cheng 1987 and Sibley & Monroe 1990) *Rhodopechys githaginea*.

Carpodacus eos Pink-rumped Rosefinch: formerly occasionally treated as conspecific with *C. pulcherrimus* Beautiful Rosefinch, but they are sympatric over large areas in China (Cheng 1987) and there is no indication of any hybridization.

Carpodacus rodochrous Pink-browed Rosefinch: often (as in Voous 1977 and Cheng 1987) spelt *C. rhodochrous* (but see Sibley & Monroe 1990).

Carpodacus rodopeplus Spot-winged Rosefinch: often (as in Voous 1977 and Cheng 1987) spelt *C. rhodopeplus* (but see Sibley & Monroe 1990). Includes *verreauxi* of SW China which shows marked morphological differences (in the male), has a disjunct distribution and might possibly merit specific status.

Carpodacus rhodochlamys Red-mantled Rosefinch: includes *grandis* Blyth's Rosefinch, sometimes (including by Voous 1977) treated as specifically distinct. Vaurie (1956) considered it was probably a separate species, but later (1959a) he treated it as conspecific with *C. rhodochlamys* in spite of its morphological differences.

Carpodacus puniceus Red-breasted Rosefinch: alternatively (as in Stepanyan 1990) *Pyrrhospiza punicea*.

Kozlowia roborowskii Roborovski's Rosefinch: alternatively (as in Sibley & Monroe 1990) *Carpodacus roborowskii*. The taxonomic position of this little-known species is uncertain but, in view of its unusual, long-winged structure that is closer to *Leucosticte* than typical rosefinches (Roselaar 1992), it seems better not to place it in *Carpodacus*.

Pinicola subhimachalus Crimson-browed Finch: sometimes (as in Cheng 1987) spelt *P. subhimachala*. Alternatively (as in Voous 1977) *Propyrrhula subhimachala*.

Urocynchramus pylzowi Przevalski's Rosefinch: Cheng (1987) and Sibley & Monroe (1990) place this species among the buntings (the latter using the English name 'Pink-tailed Bunting') since Zusi (1978) considered that its skull structure was not cardueline. Its affinities are uncertain but it is usually (including by Voous 1977) placed amongst the Fringillidae close to *Uragus sibiricus* Long-tailed Rosefinch. Based on personal observations, I share the opinion of B. King and P. Alström (pers. comms. to Sibley & Monroe 1990) that this species is a rosefinch, albeit an atypical one.

Pyrrhula pyrrhula Eurasian Bullfinch: includes *murina* Azores Bullfinch, *cineracea* Grey Bullfinch and *griseiventris* Grey-bellied Bullfinch, any or all of which are sometimes treated as specifically distinct. Both *cineracea* and *griseiventris* are treated as full species by Stepanyan (1990), while Cheng (1987) treats *griseiventris* as specifically distinct with *cineracea* as a race. There is some hybridization between *cineracea* and nominate *pyrrhula* in the area of overlap (Vaurie 1956, 1959a), but the distributions and relationships of the different forms in eastern Asia are poorly understood.

PARULIDAE

(merged in Fringillidae by Sibley & Monroe 1990)

Dendroica petechia Yellow Warbler: includes *aestiva* Yellow Warbler, the only form recorded from the Palearctic (as a vagrant), which is sometimes treated as specifically distinct. (*D. petechia* then takes the English name 'Golden Warbler'.)

THRAUPIDAE

(merged in Fringillidae by Sibley & Monroe 1990)

EMBERIZIDAE

(merged in Fringillidae by Sibley & Monroe 1990)

Passerculus sandwichensis Savannah Sparrow: alternatively (as in Voous 1977 and Stepanyan 1990) *Ammodramus sandwichensis*. Includes *princeps* Ipswich Sparrow, which has also occurred as a vagrant in the Palearctic, formerly sometimes treated as specifically distinct.

Passerella iliaca Fox Sparrow: alternatively (as in Voous 1977) *Zonotrichia iliaca*.

Melospiza melodia Song Sparrow: alternatively (as in Voous 1977) *Zonotrichia melodia*.

Latoucheornis siemsseni Slaty Bunting: alternatively (as in Voous 1977 and Cheng 1987) *Emberiza siemsseni*. This little-known species favours very dense forest undergrowth, is highly terrestrial and has an atypical song for a bunting (pers. obs. in Sichuan), so placing it in a separate genus may be the best course of action. Further studies are needed.

Emberiza leucocephalos Pine Bunting: sometimes (as in Cheng 1987 and Stepanyan 1990) spelt *E. leucocephala*. Sometimes treated as conspecific with *E. citrinella* Yellowhammer, with which it overlaps with limited hybridization in the Urals and western Siberia (Mauersberger 1971).

Emberiza godlewskii Godlewski's Bunting: sometimes (including by Voous 1977 and Cheng 1987) treated as conspecific with *E. cia* Rock Bunting. The ranges of the two forms come into close proximity in the Altai mountains without interbreeding and in Mongolia *E. cia* is found locally within the range of *godlewskii* but apparently there is no interbreeding (G. Mauersberger and L. A. Portenko in Stresemann *et al.* 1971, Mauersberger 1972), so specific status for *godlewskii* seems appropriate.

Emberiza bruniceps Red-headed Bunting: formerly sometimes treated as conspecific with *E. melanocephala* Black-headed Bunting. Hybridization between the two forms is limited to a narrow zone of contact in the north and south Caspian areas (Haffer 1977) and they are usually regarded as members of a superspecies.

Miliaria calandra Corn Bunting: alternatively (as in Cheng 1987 and Stepanyan 1990) *Emberiza calandra*.

ICTERIDAE

(merged in Fringillidae by Sibley & Monroe 1990)

NOTES ON ENGLISH NAMES

GAVIIDAE

Red-throated Loon: The use of 'loon' in North America and 'diver' in the Old World for the members of the Gaviidae is a long-established dichotomy but one that must be addressed if a standardized world list of English bird names is to be achieved. Although recognizing that 'diver' is dear to the hearts of ornithologists in the British Isles, 'loon' seems to me to have the edge. Although now used mainly in North America, 'loon' originated as a bird name in Britain and has a long history of use, dating back to at least 1634 in the literature (Simpson & Weiner 1989). The word derives from the Old Norse *lómr* (the primary sense of which is moan, i.e. moaning bird: see Lockwood 1984), by way of 'loom' and 'loone', and so has an ancient lineage. To my mind 'loon' has the advantage of being unique to the Gaviidae in the same way that 'grebe' is unique to the Podicipedidae, while 'diver' has a much wider range of meaning that extends well beyond bird names. Even if the two rival names are considered to have equal merit, the claims of 'loon' to become the standard name for worldwide use are strengthened by the fact that all five *Gavia* species breed in North America and particularly because, owing to the much larger population of English-speakers in that continent, a greater number of people are familiar with that name. (The idea, prevalent in some quarters in the British Isles, that the name 'loon' stems from the fact that the eerie, wailing cries of these birds recall the strange sounds made by lunatics or 'loonies' is a misconception.)

Black-throated Loon: Although the current North American name 'Arctic Loon' reflects the scientific name, this is not the most Arctic of the loons in distribution (that honour falls to Red-throated Loon *G. stellata* and, to a lesser degree, Yellow-billed Loon *G. adamsii*), so the name is misleading. The throat patch (although glossed with purple or green depending on the subspecies) typically appears black and so the name 'Black-throated Loon' (which was commonly used in North America earlier this century: see, for example, Pearson 1936) is appropriate. This name also has the advantage of being close to the current Old World name 'Black-throated Diver'. Reverting to this former, more suitable name (and likewise 'Great Northern Loon': see below) seems a small price for North American ornithologists to have to pay for a worldwide acceptance of 'loon'. See also Red-throated Loon.

Pacific Loon: see Red-throated Loon.

Great Northern Loon: The epithet 'common' not only tends to devalue a bird (admittedly a subjective judgement) but is often misleading. The current North American name 'Common Loon' (formerly it was often just called 'Loon') dates from the period when *G. adamsii* was treated as conspecific, thus giving *G. immer* a circumpolar distribution. Now that its breeding range is primarily North American, and as it is not even the commonest species in many parts of that continent, the name has become less appropriate. The name 'Great Northern Loon' has a long pedigree in North America and was used by the great Alexander Wilson in his *American Ornithology* (1831). A noble and appropriate name for a splendid bird (and currently in use in modified form in the Old World as 'Great Northern Diver'), this should be the preferred choice rather than the dreary and frequently inappropriate 'Common Loon'. See also Red-throated Loon.

Yellow-billed Loon: Of the Old World 'white-billed' and North American 'yellow-billed', the latter better describes the breeding adult and is marginally more accurate overall. See also Red-throated Loon.

PODICIPEDIDAE

Horned Grebe: The word 'Slavonian' derives from the medieval Latin 'S(c)lavonia', meaning 'country of the Slavs' (Simpson & Weiner 1989) and this wider meaning was the one intended when the name 'Sclavonian Grebe' was first used in Britain (see Montagu 1802). Nowadays, however, 'Slavonia' is mainly used with reference to a specific part of Croatia (Simpson & Weiner 1989). The name 'Horned Grebe', now mostly in use in North America, also originated in Britain and was in use before 'S(c)lavonian Grebe', being first used by Pennant (1785) but itself deriving from the still older 'Hooded Dabchick' (Lockwood 1984). The two names were for a long time used in parallel (e.g. Saunders 1899, Coward 1920). Both names are unique but not without their drawbacks. There are several grebe species with 'horns', while the modern restriction of 'Slavonia' to a region far from the area in northeast Europe that the bird's name was intended to refer to is particularly unfortunate. Given that a choice has to be made, I prefer 'Horned Grebe' as being less ambiguous in a present day context.

Black-necked Grebe: The Old World 'Black-necked Grebe' is more appropriate than the North American 'Eared Grebe' as the former describes an important plumage feature while several grebe species have 'ears'.

PROCELLARIIDAE

Fea's Petrel: This name reflects the scientific name of this recently elevated species and was the English name originally given to this form before it was lumped in Soft-plumaged Petrel *P. mollis*. It is to be preferred to the newly-coined 'Cape Verde Petrel' (used by Sibley & Monroe 1990), a name which only refers to part of the breeding distribution of the species and which, when juxtaposed with the name 'Madeira Petrel' for *P. feae*, is potentially misleading since it suggests that it is the local representative of the *mollis* complex in the Cape Verde Islands while *feae* is the local representative in the Madeira group of islands. In reality, of course, both species breed in the Madeira group. The name 'Cape Verde' is in any case ambiguous without the addition of 'islands' as Cape Verde itself is situated on the West African mainland in Senegal, so use of 'Cape Verde' for species that are not endemic to the Cape Verde Islands is best avoided. The local name 'Gon-gon' is interesting enough but suffers from the disadvantage of being meaningless in English.

Zino's Petrel: This newly-coined name honours P. A. Zino and F. Zino whose work helped to raise the form *madeira* to full species status and is preferable to the newly-coined 'Madeira Petrel' (used by Sibley & Monroe 1990), a name which simply invites confusion with the commonly used name 'Madeiran Petrel' for *Oceanodroma castro*. 'Madeira Petrel' is made even less appropriate by the fact that Fea's Petrel *P. feae* also breeds in the Madeiran archipelago. The local name of 'Freira' is interesting enough but, like Gon-gon, suffers from the disadvantage of being meaningless in English. It has also been used for both this species and *P. feae*.

Providence Petrel: This name is more widely used than 'Solander's Petrel' and is the name adopted in Australasia where the species breeds. The name stems from 'bird of providence', the name given to it by the inhabitants of Norfolk Island who survived famine in 1790 by eating many of the luckless creatures.

Atlantic Petrel: This name is much more widely used than 'Schlegel's Petrel' and the latter suffers from the fact that it has also been used in the past as a name for Kermadec Petrel *P. neglecta*. 'Atlantic Petrel' is, however, less than ideal as a number of different petrels occur in the Atlantic.

Black-capped Petrel: While accepting the argument that 'black' is redundant in this name (as there is no 'Brown-capped Petrel' or suchlike), the North American 'Black-capped Petrel' is not actually misleading (even when the cap coloration is dark brown, it appears black) and surely ought to take precedence over the British 'Capped Petrel' for a species that is merely a vagrant to the Palearctic.

Dark-rumped Petrel: Use of the name 'Hawaiian Petrel' for *P. phaeopygia* should be avoided as this name refers to the form *sandwichensis*, which is sometimes treated as a full species (see 'Taxonomic notes').

Flesh-footed Shearwater: The word flesh in this context refers to the pink colour of meat, not the skin colour of Europeans (a common misconception). 'Flesh-footed Shearwater' is a reflection of the scientific name, which derives from the Latin *carneus* 'flesh-coloured' and *pes* 'foot', and is marginally more appropriate for this pink-footed species than the less widely-used 'Pale-footed Shearwater'.

Christmas Shearwater: This is much the most widely used version of the name and adding 'island' to clarify that it is Christmas Island that is being referred to, rather than the festival, is probably unnecessary.

Mediterranean Shearwater: An appropriate name and one that has more meaning for English speakers than 'Yelkouan Shearwater', which derives from the Turkish word *yelkovan* = shearwater. More importantly, the latter name is associated in the minds of many people with the eastern race *yelkouan* in particular. The name 'Mediterranean Shearwater' has been used in the past for Cory's Shearwater *Calonectris diomedea*, but this was so long ago as to be unlikely to cause confusion. In the event of *mauretanicus* (Balearic Shearwater) being treated as a full species (see 'Taxonomic notes'), then the better-known 'Yelkouan Shearwater' is marginally preferable for the residual *P. yelkouan* than 'Levantine Shearwater'.

HYDROBATIDAE

European Storm-petrel: The modifier 'European' is more appropriate than 'British' for the traditional name 'Storm Petrel' as the breeding distribution of the species extends from Iceland to the central Mediterranean (and even within the British Isles the majority nest on small islands off Ireland). 'British Storm-petrel' has, however, been in use for considerably longer (primarily in North America).

Madeiran Storm-petrel: While this name only refers to a small part of the world range of the species, it is the area from which it was first described by Harcourt in 1851 and is thus of historical interest in the same way that the name 'Kentish Plover' is for *Charadrius alexandrinus*. Just because a name is geographically restricted is not strong justification for its replacement, otherwise well-known names like 'Connecticut Warbler' for *Oporornis agilis* should also be abandoned. The largely North American name 'Band-rumped Storm-petrel' is an unsatisfactory alternative when so many other storm petrels have a white band across the rump. The name 'Harcourt's Storm-petrel' is not in widespread use, which is unfortunate as it is both unique and appropriate.

PHALACROCORACIDAE

Temminck's Cormorant: This name, which honours the ornithologist who jointly described the species with Schlegel in 1850, is more appropriate than 'Japanese Cormorant' for a species that breeds from north China to Sakhalin and the Kuril Islands (even being used in books on Japanese birds, e.g. Brazil 1991).

Long-tailed Cormorant: Both this name and 'Reed Cormorant' are reasonably appropriate, but 'Long-tailed Cormorant' is more widely used.

ANHINGIDAE

African Darter: This is the usual name for the form *rufa* when it is split from *A. melanogaster* (see 'Taxonomic notes'). The latter is known simply as 'Darter' when it includes all three forms, but as 'Oriental Darter' if the African and Australasian forms are treated as full species.

PELECANIDAE

Great White Pelican: A modifier is necessary to differentiate the well-established English name 'White Pelican' for *Pelecanus onocrotalus* from the name 'American White Pelican' for *P. erythrorhynchos*. The name 'Eastern White Pelican' has sometimes been used, but is unsatisfactory when the only other 'white pelican' is found in North America (the usual use of 'western' and 'eastern' being for pairs of species inhabiting the same continental landmass). The old name 'Rosy Pelican' (which refers to the rosy tinge to the plumage in the breeding season, a feature that is far less distinctive than the overall white coloration) is likewise rather inappropriate. Although *P. onocrotalus* is not strikingly larger than the American species (indeed there is some overlap in measurements), 'Great White Pelican', a name already widely used in subsaharan Africa, is probably the best of the available options.

ARDEIDAE

Great Bittern: This name is marginally preferable to 'Eurasian Bittern' as the name for the largest of all the bitterns, contrasting nicely with the English name 'Little Bittern' for *Ixobrychus minutus*. The species breeds in subsaharan Africa, as well as the Palearctic.

Striated Heron: This name is the standard in the Americas and now also Australasia. While only being descriptive of the immature, it has the slight advantage of reflecting the scientific name. The other existing names are also less than ideal. The back is not very green and several other heron species are little. On balance, especially as it is the name known to a greater number of English-speakers, 'Striated Heron' is to be preferred.

Cattle Egret: In the event of the form *coromanda* (Eastern Cattle Egret) being treated as a full species (see 'Taxonomic notes'), it becomes necessary to change the English name for the residual *B. ibis* to 'Western Cattle Egret' (or perhaps 'Common Cattle Egret').

Black Heron: This name is more widely used than 'Black Egret' and, as this bird is not a typical egret (often being placed in a separate genus, *Hydranassa*), is marginally to be preferred.

Western Reef Egret: Although at present usually referred to as 'Western Reef Heron', the eastern counterpart of this species, *E. sacra*, is usually known as 'Pacific Reef Egret' and there is a close taxonomic relationship with Little Egret *E. garzetta*, so retaining the name 'heron' in this instance creates an unhelpful anomaly.

Intermediate Egret: This name reflects the scientific name and the relative size of the species. It is much to be preferred to either 'yellow-billed' or 'plumed', both of which refer to features common to a number of egret species.

Great Egret: This name is now more widely used than 'Great White Egret'. As most egrets are white, the word 'white' is redundant.

SCOPIDAE

Hamerkop: This spelling is more widely used than 'Hammerkop', which is an anglicized version of the Afrikaans word.

CICONIIDAE

Oriental Stork: Removing 'white' from the name for this species is preferable, to my mind, to adding a modifier to the very well-known name 'White Stork' for *C. ciconia*.

THRESKIORNITHIDAE

Northern Bald Ibis: The replacement of 'Bald Ibis' with the German name 'Waldrapp' (meaning 'wood raven') or the old name 'Hermit Ibis' seems unnecessary when the simple modifier 'northern' can be added to differentiate the species from the related Southern Bald Ibis *G. calvus*.

PHOENICOPTERIDAE

Greater Flamingo: In the event of the Old World form *roseus* (Greater Flamingo) being treated as a full species, *P. ruber* is renamed 'American Flamingo'.

ANATIDAE

Tundra Swan: This name has been in use for some time (especially in North America, where 'Whistling Swan' was the former name for *C. columbianus*). Now that *bewickii* is treated as conspecific with *C. columbianus* it is inappropriate and unhelpful to try to apply the name 'Bewick's Swan' to that species.

Brent Goose: The Old World 'Brent Goose' has the advantage, compared to the North American 'Brant', of indicating the kind of bird involved. Whether 'Brent' is spelt with an 'e' or an 'a' is of little significance.

Common Teal: This name is preferable to 'Green-winged Teal' as it is the commonest teal over a large part of the world and only a small part of the wing is green. Moreover, the name 'Green-winged Teal' is strongly associated with the North American form *carolinensis* and should be kept available in case this form is treated as a full species (see 'Taxonomic notes'). For the dangers inherent in using a name for a form that is sometimes treated as specifically distinct as the standard name for the species with which it is currently treated as conspecific, see Common Scoter.

Spot-billed Duck: In the event of the form *zonorhyncha* (Eastern Spot-billed Duck) being treated as a full species (see 'Taxonomic notes'), it becomes necessary to change the English name for the residual *A. poecilorhyncha* to 'Western Spot-billed Duck'.

Red-billed Teal: This name is in much more widespread use than 'Red-billed Duck' and was the name preferred both by Brown *et al.* (1982) for *The Birds of Africa* and by Dowsett & Forbes-Watson (1993).

Marbled Duck: This name is now in more widespread use and is to be preferred to 'Marbled Teal' for this distinctive duck that is the sole member of the genus *Marmaronetta.*

Ferruginous Duck: This name is more widely known than 'Ferruginous Pochard' and, as the genus *Aythya* includes a series of both 'ducks' and 'pochards', there is no advantage in replacing it.

Long-tailed Duck: Traditional as the North American name 'Oldsquaw' is, 'Long-tailed Duck' is a more meaningful and uncontentious name and so must be preferable in a worldwide context.

Common Scoter: This is a particularly tricky case. Although the North American name 'Black Scoter' is marginally more appropriate for the species *M. nigra* than the Old World 'Common Scoter' (as this is the most all-black of the scoters but not always the commonest), the possibility that the North American and east Siberian race *americana* will be more widely treated as a full species in the future (see 'Taxonomic notes') means that one can envisage a bizarre scenario in which North Americans give up a well-established and appropriate name (i.e. 'Black Scoter') for the rarely used 'American Scoter' (adopted for *americana* by Sibley & Monroe 1990) while English-speaking ornithologists in the Old World give up 'Common Scoter' only to find that it is no longer necessary, but that they are landed with 'Black Scoter'! I believe common sense dictates the use of 'Common Scoter' for *M. nigra*, leaving the name 'Black Scoter' free to be applied to *americana* if it is treated as a full species.

Velvet Scoter: A similar situation applies for this species as for Common Scoter *M. nigra*.The Old World 'Velvet Scoter', which has a long pedigree (see Inskipp & Sharrock 1992), should be kept for this species. The North American name 'White-winged Scoter' is appropriate enough (even if the white on the wings is restricted to the secondaries), but as *deglandi* of North America and E Asia may well be widely treated as a full species in the future (see 'Taxonomic notes') it is sensible to keep the name 'White-winged Scoter' available for this form rather than end up with another bizarre situation where 'White-winged Scoter' is applied only to the European and W Asian form and North Americans are forced to think up a new name for *deglandi.*

Goosander: The Old World name 'Goosander' (deriving from 'goose' and old Norse *önd*, plural *ander*, meaning duck) dates back in the literature, in the form 'Gossander' to at least 1622 (Simpson & Weiner 1989). If it was a question of resisting some attempted 'tidying up', I would wholeheartedly opt for this traditional name, but unfortunately it is necessary to of compare the merits of two well-established names and adopt one as the standard. 'Goosander' is, I believe, marginally preferable to the North American 'Common Merganser' as this species is outnumbered by Red-breasted Merganser in many areas. It is also a more pleasing name that resists the encroachment of dull uniformity. Nonetheless a good case can be made for 'Common Merganser', which indicates the affinities of the species, unlike 'Goosander'.

ACCIPITRIDAE

European Honey Buzzard: The name 'Eurasian Honey Buzzard' is only appropriate if the form *ptilorhyncus* (Crested Honey Buzzard) is treated as conspecific (see 'Taxonomic notes'), otherwise 'European Honey Buzzard' is preferable on geographic grounds (*apivorus* extends only as far east as Western Siberia).

Crested Honey Buzzard: This is the well-established name for the species and I see no reason to change to the newly-coined 'Oriental Honey Buzzard' (used by Sibley & Monroe 1990). The crest is shared with another species (Barred Honey Buzzard *P. celebensis*), but I do not accept that this kind of thing represents a serious problem that merits a well-established name being replaced. If this principle were to be accepted then numerous species on the Palearctic list that have names that describe features not peculiar to them should also be renamed. In any case, why replace one name with another that is no more precise? This species breeds far beyond the bounds of the Oriental region.

Black-winged Kite: The former name 'Black-winged Kite' was reinstated for this species by Sibley & Monroe (1990) to avoid confusion with the Australian species *E. axillaris* (synonym *E. notatus*), which has been known as 'Black-shouldered Kite' or sometimes 'Australian Black-shouldered Kite' since at least the beginning of this century. Although 'Black-winged Kite' is a less accurate name for a species with black only on the 'shoulders', one cannot expect Australian ornithologists to willingly give up a highly appropriate name, on which they have prior claim, just to help us out of a mess. They would, in any event, face difficulties in doing so: an alternative such as 'Australian Kite' would be a poor substitute in a land with a whole series of resident kites. I considered proposing the name 'Common Black-shouldered Kite' for the widespread Eurasian and African *E. caeruleus*, but concluded that this was an even less attractive option than reverting to 'Black-winged Kite'.

African Swallow-tailed Kite: Although the newly-coined 'Scissor-tailed Kite', used by Sibley & Monroe (1990) to avoid confusion with the name 'Swallow-tailed Kite' for *Elanoides forficatus* of the New World, is pleasing enough, 'Swallow-tailed Kite' or 'African Swallow-tailed Kite' are such well-established and appropriate names for the African species that I am reluctant to opt for a major change. *E. forficatus* has often been called 'American Swallow-tailed Kite' in New World literature, and the fact that the two species are not very closely related seems unimportant when one is considering vernacular names. Using the modifiers 'African' and 'American' allows both species to go on being called 'swallow-tailed kite' in popular parlance.

Pallas's Fish Eagle: This name is much to be preferred to 'Pallas's Sea Eagle' for a species that is almost never found in coastal areas.

Indian White-backed Vulture: The name 'White-rumped Vulture' has only been in use in SE Asia since its coining two decades ago and the species is now rare almost throughout that region. The vast majority of the population inhabit the Indian subcontinent, where this species is always known as 'Indian White-backed Vulture'. Both the back and the rump are white, so both names are descriptively accurate, but 'Indian White-backed Vulture' is more informative and complements the name 'African White-backed Vulture' for *Gyps africanus*.

Eurasian Griffon Vulture: It is helpful to retain 'vulture' in the name, although I feel this is a marginal instance as the word 'griffon' already signifies vulture to many ornithologists.

Himalayan Griffon Vulture: See Eurasian Griffon Vulture.

Rüppell's Griffon Vulture: In this international era 'Rüppell's' should be spelt with an umlaut rather than 'Rueppell's' (as per Sibley & Monroe 1990). See also Eurasian Griffon Vulture.

Eurasian Black Vulture: I can understand the argument that English names which might imply a non-existent taxonomic relationship are not a good thing in theory, but if we can live with 'Eurasian Tree Sparrow' and 'American Tree Sparrow', let alone all those Old World and New World warblers, sparrows, orioles and blackbirds, we can surely use common sense and call this species by a sensible name that well describes the coloration of the species and its distribution, rather than re-introduce an old and misleading name like 'Cinereous Vulture' just to avoid a clash with another species which currently shares the name 'Black Vulture'. The term 'cinereous' means ashen-grey, or ash-coloured (Simpson & Weiner 1989) and the plumage coloration of this species certainly does not qualify: although not pure black, it is very dark. Surely it is the role of the taxonomic categories and the scientific nomenclature to indicate relationships, or the lack of them. I do not believe that harm will result from calling this species 'Eurasian Black Vulture' and *Coragyps atratus* by the English name 'American Black Vulture'. The name 'Monk Vulture', which reflects the scientific name, has been proposed as an alternative to Cinereous Vulture (see Inskipp & Sharrock 1992), but why go to the lengths of introducing an entirely new name, that few people will relate to, when a more appropriate English name already exists?

Short-toed Eagle: Although the other *Circaetus* species in subsaharan Africa often carry the group name 'snake eagle' (reflecting their primary food source), 'Short-toed Eagle' is such a well-established name that adding 'snake' to it must surely qualify as unnecessary tidying.

Western Marsh Harrier: This is the most appropriate name when *spilonotus* Eastern Marsh Harrier is treated as a full species (see 'Taxonomic notes'). If, on the other hand, it is treated as conspecific then 'Eurasian Marsh Harrier' is appropriate for the enlarged species.

Hen Harrier: This name is very long-established in the Old World, dating back in the British literature, in the form 'henne harroer', to at least 1565 (Simpson & Weiner 1989). The name, as pointed out by Ray (1691), derived from the species' habit of "chasing, preying upon, and destroying of poultry" back in those bygone days of peasant farming and free-range hens. The current North American name 'Northern Harrier' replaced 'Marsh Hawk' some decades ago and, while appropriate enough, is a dull alternative. Arguments that having 'hen' in the English name for this species can harm efforts to persuade country people of the need to conserve the species are valid, but any bird with the name 'harrier' is likely to encounter prejudice.

Swainson's Hawk: While 'buzzard' is a much more specific and therefore appropriate name for *Buteo* species (see Rough-legged Buzzard), I feel it should be left to North American ornithologists to address the issue of what to do about the name for a New World species that is merely a vagrant to the Palearctic.

Rough-legged Buzzard: Adopting the name 'Rough-legged Hawk' rather than 'Rough-legged Buzzard' as the standard name for this circumpolar species would be a highly retrograde step. Just because a wide variety of raptors, including *Buteo* species, are known as 'hawks' in the Americas does not justify exporting this confusing simplification to the rest of the world. The name 'buzzard', which dates back in the literature, in the form 'busard' to about 1300 (Simpson & Weiner 1989), is used for all Old World members the genus *Buteo* (and only a handful of other raptors) and should be retained for this species. Ideally, North American ornithologists will opt to use the name 'buzzard' for even the purely American *Buteo* species in the future, although one sympathizes with the problems they face due to the belief of the general public that 'buzzard' is synonymous with 'vulture'.

Tawny Eagle: If the form *vindhiana* (Asian Tawny Eagle) is treated as a full species (see 'Taxonomic notes') then the residual *A. rapax* is renamed 'African Tawny Eagle'.

Imperial Eagle: see Spanish Imperial Eagle.

Spanish Imperial Eagle: The distinctive form *adalberti* of the Iberian peninsula, which is sometimes treated as a full species (see 'Taxonomic notes'), is always referred to as 'Spanish Imperial Eagle' and it would surely be a retrograde step to replace such a well-known name with the newly-coined 'Adalbert's Eagle' (used by Sibley & Monroe 1990), especially when other solutions are available. If *adalberti* is treated as a full species the English name for the residual *A. heliaca* can be amended to 'Eastern Imperial Eagle', or that for *adalberti* shortened to 'Spanish Eagle'. I prefer the first option: empires and 'the east' are made for each other.

Verreaux's Eagle: This name, which reflects the scientific name, should be used to avoid a clash with the name 'Black Eagle' for *Ictinaetus malayensis* of south Asia.

FALCONIDAE

Eurasian Hobby: The modifier 'northern' is best avoided when a geographically more precise term, such as 'Eurasian', is available.

Gyr Falcon: This name has often been spelt in compound fashion, but as it is not widely known outside the ornithological and falconry communities it may be possible to make this simpler variant stick. The name dates back to at least the 14th century and may derive from the old Norse *geirfalki* (*geirr* spear and *falki* falcon), but its origins are disputed (Urdang *et al.* 1979, Simpson & Weiner 1989).

TETRAONIDAE

Siberian Grouse: The existing name 'Siberian Spruce Grouse' conflicts with the name 'Spruce Grouse' for *D. canadensis*. Although the loss of 'spruce' is unhelpful, this is the only 'grouse' endemic to Siberia.

Severtzov's Grouse: This existing name is unique and not problematical, so it is unnecessary to change to the newly-coined 'Chinese Grouse' (used by Sibley & Monroe 1990).

Willow Ptarmigan: All three species of *Lagopus* occur in North America, where they are all known as 'ptarmigan' (a name which derives from the Gaelic word *tarmachan* for *L. mutus*). The distinctive and well-known form *scoticus*, which is unique in its lack of a white winter plumage, will of course go on being called 'Red Grouse' long into the future, regardless of whether or not it is treated as a full species (see 'Taxonomic notes'), but it would be foolish to suggest that this name should be adopted as the worldwide standard name for *Lagopus lagopus* when it is so clearly inappropriate over the remainder of the circumpolar distribution of the species. Given that few people in the British Isles are willing to use the name 'Willow Grouse' (understandably enough as *scoticus* has no association with this habitat), I see no point in advocating this name as a compromise solution.

Rock Ptarmigan: A modifier is required to differentiate this species from the other two ptarmigan species. 'Rock Ptarmigan' is already in use in North America and is appropriate.

Caucasian Grouse: The existing name 'Caucasian Black Grouse' conflicts with the name 'Black Grouse' for *T. tetrix*. Although the loss of 'black' is unhelpful, this is the only species of grouse in the Caucasus and adjacent region.

PHASIANIDAE

Verreaux's Monal Partridge: The existing name is unique and appropriate, honouring the ornithologist who first described the species in 1870, so adopting the newly-coined 'Chestnut-throated Partridge' (used by Sibley & Monroe 1990) is not only unnecessary but also replaces a distinctive name with one which is similar to the names of many other Asian partridges and thus instantly forgettable. Further, in the event that *szechenyii* is treated as conspecific (see 'Taxonomic notes'), one is then left with the inappropriate 'Chestnut-throated Partridge' as the name for an enlarged species where one of the populations has a buff-coloured throat. I prefer to see 'monal' retained in the name to point up the fact that the distinctive *Tetraophasis* species, like the snowcocks (*Tetraogallus*), are not typical partridges.

Széchenyi's Monal Partridge: The existing name is unique, so it is unnecessary to adopt the newly-coined 'Buff-throated Partridge' (used by Sibley & Monroe 1990). Further, adopting the latter name has positive disadvantages: see Verreaux's Monal Partridge.

Chukar: This version of the name is so well-known that it seems unnecessary to insist on the longer 'Chukar Partridge'. See also Sora below.

Przevalski's Partridge: The existing name is unique and appropriate, honouring the great ornithologist-explorer of the Tibetan plateau who first described the species in 1876, so it is unnecessary to adopt the newly-coined 'Rusty-necklaced Partridge' (used by Sibley & Monroe 1990).

See-see Partridge: Unlike 'Chukar', which is such a well-known name that adding the modifier 'partridge' is probably unnecessary, this is not a bird familiar to many people and so the longer version of the name is to be preferred.

Common Pheasant: Much the more appropriate name for this most widespread species of pheasant. Only some races have 'ring-necks', so 'Ring-necked Pheasant' is less satisfactory.

TURNICIDAE

Small Button-quail: While I am loath to see the end of the wonderful British name 'Andalusian Hemipode', this species is most often called 'Little Button-quail' in its main area of distribution in Asia and Africa (sometimes 'Kurrichane Button-quail' in the latter continent), and all other members of the family bear the name 'button-quail'. Unfortunately the name 'Little Button-quail' is also used for the Australian *T. velox* and so, since none of the current names for *T. sylvatica* is pre-eminent, the adoption of the newly-coined 'Small Button-quail' (used by Sibley & Monroe 1990) is an acceptable solution.

RALLIDAE

Sora: The addition of 'crake' to this well-established North American name (as proposed by Inskipp & Sharrock 1992), seems an unnecessary step to me and this kind of thinking leads inexorably to 'Dunlin Sandpiper', 'Fieldfare Thrush', 'Blackcap Warbler' and 'Brambling Finch'. Do we really want such crushing uniformity? In any case, North American ornithologists should decide on the English names of species that are merely vagrants to the Palearctic.

Swinhoe's Rail: The existing names 'Swinhoe's Yellow Rail' and 'Asian Yellow Rail' both conflict with the name 'Yellow Rail' for *C. noveboracensis* of North America.

Corn Crake: The name of this species is usually compounded (see any dictionary), but as it is no longer well-known to the general public in the British Isles it should be possible to make this simpler variant stick.

Purple Gallinule: The long-running English name conflict between this species and *Porphyrio porphyrio* has been resolved by the widespread adoption of the new name 'Purple Swamp-hen' for the latter. While there is a good case for retaining the name 'American Purple Gallinule' for this species for a few more years in Europe, in order to reduce confusion, it would be foolish to suggest that this Old World name for a transatlantic vagrant should be adopted for use worldwide and then be shortened to the more usual 'Purple Gallinule' after an interval!

Purple Swamp-hen: The name conflict with the American 'Purple Gallinule' *Porphyrula martinica* is happily resolved by the adoption of the new name 'Purple Swamp-hen' for *Porphyrio porphyrio*. I find the latter, which reflects the unique character of this sole member of the genus, has grown on me and it now seems an appropriate name for this hulking and distinctive inhabitant of the marshlands. (Using a hyphen avoids the potentially confusing combination of 'p' and 'h'.)

Eurasian Coot: This name is already in very widespread use in Asia, Australasia, subsaharan Africa and North America. Given this situation, retaining the existing name must be preferable. The name 'Common Coot' is, however, also appropriate for such a wide-ranging species.

Red-knobbed Coot: Long-established in Africa, where the bulk of the range of this species lies, this name is much more appropriate than the misleading 'Crested Coot', the name in traditional use in the British Isles.

GRUIDAE

Red-crowned Crane: This bird is very strongly associated with the culture and image of both China and Japan. In view of the continuing need for vigorous conservation measures to preserve the population of this evocative species, use of the politically uncontentious 'Red-crowned Crane' is preferable to either 'Japanese Crane' or 'Manchurian Crane'. The red crown patch is, however, hardly its most distinctive feature.

Siberian Crane: This name is in much more widespread use, especially in Asia where the species occurs, than 'Siberian White Crane'.

OTIDIDAE

Denham's Bustard: This name is much more widely used than 'Stanley Bustard' (a name in use only in southern Africa) and reflects the scientific name. (If the latter name is used then it should be spelt 'Stanley's Bustard' to conform to modern practice.)

Houbara Bustard: The word 'Houbara' derives from the Arabic *hubari*, meaning bustard (Simpson & Weiner 1989), so the name 'Houbara Bustard' does involve some duplication. Nonetheless, this is the better-established English name and has the advantage of revealing the affinities of the species.

ROSTRATULIDAE

Greater Painted-snipe: A modifier needs to be added to the traditional name 'Painted Snipe' to differentiate this species from the 'American Painted-snipe' *R. semicollaris* of South America. It is helpful to hyphenate the name 'painted-snipe' to indicate that these are members of a distinct family and not closely related to the true snipes.

HAEMATOPODIDAE

Canary Islands Oystercatcher: Dropping 'islands' from the name is unhelpful because of the association of the word 'canary' with the colour yellow.

DROMADIDAE

Crab-plover: It is helpful to hyphenate the name to indicate that this unusual species (the sole member of the family) is not a true plover.

BURHINIDAE

Stone-curlew: This is a very well-liked name and, as with storm-petrel, painted-snipe and crab-plover, hyphenation can easily be used to indicate that this species is not a true curlew. I accept that 'thick-knee' is an old East Anglian name for this species and that this group name is already widely used for the other members of the family, but I find 'Eurasian Thick-knee' an ugly mouthful. In any case, it is hard to believe that many people would have difficulty appreciating that this species is not a typical curlew (of the genus *Numenius*). As with 'Dunnock' *versus* 'Hedge Accentor', I see the attempt to replace 'Stone-curlew' as an unnecessary attempt to 'tidy up' which should be resisted not only because diversity of English names enriches our ornithology, but also because if we accept the argument in individual cases like this then how can one argue against wholesale 'standardization' in the future that would sweep away dozens of individual names like 'Whimbrel', 'Chiffchaff' and 'Yellowhammer' just because they fail to indicate the affinities of the species. Surely it is part of the sheer pleasure of ornithological study, and instructive to boot, to discover just how diverse and inconsistent the English names of birds actually are, and thus begin to appreciate the importance of taxonomy and the scientific nomenclature.

GLAREOLIDAE

Egyptian Plover: This species is of uncertain affinities and while probably closest to the coursers it has sometimes been considered closer to the pratincoles or even placed in its own family (Urban *et. al.* 1986). Although the existing name 'Egyptian Plover' is not ideal, as the species is not a true plover of the family Charadriidae, changing the name to 'Egyptian Courser' (suggested by Inskipp & Sharrock 1992) would simply replace a well-known name with a new one that was no better, for this species certainly does not look much like a courser. While there are instances when a revision to the group name, to reflect both visual appearance and taxonomic position, is appropriate, I have serious doubts in this particular instance. If the taxonomic status changes again in the future there would be no point in keeping the name 'Egyptian Courser', leading to pressure for yet another change of name. Likewise restoring the old name 'Crocodile Bird' (used by Sibley & Monroe (1990) is unsatisfactory as there is no scientific evidence for any association with crocodiles. Seeing no obvious advantage in a change of English name, but instead some disadvantages, I would advocate retaining the current name for this distinctive species.

CHARADRIIDAE

Little Ringed Plover: The simplification of the name to 'Little Plover' to avoid having to add a modifier such as 'common' or 'great' to the traditional name 'Ringed Plover' for C. *hiaticula* would be a retrograde step as many plovers are small and the existing name points up the considerable similarity to C. *hiaticula*.

Common Ringed Plover: This name, already in use in North America and elsewhere, is a marginally better choice than the newly-coined 'Great Ringed Plover'. Although the species is not the more commonly encountered of the two Palearctic 'ringed plovers' in some areas, it cannot by any means be described as 'great' in size, either in general terms or in relation to C. *dubius*.

Killdeer: The addition of 'plover' to this commonly used North American name seems an unnecessary 'standardization': See also Sora.

Kentish Plover: The name 'Kentish Plover' is perhaps more widely used than the North American 'Snowy Plover', being the standard throughout the Old World. Neither name stands out as being obviously superior to the other. The name 'Kentish Plover' is kept because of its historical interest, in the same way that the name 'Terek Sandpiper' is kept for *Xenus cinereus* even though it refers to an area where the bird only occurs on migration. Although this is a rather pale species, several other small plovers are just as 'snowy'. The American *occidentalis* group is sometimes treated as a full species under the name 'Snowy Plover'. Given this situation, its seems preferable to retain 'Kentish Plover' as the standard name for C. *alexandrinus*.

Lesser Sand Plover: This name, which well reflects the relationship to Greater Sand Plover C. *leschenaultii*, is more appropriate than 'Mongolian Plover' for a species that is not by any means restricted to, or even common in, that part of the world.

Eurasian Dotterel: The traditional name 'Dotterel' requires a modifier to differentiate it from the other 'dotterels' of Australasia and South America. The name 'Eurasian Dotterel' is appropriate enough and already widely used, so should have priority, although the newly-coined 'Mountain Dotterel' is also apt. Unfortunately the latter name is close to the name 'Mountain Plover' for C. *montanus* of North America and so, as Eurasian Dotterel breeds in Alaska, might possibly lead to confusion.

American Golden Plover: With the splitting off of the form *fulva* (Pacific Golden Plover), this has become a more appropriate name for the species than 'Lesser Golden Plover'.

European Golden Plover: With the demise of the name 'Lesser Golden Plover' for P. *dominica* it would be inappropriate to use the North American name 'Greater Golden Plover' for this species (and in any case the size difference is only slight), but the standard name should be 'European Golden Plover' rather than 'Eurasian Golden Plover' (as used by Sibley & Monroe 1990) since the species' range only marginally extends into Asia.

Grey Plover: The Old World 'Grey Plover' is preferable to the North American 'Black-bellied Plover' for the species as it is grey rather than golden at any season, but shares a black belly in breeding plumage with all three golden plovers.

Spur-winged Lapwing: Use of the name 'lapwing' for the broad-winged plovers of the genus *Vanellus* (and *Hoplopterus* and/or *Chettusia* if treated as distinct) has for a long time been more common than the use of 'plover' in Asia and was also adopted by Urban *et al.* 1986 in *The Birds of Africa*. 'Lapwing' is now the standard in Australasia also. It is hard to argue against the merits of a separate group name for these distinctive species.

Black-headed Lapwing: See Spur-winged Lapwing.

Grey-headed Lapwing: See Spur-winged Lapwing.

Red-wattled Lapwing: See Spur-winged Lapwing.

Sociable Lapwing: See Spur-winged Lapwing.

White-tailed Lapwing: See Spur-winged Lapwing.

SCOLOPACIDAE

Red-necked Stint: This is by far the best-known version of the English name in the Old World (which includes almost all the normal area of occurrence of the species) and, since it is just as appropriate as 'Rufous-necked Stint', it therefore has the better claim to become the worldwide standard. The colour of the neck is not a typical red, but if 'Red Knot' qualifies as red rather than rufous then so does this species.

Spoon-billed Sandpiper: This is the name in use by English-speaking ornithologists throughout the Old World, including all the areas where this species normally occurs, and is to be preferred to the North American 'Spoonbill Sandpiper'. The bill is, after all, spoon-shaped and nothing to do with spoonbills.

Pintail Snipe: In parallel with 'Spoon-billed Sandpiper', the construction 'pin-tailed' is preferable to 'pintail', but 'Pintail Snipe' is now so well-established in the Old World, including all the areas in which this species is normally found, that I see little prospect of making a revision stick.

Asian Dowitcher: This name is more widely used and just as appropriate as 'Asiatic Dowitcher'.

Little Curlew: This is the name in use in Australia, where the species winters, and in view of the close relationship with Eskimo Curlew *N. borealis* is to be preferred to the largely British 'Little Whimbrel'. In addition, use of the latter name would require the modifier 'common' to be added to the traditional name 'Whimbrel' for *N. phaeopus*.

Eurasian Curlew: Although this species does not breed right across Eurasia, it nests as far east as Mongolia and Transbaicalia and is found as a migrant and winter visitor across much of eastern Asia. Consequently 'Eurasian Curlew' is preferable to 'Western Curlew' or 'European Curlew'.

Far Eastern Curlew: This species nests only in the 'Far East', having a comparatively restricted breeding distribution in NE China, easternmost Mongolia and the Russian Far East. With *N. arquata* qualifying for the description 'Eurasian Curlew', I marginally prefer 'Far Eastern Curlew' to 'Eastern Curlew'.

Red Phalarope: The North American name 'Red Phalarope', which refers to the distinctive breeding coloration, is preferable in a worldwide context to the Old World name 'Grey Phalarope' (the latter having become established largely because this species is almost never observed in breeding plumage in the British Isles). All three phalarope species are rather grey in winter plumage and the name 'Red-necked Phalarope' for *P. lobatus* also refers to the breeding plumage and thus fits in well with 'Red Phalarope'. The name for *Calidris canutus* is 'Red Knot', not 'Grey Knot', in spite of the fact that most people only see this species in winter plumage.

STERCORARIIDAE

Pomarine Jaeger: As with 'loon' and 'diver', the use of 'jaeger' in North America and 'skua' in the Old World for the smaller Stercorariidae is a long-established dichotomy. Most people think of 'jaeger' (which is the German word for hunter, and is pronounced 'yey-ger') as a purely American usage, but in fact it was used in the British Isles also, dating back in the literature, in the form 'jager', to at least 1826. The word 'skua' dates back to about 1604 and its origins lie in the Faeroese *skugvur*, their name for *Catharacta skua* (see Simpson & Weiner 1989). In the first half of the nineteenth century the usual practice in the British Isles was to reserve the term 'skua' for what we now call the 'Great Skua' *Catharacta skua* and use 'jager' for the smaller species. This practice continued in North America, but on this side of the Atlantic all the species later became known simply as 'skuas'. Virtually all authorities now divide the Stercorariidae into two genera and, although I personally prefer 'skua', I find it hard to argue convincingly against the merits of a name that helps to differentiate the smaller *Stercorarius* species with their projecting central tail feathers from the heavy, gull-like *Catharacta* species. The division into 'jaegers' and 'skuas' has recently been officially adopted in Australia also.

Parasitic Jaeger: All jaegers (or smaller skuas) are 'parasitic' (strictly speaking, kleptoparasitic) to some degree but this species is much the most reliant on food piracy (see Cramp & Simmons 1983), a fact that is reflected in the scientific name. All three *Stercorarius* species are primarily 'arctic' in breeding distribution and, although this species breeds as far north as 82°N in Franz Josef Land, Long-tailed Jaeger *S. longicaudus* reaches even further into the Arctic region in northern Canada and Greenland, while *S. parasiticus* nests further to the south than any other jaeger. Given that it is necessary to resolve the conflicting claims of the North American 'Parasitic' and Old World 'Arctic', the former is clearly more appropriate and also has the further advantage of reflecting the scientific name. See also Pomarine Jaeger.

Long-tailed Jaeger: See Pomarine Jaeger.

Southern Skua: A preferable name to 'Antarctic Skua' as many populations breed well to the north of Antarctica proper.

South Polar Skua: This is now a much more widely used name than 'McCormick's Skua'. Although this species only occasionally reaches the South Pole (where it has been observed feeding at the garbage dump at the American base: K. Kaufman *in litt.*), it certainly has the most southerly distribution of any skua.

LARIDAE

Pallas's Gull: The name 'Pallas's Gull' was coined to avoid having to add the modifier 'common' to the name 'Black-headed Gull' for *L. ridibundus* (see Inskipp & Sharrock 1992). Although I much prefer to see existing names retained, where no nomenclatural problem exists, this is a particularly difficult situation (see entries for Black-headed Gull and Mew Gull) and so, as this new name is appropriate (honouring the famous ornithologist and explorer who first described the species in 1773), I am making a pragmatic exception in this instance.

Black-headed Gull: The name 'Common Black-headed Gull' was coined in North America, where this species was then only a vagrant, and unfortunately without any reference to English-speaking ornithologists in Europe. Adding the modifier 'common' in order to differentiate this species from 'Great Black-headed Gull' *L. ichthyaetus* is highly unsatisfactory as it simply invites confusion with the well-established Old World name 'Common Gull' for *L. canus*, especially at a time when it is proposed that this name should be replaced by 'Mew Gull'. A better solution is to leave the well-established name 'Black-headed Gull' in place and change the name for *L. ichthyaetus* (see Pallas's Gull).

Mew Gull: The origins of the rival names 'Mew Gull' and 'Common Gull' are obscure, but probably stem from the fact that small gulls were once called 'mews' or 'sea-mews'. In this same period *L. ridibundus* was typically referred to as the 'Pewit' (later 'Pewit-Gull'), after its call. This may explain why *L. canus* ultimately achieved its current names. At first 'Common Mew' (as in 'commonest other mew' after the

Pewit), later becoming 'Common Gull' or 'Mew Gull'. Whatever the origins of 'Common Gull', this has always been a highly inappropriate name for a species that is by no means the common gull of Eurasia and undoubtedly represents one of the most misleading uses of the epithet 'common' in ornithology today. The name 'Mew Gull' may not be perfect (effectively meaning 'small-gull gull'), but in comparison with 'Common Gull' it wins by default. No other suitable English name has ever been suggested for this species, and 'Mew Gull' (which was at one time used in the British Isles) has recently advanced to the point that it is now widely used in Asia as well as North America, and was adopted by Urban *et al.* (1986) as the preferred name for *The Birds of Africa*. In the event of the North American form *brachyrhynchus* being treated as a full species (see 'Taxonomic notes'), use of the names 'Eurasian Mew Gull' and 'American Mew Gull' would be preferable to reverting to the highly unsatisfactory 'Common Gull' for *L. canus*.

Heuglin's Gull: Preferable to 'Siberian Gull' both because so many other gulls occur in Siberia and because the taxonomic situation is unclear (and the geographical distribution of this 'species' likewise uncertain).

STERNIDAE

Greater Crested Tern: This name is marginally preferable to 'Great Crested Tern' in contrast to 'Lesser Crested Tern', and both are preferable to the rather ambiguous 'Swift Tern'.

Grey-backed Tern: Both this name and 'Spectacled Tern' are widely used, but this species has a contrastingly grey back and does not show prominent 'spectacles'.

White-winged Tern: While accepting that the loss of 'black' from the English name for *C. leucopterus* is unhelpful, the name 'White-winged Tern' is already in such widespread use in Asia, Australasia, Africa and North America that I do not believe the alternative option, that of adding a modifier to the name 'Black Tern' for *C. niger*, is the best course of action.

Lesser Noddy: If *minutus* is treated as conspecific (see 'Taxonomic notes'), the name 'Black Noddy' is usually applied to the enlarged species.

White Tern: The well-liked name 'Fairy Tern' is far more pleasing for this appealing species than the distinctly uninspired 'White Tern'. Sadly the former conflicts with the sole English name for the Australasian species *Sterna nereis* and, as 'White Tern' is very widely used already, I reluctantly adopt it here. The modifier 'common' is only needed if the extralimital form *microrhyncha* ('Little White Tern') is treated (as by Pratt *et al.* 1987 and Sibley & Monroe 1990) as a full species, but the paper quoted in support of this treatment (Holyoak & Thibault 1976) reports that intermediates are frequently found in the Marquesas group and does not urge specific status for *microrhyncha*.

ALCIDAE

Common Murre: The name 'murre', currently in use mainly in North America, originated in Britain and appears in the literature as early as 1602 (Simpson & Weiner 1989). It is considered to be onomatopoeic in origin, echoing the low, guttural calls of the adults on the breeding cliffs (Lockwood 1984). The name 'guillemot' originated in France and is a pet name for *Guillaume* = William (meaning 'little William') that ultimately derives from the Old French *Willelm*. When used as a bird name, it referred to the juvenile of the species according to Belon (1555) and is also onomatopoeic, echoing the clear, high-pitched calls of the young birds. It was introduced into English by Ray (1678) and has generally replaced local British names such as 'Will' and 'Willock' that similarly derive from *Willelm*, once a common name in England also (Lockwood 1984). Regardless of the history and meaning of the names, 'murre' has the advantage of differentiating the members of the genus *Uria* from the members of the genus *Cepphus* (which are called 'guillemots' in both the New World and the Old). For this reason alone it would be hard to argue that 'guillemot' should be adopted as the worldwide standard name for the members of both genera, thus removing a helpful (and linguistically enriching) differentiation. Use of 'murre' also links with the name 'murrelet' given to a number of smaller alcids. As with 'loon' *versus* 'diver', even if the two names are considered to have equal merit, the claims of 'murre' as the worldwide standard are strengthened by the greater number of English-speakers familiar with the name. Murre is not, however, the easiest word to pronounce correctly: it should sound roughly like myrrh, as in 'gold, frankincense and myrrh'.

Brünnich's Murre: The current North American modifier 'thick-billed' is appropriate enough, but Brünnich was the first person to realize that there was a second species of *Uria* (he described the differences between the two species in 1764) and such an early triumph of careful observation ought to be honoured. In fact the name 'Brünnich's Murre' was formerly in widespread use in North America (see, for example, Pearson 1936), so its restoration seems a small price for North American ornithologists to pay in return for a worldwide acceptance of murre. See also Common Murre.

Little Auk: Delightful as the North American name 'Dovekie' is, the Old World 'Little Auk', which indicates the affinities of the species and its relative size, has the better claim for worldwide usage.

COLUMBIDAE

Rock Dove: While I accept that most other *Columba* species are called 'pigeon' rather than 'dove', I do not believe that a quest for uniformity in English names is sufficient justification for replacing perfectly adequate existing names. This species is usually referred to as 'Rock Dove' throughout North America and Europe, as well as in Africa. Changing the name to 'Rock Pigeon' is the kind of unnecessary 'tidying' that is only likely to alienate many people who could otherwise be persuaded of the need for a worldwide standardization of English names of birds. (Feral individuals of this species are, however, often referred to as 'Feral Pigeons' rather than feral Rock Doves, an inconsistency which only augments the sheer pleasure of ornithological study.)

Stock Dove: See Rock Dove.

Yellow-eyed Dove: The epithet 'yellow-eyed' has long been in use for this species and, since it is both appropriate and unique amongst the Columbidae, there is no good reason to adopt the newly-coined 'Pale-backed Pigeon' (used by Sibley & Monroe 1990). See also Rock Dove.

Trocaz Pigeon: This English name, apparently first used by Goodwin (1970), derives like the scientific name from the local Portuguese name *pombo trocaz* (see Jobling 1991). The rather uninspired 'Long-toed Pigeon' is also of relatively recent origin, replacing 'Madeiran Laurel Pigeon' and other earlier names.

Ryukyu Wood Pigeon: As other island forms in the region are all called 'wood pigeon' it is inappropriate to shorten the name of just this particular species (as done by Sibley & Monroe 1990).

African Collared Dove: This species is thought to be closely related to the Eurasian Collared Dove *S. decaocto*, so this is an appropriate name. The species is not noticeably 'pink-headed' and the 'rose-grey' coloration is shared by other subsaharan *Streptopelia* species.

African Mourning Dove: The addition of the modifier 'African' differentiates this species from the well-known Mourning Dove *Zenaida macroura* of North America. Sibley & Monroe (1990), following Goodwin (1970), used the name 'Mourning Collared Dove' for the African species, but this name is such a mouthful and the name 'Mourning Dove' so well-established for the African species that I believe the use of the modifiers 'African' and 'American' , in spite of the lack of a close taxonomic relationship, to be preferable. The name 'African Mourning Dove' was adopted by Urban *et al.* (1986) for *The Birds of Africa* and by Dowsett & Forbes-Watson (1993).

Red Turtle Dove: This is by far the most widely used name for this species and, since most ornithologists merely associate the name 'turtle dove' with the genus *Streptopelia*, rather than any particular sub-group within it that shows particular plumage characters, I do not feel there is a pressing need to adopt the name 'Red Collared Dove' (as used by Sibley & Monroe 1990, following Goodwin 1970), especially when so many of the *Streptopelia* species of subsaharan Africa which have solid black half collars are not called 'collared doves'.

Oriental Turtle Dove: This is the name almost always used in Asia, where the species occurs and, as this bird is less rufous than European Turtle Dove *S. turtur*, it is more appropriate than the alternative 'Rufous Turtle Dove'.

Emerald Dove: Both names for this species are widely used and both are appropriate, but this name is to be preferred to 'Green-winged Pigeon' as the only other member of the genus, *C. stephani*, is called 'Stephan's Dove' (or 'Stephan's Ground Dove').

American Mourning Dove: see African Mourning Dove.

Wedge-tailed Green Pigeon: Retaining 'green' in the names for the distinctive *Treron* species is helpful.

White-bellied Green Pigeon: See Wedge-tailed Green Pigeon.

PSITTACIDAE

Rose-ringed Parakeet: This, rather than 'Ring-necked Parakeet', is the name in most widespread use.

Lord Derby's Parakeet: The name 'Derbyan Parakeet' (used by Sibley & Monroe 1990) is a completely unnecessary and indeed ugly replacement for a widely used and unique name.

CUCULIDAE

Jacobin Cuckoo: As this name (which reflects the scientific name) is widely used in subsaharan Africa, which forms the greater part of the range of the species, it is marginally to be preferred to the Asian name 'Pied Cuckoo', especially as all-dark individuals are of frequent occurrence in southern Africa.

Didric Cuckoo: This is the most widely used version of the English name. The typical songs of this species sound like 'day-dee-dee-diric' and 'dee-dee-dee-di-di-c' according to Fry *et al.* (1988), so all three versions of the English name can claim to be reasonably accurate renditions.

Common Koel: When an existing name is well-established and appropriate enough, why change it? The newly-coined 'Asian Koel' (used by Sibley & Monroe 1990) is not a very accurate description for a species that still ranges as far as New Guinea even when *cyanocephala* Australian Koel and *melanorhyncha* Black-billed Koel are treated as full species.

TYTONIDAE

Barn Owl: It is not necessary to add the modifier 'common' to the English name for this species if the word 'barn' is dropped from the English names for *T. inexspectata* (now usually called 'Minahassa Owl' or 'Minahassa Masked Owl'), *T. aurantia* (now usually called 'Golden Owl' or 'Bismarck Masked Owl'), *T. rosenbergii* (now usually called 'Sulawesi Owl') and *T. glaucops* (now often called 'Ashy-faced Owl').

Grass Owl: In the event of the form *longimembris* (Eastern Grass Owl) being treated as a full species (see 'Taxonomic notes'), the residual *T. capensis* is renamed 'African Grass Owl'.

STRIGIDAE

Collared Scops Owl: If the form *lempiji* is treated as a full species (see 'Taxonomic notes') and given the English name 'Collared Scops Owl', then the name 'Indian Scops Owl' is probably the most appropriate choice for the residual *O. bakkamoena*, although this name has been used for *O. sunia* (Oriental Scops Owl) in the past.

Pallid Scops Owl: This name has been in use for many years in Asia and is preferable to 'Striated Scops Owl' (which only relatively recently replaced the old name 'Bruce's Scops Owl' in the Western Palearctic) as this species is always very pale in appearance while many scops owls have obvious striations. A case can also be made for 'Bruce's Scops Owl', a name which reflects the scientific name.

European Scops Owl: The name 'Common Scops Owl' is only appropriate when the form *senegalensis* (African Scops Owl) is treated as conspecific, giving the species a huge distribution throughout Europe, Africa and western Asia. It becomes even more appropriate when (as in Sibley & Monroe 1993) the form *sunia* (Oriental Scops Owl) is also treated as conspecific. Similarly, the name 'Eurasian Scops Owl' is best avoided unless *sunia* is treated as conspecific. The name not only suggests a wider range in Asia than *O. scops* (*sensu stricto*) actually has (it reaches only as far as Lake Baikal and the borders of Pakistan) but, because of the frequency with which *sunia* has been treated as conspecific in the past, it implies that this is the taxonomic treatment being followed.

Ryukyu Scops Owl: The name 'Elegant Scops Owl' was recently coined by B. King and adopted by Sibley & Monroe (1990). B. King (*in litt.*) has now had second thoughts, concluding that this species is no more elegant than any other scops owl, and advocates return to 'Ryukyu Scops Owl', a name referring to the bulk of the range of this newly elevated species. The latter name was used by Brazil (1991) and was the name most often used in the past.

Eurasian Eagle Owl: The modifier 'northern' is best avoided when a geographically more precise term, such as 'Eurasian', is available.

Père David's Owl: If *davidi* is treated as a full species (see 'Taxonomic notes') then I favour the name 'Père David's Owl', which reflects the scientific name, over 'Sichuan Wood Owl'.

Tengmalm's Owl: The Old World name 'Tengmalm's Owl' is unique and more appropriate than the North American 'Boreal Owl' for this species as several owls are characteristic of the boreal forest and *Aegolius funereus* also breeds well to the south of the boreal zone as such. The Swedish ornithologist Tengmalm was for a time believed to have discovered the species (and it was described as *Strix tengmalmi* by Gmelin before it was realized that it was the same as *Strix funerea* of Linnaeus) and during his lifetime he made a significant contribution to the knowledge of northern owls (see Mearns & Mearns 1988).

CAPRIMULGIDAE

Mountain Nightjar: This name was used by both Fry *et al.* (1988) in *The Birds of Africa* and by Dowsett & Forbes-Watson (1993). As it is so well-established I have adopted it here in preference to the equally suitable 'Montane Nightjar' and 'Abyssinian Nightjar'.

European Nightjar: This is a widely used name compared to 'Eurasian Nightjar' and is to be preferred for a species that does not extend right across Asia as a breeding bird and which winters largely in subsaharan Africa, so is virtually unknown over most of south and east Asia. 'European Nightjar' also has the helpful advantage of reflecting the scientific name.

APODIDAE

White-throated Needletail: Adding 'swift' to the name for this species, while better indicating its affinities, would be out of line with the English names for all the other 'needletails' of Asia.

Cape Verde Swift: This is the name in most widespread use and, since it is both unique and appropriate, a reversion to 'Alexander's Swift' is unnecessary.

Fork-tailed Swift: This is the name by which the species is usually known throughout its breeding and wintering ranges in east Asia and Australasia. While not describing a feature peculiar to the species (a failing which applies to numerous bird names), this is the only swift with a markedly forked tail over much of its range. The less well-established name 'Pacific Swift' is no more appropriate as the breeding range of the species extends far from the Pacific fringe of Asia.

Little Swift: It is desirable to use this well-known name for the species *A. affinis*. The name 'House Swift' is mainly used in Asia and is mostly applied to the form *nipalensis*, which is sometimes treated as a full species (see 'Taxonomic notes').

ALCEDINIDAE

White-throated Kingfisher: This name or the alternative 'White-breasted Kingfisher' are used throughout south and east Asia, where most of the distribution of the species is situated. 'White-throated' is marginally preferable to 'white-breasted' as all races have white throats, but sometimes the white barely extends onto the centre of the breast. The old name 'Smyrna Kingfisher', although reflecting the scientific name, is now only infrequently used and it is hard to argue the case for restoring it in the face of competition from two appropriate and well-established competitors.

Grey-headed Kingfisher: Both this name and 'Chestnut-bellied Kingfisher' are appropriate, but 'Grey-headed Kingfisher' is more widely used (including by by Fry *et al.* 1988 in *The Birds of Africa*).

Miyako Kingfisher: The form *miyakoensis* is known from only a single specimen from the island of Miyako and its taxonomic status, and provenance, is uncertain (see 'Taxonomic notes'). The name 'Miyako Kingfisher' is used more often for this form than 'Ryukyu Kingfisher' and is geographically more precise.

Common Kingfisher: This is much the most widely used 'modified' version of the traditional name 'Kingfisher' and appropriate for a species with such a wide distribution.

MEROPIDAE

Green Bee-eater: The name 'Little Green Bee-eater' conflicts with the name 'Little Bee-eater' for the widespread subsaharan species M. *pusillus*. The name 'Green Bee-eater' is already used for M. *orientalis* throughout its Asian range.

UPUPIDAE

Eurasian Hoopoe: If, as is done here, the form *africana* (African Hoopoe) is treated as a full species (see 'Taxonomic notes'), it is necessary to add a modifier to the name 'Hoopoe' for U. *epops*. Even if *africana* is not treated as specifically distinct, it is still necessary to add a modifier if one follows Dowsett & Forbes-Watson (1993) in treating the form *marginata* (Madagascar Hoopoe) as a full species.

PICIDAE

Eurasian Wryneck: The modifier 'northern' is best avoided when a geographically more precise term, such as 'Eurasian', is available.

Grey-headed Woodpecker: It is bizarre to change this well-known name to 'Grey-faced Woodpecker' just to avoid a clash with the newly split 'Grey-headed Woodpecker' *Dendropicos spodocephalus* of subsaharan Africa (as was done by Sibley & Monroe 1990). The latter species is of dubious validity (see Dowsett & Dowsett-Lemaire 1993), but in any event *spodocephalus* should be given a different English name.

European Green Woodpecker: The range of this species barely reaches Asia, so the name 'Eurasian Green Woodpecker' (used by Sibley & Monroe 1990) is inappropriate. Regardless of whether 'green' is included or excluded from the English names for the other Palearctic *Picus* species, a modifier still needs to be added to the traditional name 'Green Woodpecker' for this species to differentiate it from the name 'Cuban Green Woodpecker' for *Xiphidiopicus percussus* and the name 'Little Green Woodpecker' for *Campethera maculosa* of subsaharan Africa.

Levaillant's Green Woodpecker: It is helpful to retain 'green' in the name as a reminder of the close relationship with European Green Woodpecker P. *viridis*.

Japanese Green Woodpecker: It is helpful to retain 'green' in the name to help differentiate the species from the other endemic Japanese woodpecker, Okinawa Woodpecker *Sapheopipo noguchii*, and especially the name 'Japanese Pygmy Woodpecker' for *Dendrocopus kizuki* (see entry for that species).

Okinawa Woodpecker: Of the two existing names, 'Okinawa Woodpecker' is to be preferred as the species occurs only on that island while Pryer appears to have no connection with this species, or indeed ornithology in general (T. P. Inskipp *in litt.*).

Japanese Pygmy Woodpecker: With 'pygmy woodpecker' often being included in the English names for other small woodpeckers species in Asia it is unhelpful to shorten the established name for *D. kizuki* to plain 'Pygmy Woodpecker'. Japan forms a large portion of its range and the retention of 'Japanese' will prevent confusion.

ALAUDIDAE

Singing Bush Lark: The larks are a large and confusing group and so it is unhelpful to drop the word 'bush' from the English names for many *Mirafra* species.

Greater Hoopoe Lark: The modifier 'greater' is necessary to differentiate this species from the Lesser Hoopoe Lark *A. hamertoni* of Somalia.

Tibetan Lark: Unfortunately 'Long-billed Calandra Lark' cannot be shortened to 'Long-billed Lark' without clashing with the English name for *Certhilauda curvirostris* of southern Africa and so, rather than add a modifier to the name 'Calandra Lark' for *M. calandra*, the adoption of the newly-coined 'Tibetan Lark' (used by Sibley & Monroe 1990) seems preferable. This is the most widespread lark of the Tibetan Plateau after Horned Lark *Eremophila alpestris*.

Hume's Short-toed Lark: It is unnecessary and unhelpful to shorten the name to 'Hume's Lark'.

Sand Lark: This unique name is well-known and, as the species is by no means the only 'short-toed lark' occurring in India, changing the name to 'Indian Short-toed Lark' is undesirable.

Wood Lark: The name of this species, like 'skylark', is usually compounded (see any dictionary), but as it is not well-known outside the ornithological community it should be possible to make this simpler variant the standard.

Oriental Skylark: Simplifying the name to 'Oriental Lark' to avoid having to add the modifier 'Eurasian' to Skylark is an unhelpful strategy when so many species of lark occur in the Oriental region. 'Oriental Skylark' is the name in most widespread use and is preferable to 'Small Skylark' in view of the rather slight size difference.

Eurasian Skylark: This is a well-known bird name to the English-speaking general public and the name is always compounded in English literature and in dictionaries, so attempts to promote 'Sky Lark' are unlikely to succeed. The name 'Eurasian Skylark' is preferable to 'Common Skylark' as the former is already widely used in Asia and North America and well reflects the distribution of the species.

Raso Lark: The correct spelling for the island on which the species is found is 'Raso' and not 'Razo'.

Horned Lark: The largely British name 'Shore Lark' (which refers to an uncommon and marginal habitat of the species) is so much less appropriate on a worldwide scale than 'Horned Lark' that the latter is greatly to be preferred. 'Horned Lark' is the standard name in both North America and Asia.

HIRUNDINIDAE

Plain Martin: This species has several current names, none of which stand out as being more widely used. The name 'Plain (Sand) Martin' is well-established in Asia and is marginally more appropriate for this rather nondescript bird than the African and Western Palearctic name 'Brown-throated Sand Martin' as the throat does not stand out as contrastingly brown but is merely tinged darker than the rest of the underparts. 'African Sand Martin' is unsuitable as the standard name for a species with an equally wide range in Asia. Note: the word 'sand' is dropped to avoid having to modify the name 'Sand Martin' for the widespread *R. riparia*.

Sand Martin: All other *Riparia* species are called 'martin' and so, given that a choice must be made, 'Sand Martin' is preferable to the North American name 'Bank Swallow'. As long as 'sand' is dropped from the name for *R. paludicola*, there is no need to add the modifier 'Common' to the name for *R. riparia* unless the form *diluta* (Pale Sand Martin) is treated as a full species (see 'Taxonomic notes'), in which case the name 'Common Sand Martin' is appropriate for the residual *R. riparia*.

Eurasian Crag Martin: Even when the form *obsoleta* (Pale Crag Martin) is treated as conspecific with Rock Martin *H. fuligula*, a modifier still needs to be added to the name 'Crag Martin' for *H. rupestris* to avoid conflict with the name 'Dusky Crag Martin' for the Asian *H. concolor*. The name 'Eurasian Crag Martin' is geographically more precise than 'Northern Crag Martin'.

American Cliff Swallow: The modifier 'American' needs to be added to the name for this species to differentiate it from the established names 'Preuss's Cliff Swallow' for *H. preussi*, 'Red-throated Cliff Swallow' for *H. rufigula*, 'South African Cliff Swallow' for *H. spilodera*, 'Red Sea Cliff Swallow' for *H. perdita* and 'Indian Cliff Swallow' for *H. fluvicola*. As all these species are known to be (or presumed to be in the case of *H. perdita*) colonial nesters and frequently use cliffs, overhanging riverside rocks and the undersides of bridges for nest sites, it seems unjustified and unhelpful to avoid the need for a modifier for the American *H. pyrrhonota* (which has a similar range of nesting habits) by removing 'cliff' from the name for no less than five other species (as done by Sibley & Monroe 1990).

Nepal House Martin: See Common House Martin.

Asian House Martin: See Common House Martin.

Common House Martin: All three *Delichon* species are traditionally called 'house martins' and, although Asian House Marin *D. dasypus* only occasionally nests on houses and Nepal House Martin *D. nipalensis* apparently never does, this group of three species share such similar and distinctive plumage characters that I feel it would be an unhelpful step to remove the word 'house' from their names in order to avoid adding a modifier to the traditional name 'House Martin' for *D. urbica*. 'Common House Martin' is the established name for the latter in Asia, where all three *Delichon* species occur, and so it is preferable to retain this version, especially as *D. urbica* has a far wider distribution than the other two. Its claims are further strengthened by the fact that the alternative name 'Northern House Martin' loses its meaning in Europe, western Asia and Africa where there are no other *Delichon* species.

MOTACILLIDAE

Olive-backed Pipit: This name is much more widely used than the equally appropriate 'Olive Tree Pipit', so should have preference. The name 'Indian Tree Pipit' only refers to a small part of the distribution and is not in widespread use.

Tree Pipit: There is no need to add the modifier 'brown' to this well-known name if 'Olive-backed Pipit' is used for *A. hodgsoni*.

Rock Pipit: This is the long-established, well-known name for *A. petrosus*, but there is a conflict with the name 'Rock Pipit' (or 'African Rock Pipit') for the localized southern African species *A. crenatus*. As the latter species is known to so few English-speakers, it seems preferable to change its name rather than add a modifier to the name for a far better known species. Sibley & Monroe (1990) adopted the newly-coined 'Yellow-tufted Pipit' for *crenatus*, but this not a particularly accurate description for a bird with a little yellow at the bend of the wing. A name such as 'Drakensberg Pipit' might be a better option.

Buff-bellied Pipit: This fairly new name seems preferable to 'American Pipit' for this recent split. Although the latter name is of long standing, having been applied for many years to *A. spinoletta rubescens* in North America prior to the elevation of *rubescens* (together with *japonicus*), it refers to only a part of the distribution of the species (which extends across an immense area in eastern Asia also).

Citrine Wagtail: This is a much better-known English name than 'Yellow-headed Wagtail' or the relatively recent 'Yellow-hooded Wagtail' and so (being equally appropriate) it should have precedence. In addition 'Yellow-headed Wagtail' clashes directly with the English name for *M.* (*f.*) *lutea* and 'Yellow-hooded Wagtail' is unfortunately close to it.

White Wagtail: This is much the most widely used name for the species, being the standard in Asia, subsaharan Africa and North America, and a well-known alternative in Europe. I have therefore reluctantly given it priority over 'Pied Wagtail', even though this is patently a pied rather than a white bird (regardless of subspecies).

African Pied Wagtail: If the name 'White Wagtail' is used for *M. alba* there is no need to drop 'pied' from the name for this species, which would be a retrograde step when the African continent is home to a number of wagtail species.

PYCNONOTIDAE

Chinese Bulbul: The name 'Light-vented Bulbul' is awkward and misleading. It suggests, wrongly, that this species has a contrastingly pale-coloured vent when in reality it simply has plain whitish underparts (without the contrasting yellow or red colour on the vent shown by a number of *Pycnonotus* species). The longer-established name 'Chinese Bulbul' reflects the scientific name and is highly appropriate for this characteristic species of lowland China that extends only marginally into Southeast Asia and the southernmost Nansei (or Ryukyu) Islands.

Himalayan Bulbul: The current name 'White-cheeked Bulbul' is unique and descriptively accurate. Unfortunately the western form *leucotis* is known as 'White-eared Bulbul' and if this form is treated as a full species (see 'Taxonomic notes') a confusing situation results. While reluctant to see existing names replaced without good reason, this is clearly an exceptional case and the newly-coined 'Himalayan Bulbul' (used by Sibley & Monroe 1990) is appropriate enough for a species with a purely Himalayan distribution. If the two forms are regarded as conspecific then 'White-cheeked Bulbul' is an appropriate name for the enlarged species.

White-spectacled Bulbul: This name is greatly preferable to 'Yellow-vented Bulbul' in view of the number of other bulbul species with yellow vents and avoids a clash with the name 'Yellow-vented Bulbul' for *Pycnonotus goiavier* of SE Asia.

Common Bulbul: This is by far the best-known name for this species, which has the most extensive distribution of any bulbul in Africa (even when some forms are split off, as in Sibley & Monroe 1990). 'Common Bulbul' may be an unexciting name, but it is appropriate for such a widespread and numerous species and, since it was used by both Keith *et al.* (1992) in *The Birds of Africa* and Dowsett & Forbes-Watson (1993), I see no compelling reason to replace it with the name 'Garden Bulbul'.

TROGLODYTIDAE

Winter Wren: As the only member of the Troglodytidae inhabiting the Old World, this circumpolar species has generally been known in the Palearctic simply as *the* Wren. In North America it is called 'Winter Wren'. The origins of the name are uncertain, but it probably derives not only from its status as a winter visitor in much of the eastern United States but also from this species' habit of singing loudly even in the depths of winter, making it doubly obvious as the 'winter wren' of much of the eastern USA. Its association with winter was enshrined in the scientific name *T. hiemalis*, which it bore before being lumped in *T. troglodytes*. The association with winter is not restricted to North America either, as the species often features on Christmas cards in the British Isles and the Dutch name for the species, *Winterkoning*, means 'winter king'. Although initially sceptical, on reflection I find 'Winter Wren' not a bad choice for a bold little sprite that is particularly obvious during the north European winter. The name 'Northern Wren', which has been used occasionally in Asia, is inappropriate in an Old World context (where there are no other wrens). Consequently there seems little point in trying to persuade North American ornithologists to replace their own well-established name with this one (although in that continent the name would in fact be apt, this being the wren with the most northerly breeding distribution). 'Common Wren', a name rarely seen, similarly suffers from a lack of meaning in an Old World context and would be equally unsuitable in North America where this is by no means the commonest or the most widespread species of wren.

PRUNELLIDAE

Dunnock: This name (which means 'small and dusky brown') may only have been adopted as the 'official' name for the species by *British Birds* in 1954 and by the British Ornithologists' Union in 1971, to replace the misleading 'Hedge Sparrow', but it is a traditional English name for the species of very long standing, dating back in the literature, in the form 'donek', to about 1475. This predates even 'hedge-sparrow', which first appeared, in the form 'hedge-sparowe', in 1530 (Simpson & Weiner 1989). I strongly advocate keeping it both as a pleasing name for a loveable little bird and as a barrier against the creeping tide of uniformity that will otherwise overwhelm 'Dunlin', 'Whimbrel', 'Fieldfare', 'Chiffchaff', 'Brambling' and all the rest of those traditional English names which so enrich our ornithology, but which fail to reveal the taxonomic affinities of the species. 'Hedge Accentor' may have been used in the literature last century (see British Ornithologists' Union Records Committee 1988), but this is not a compelling justification for replacing a unique and well-liked name.

Arabian Accentor: The existing name is unique and appropriate, reflecting the geographical region of occurrence, so it is unnecessary to adopt the newly-coined 'Yemen Accentor' (used by Sibley & Monroe 1990).

Kozlov's Accentor: The existing name is unique and appropriate, honouring a great ornithologist-explorer of Central Asia and Tibet, so it is unnecessary to adopt the newly-coined 'Mongolian Accentor' (used by Sibley & Monroe 1990).

Altai Accentor: Both 'Himalayan Accentor' and 'Altai Accentor' are unique names, with the latter being more appropriate as the species breeds in the Altai and other mountain ranges in Central Asia but only winters in the Himalayas, so it is unnecessary to adopt the newly-coined 'Rufous-streaked Accentor' (used by Sibley & Monroe 1990), a name which invites confusion with the equally rufous-streaked Alpine Accentor *P. collaris*.

TURDIDAE

Rufous-tailed Scrub Robin: *Cercotrichas* species are now usually referred to as 'scrub robins' than 'bush robins'. The revised name recommended for this species by the British Ornithologists Union Records Committee (1988) was 'Rufous Scrub Robin', but this changed to 'Rufous-tailed Scrub Robin' in Inskipp & Sharrock (1992) following Sibley & Monroe (1990). No explanation was given for this further change, which presumably reflects the fact that all forms have rufous tails but not all are rufous on the upperparts. This species has suffered a series of changes to its English name and, while reluctantly going along with this one, it is greatly to be hoped that we will all be spared further disruption.

Black Scrub Robin: See Rufous-tailed Scrub Robin.

Common Nightingale: While the juxtaposition of 'common' and 'nightingale' is not ideal, the alternative name 'Rufous Nightingale' overstates the coloration of the species.

Blackthroat: I am very reluctant to coin new names, but here is an exception. Sibley & Monroe (1990) use the name 'Black-throated Blue-robin' for the species to avoid a clash with the name 'Black-throated Robin' for *Poecilodryas albonotata* of New Guinea, but although this is a name that has been used for the species in the past, it is inappropriate as there is no blue in the plumage! In view of the fact that this form was formerly considered a black-throated colour morph of Firethroat *L. pectardens*, 'Blackthroat' seems appropriate and also goes well with 'Bluethroat' for *L. svecica*.

Red-flanked Bluetail: This name is so wonderfully apt, as well as pleasing to the ear, that it should be retained in spite of the fact that other *Tarsiger* species are called 'bush robins'. The name 'Orange-flanked Bush Robin' is in use in some parts of Asia, but far fewer people are familiar with this name.

White-throated Robin: The English name 'Irania' is widely used in subsaharan Africa to differentiate this species from *Cossypha humeralis*, which is often called 'White-throated Robin'. This problem is largely avoided if the latter is referred to as 'White-throated Robin-chat', the name used by Keith *et al.* (1992) in *The Birds of Africa*. Likewise, *Turdus assimilis* of Central and South America is better referred to as 'White-throated Thrush' rather than 'White-throated Robin'.

Eversmann's Redstart: The existing name is unique and appropriate, honouring the ornithologist who first described the species in 1841, so it is unnecessary to adopt the newly-coined 'Rufous-backed Redstart' (used by Sibley & Monroe 1990).

Przevalski's Redstart: The existing name is unique and appropriate, honouring the great ornithologist-explorer of the Tibetan plateau who first described the species in 1876, and is in more widespread use than 'Alashan Redstart', a name which refers to only a small part of the range of the species.

Blue-capped Redstart: The existing name 'Blue-headed Redstart' often leads to confusion with the name 'Blue-fronted Redstart' for *P. frontalis*, a species which appears far more 'blue-headed'. In this instance, faced with an unusually problematic existing name, it is advantageous to adopt the newly-coined 'Blue-capped Redstart' (used by Sibley & Monroe 1990).

Güldenstädt's Redstart: The current name is unique and appropriate, honouring the ornithologist who first described the species in 1775, so it is unnecessary to resurrect the old name 'White-winged Redstart' (used by Sibley & Monroe 1990). Only a part of the wing is white.

White-capped Redstart: If this species is treated as closely related to the redstarts of the genus *Phoenicurus* (see 'Taxonomic notes'), then this name is more appropriate than 'River Chat', the only other English name in frequent use. The name 'River Redstart' reflects the affinity with water, but has not been commonly used. Lengthening the well-established name to 'White-capped Water Redstart' (used by Sibley & Monroe 1990) seems unnecessary to me.

Plumbeous Redstart: Lengthening this very well-established name to 'Plumbeous Water Redstart' seems unnecessary, even if *R. bicolor* is usually called 'Luzon Water Redstart'.

Familiar Chat: This name is more commonly used than 'Red-tailed Chat' and is the name adopted both by Keith *et al.* (1992) for *The Birds of Africa* and by Dowsett & Forbes-Watson (1993).

Stoliczka's Bushchat: The existing name is unique and appropriate, honouring the ornithologist who first described the species in 1872, so it is unnecessary to adopt the newly-coined 'White-browed Bushchat' (used by Sibley & Monroe 1990). The supercilium is only whitish-buff and is not a particularly prominent feature.

Canary Islands Stonechat: It is unhelpful to coin new names for *Saxicola* species that simplify 'stonechat' to 'chat' as the latter is not specific to the genus. (The newly-coined 'Canary Chat' also suffers from the fact that it could imply a canary-yellow coloration.). This species is generally considered closely related to Common Stonechat *S. torquata*, forming a superspecies with it and other related forms (C. S. Roselaar in Cramp 1988), so the existing name 'Canary Islands Stonechat' is appropriate enough. Although the species is mainly restricted to Fuerteventura, it has also been found on Alegranza and Montaña Clara off Lanzarote, and may still occur there.

Common Stonechat: Even if the form *maura* (Siberian Stonechat) is treated as conspecific and all other Palearctic *Saxicola* species are called 'bushchat' (or 'chat') rather than 'stonechat', the English name for this species still requires the addition of the modifier 'common' to avoid conflict with names for the closely related Reunion Stonechat *S. tectes* and the White-tailed Stonechat *S. leucura*.

Hodgson's Bushchat: The existing name is unique and appropriate, honouring the ornithologist responsible for its discovery, so it is unnecessary to adopt the newly-coined 'White-throated Bushchat' (used by Sibley & Monroe 1990). 'Hodgson's Bushchat' is more widely-known than 'Hodgson's Stonechat'.

Pied Bushchat: This name is in much more widespread use than 'Pied Stonechat' in the areas where the species occurs in Asia and Australasia and is equally appropriate.

Red-breasted Wheatear: This name is in more widespread use than 'Botta's Wheatear' although, as the red tinge on the breast is not always very strong, a case can be made for the latter.

Red-tailed Wheatear: This well-established name is unique but not particularly accurate as only the base of the tail and the rump are red and most adults of the nominate race have white at the base of the tail instead! Unfortunately the name 'Red-rumped Wheatear' is already taken by *O. moesta*, otherwise that name would be much more appropriate. While the rump and tail base colour is not pure red, it is richer and darker (in fresh plumage) than normally implied by the term 'rufous', so changing over to the name

'Rufous-tailed Wheatear' (used by Sibley & Monroe 1990) would not offer any improvement. The distinctive form *chrysopygia* always shows a reddish tail base and may be worthy of specific status (see 'Taxonomic notes'). If treated as specifically distinct it should keep the name 'Red-tailed Wheatear' and the residual *O. xanthoprymna* should be renamed. No single plumage character is distinctive and unique enough to assist with naming the latter, but 'Turkish Wheatear' would be reasonably appropriate (although *xanthoprymna* occurs in SW Iran also).

Variable Wheatear: A highly appropriate name for such a variable species and one that removes the need to modify the name 'Pied Wheatear' for *O. pleschanka*.

White-crowned Wheatear: This is a difficult case. Shortening the existing name 'White-crowned Black Wheatear' to 'White-crowned Wheatear' is not ideal as a way of avoiding adding a modifier to the name 'Black Wheatear' for *O. leucura*, but is probably the best available option. Adults of this species are differentiated from the latter species by their white crowns, while the newly-coined 'White-tailed Wheatear' (used by Sibley & Monroe 1990) is neither accurate (not all the tail is white) nor a feature unique to this species (male Hooded Wheatear *O. monacha* also has a largely white tail). These failings would not be critical in an existing name, as so many species have names which describe features shared with other species), but it is surely disadvantageous to replace a well-established name, or a shortened version of it, with a new name which is no more precise. (Note: I was unable to solve this problem by keeping the existing name in full as all of the more obvious modifiers for 'Black Wheatear', such as 'common', 'European' or 'western', are misleading to some degree.)

Scaly Thrush: This is the name in most widespread use in Asia, where the species normally occurs, and is an appropriate description of the bird. Although the name 'White's Thrush' is probably known to more English speakers, it is only a vagrant where most of these individuals reside in the Western Palearctic and in addition Gilbert White had no direct connection with the species, so it is hard to argue that 'White's Thrush' has a better claim for worldwide adoption than the apt 'Scaly Thrush'. There has been a tendency to split the *Z. dauma* complex into several species. If the south Asian forms are treated as one or more full species in the future then the name 'White's Thrush' could be reinstated for the migratory northern form *aurea* (see 'Taxonomic notes').

Tickell's Thrush: This is the name by which this species is almost always called, in honour of the ornithologist who first described the species in 1833. Changing the name to 'Indian Grey Thrush' (used by Sibley & Monroe 1990, but not 1993) is unnecessary.

Japanese Thrush: Both names are widely used, but, while this species breeds locally in China as well as Japan, the name 'Japanese Thrush' seems preferable to 'Grey Thrush' as the dark areas on the adult male are mainly black rather than grey and there is another species of the region, Grey-backed Thrush *T. hortulorum*, which fits the description 'grey' far better.

Common Blackbird: This name has the advantage of already being in widespread used in Asia. In view of this fact, plus the much more restricted distributions of the other thrushes that are called 'blackbirds' and the possibility that some of the south and east Asian forms of *T. merula* may be treated as one or more full species in the future (see 'Taxonomic notes'), use of 'Common Blackbird' seems preferable to adopting 'Eurasian Blackbird'. The latter name certainly serves to distinguish this species from any of the common 'blackbirds' of the New World family Icteridae, but this Old World species is so very much *the* Blackbird that this is surely unnecessary.

Kessler's Thrush: The existing name is unique and unproblematic, so it is unnecessary to adopt the newly-coined 'White-backed Thrush' (used by Sibley & Monroe 1990). The patch on the back is not clean white even in the adult male.

Eyebrowed Thrush: The correct version is 'Eyebrowed', not 'Eye-browed'.

Dusky Thrush: This name, which strictly speaking refers to the subspecies *eunomus*, is (rather unfortunately) the best-known name for the species as a whole. If *eunomus* is treated as a full species (see 'Taxonomic notes') then the name 'Naumann's Thrush' is to be preferred for the residual *T. naumanni* rather than the infrequently used 'Rufous-tailed Thrush'.

Dark-throated Thrush: Adoption of this recently-coined name neatly sidesteps the need to decide between 'Red-throated Thrush' and 'Black-throated Thrush' for this markedly dimorphic species. Should the two forms ever be treated as separate species once more then the original English names are available.

Chinese Thrush: Removing 'song' from the name for this Chinese endemic is preferable, to my mind, to adding a modifier to the very well-known name 'Song Thrush' for *T. philomelos*.

SYLVIIDAE

Asian Stubtail Warbler: If this species is placed in *Urosphena*(see 'Taxonomic notes') then adoption of 'Asian Stubtail Warbler', which conforms with the name 'stubtail' presently used for other members of the genus, is probably a better solution than retaining either of the existing names and in consequence spreading the name 'bush warbler' across three different genera. It is distinctly unhelpful, however, to drop 'warbler' from the name for any of the three *Urosphena* species as this creates a new and (to most people) unfamiliar name that gives no indication of the affinities of the species and might even suggest that these birds, like 'spinetails' and 'needletails', were swifts! If the species is retained in *Cettia* then 'Stub-tailed Bush Warbler' is in more widespread use and marginally more descriptive than 'Short-tailed Bush Warbler'.

Large-billed Bush Warbler: Changing the existing name to the newly-coined 'Long-billed Bush Warbler' (used by Sibley & Monroe 1990) just to achieve a minor improvement in accuracy is surely unnecessary (otherwise the names for hundreds of Palearctic species merit similar revision).

Zitting Cisticola: There is no sense in trying to persuade the rest of the world to adopt the largely British name 'Fan-tailed Warbler' when this widespread species and the many other *Cisticola* species are known as 'cisticolas' virtually everywhere else. (What is more, this name conflicts with the name 'Fan-tailed Warbler' for *Euthlypis lachrymosa* of Central America and also a frequently used English name for *Schoenicola platyura* of subsaharan Africa.) The name 'Zitting Cisticola' is already in widespread use in Asia and Africa and refers to the characteristic 'zit ... zit ... zit ...' song. The name 'Fan-tailed Cisticola' is sometimes used in Africa, but the tail shape is not unique to this species.

Graceful Prinia: As with 'Zitting Cisticola', there is no point in sticking with the largely British name 'Graceful Warbler' when this species and all the other *Prinia* species are known as 'prinias' virtually everywhere in Asia and Africa.

Cricket Warbler: This is the name in most widespread use (it refers to the cricket-like song). Sibley & Monroe (1990) coined 'Cricket Longtail' for this species, presumably to try to minimize the use of 'warbler' for the members of the Cisticolidae (which they treated as a separate family), but this revision misleadingly suggests a close relationship with the 'Green Longtail' *Urolais epichlora*.

Scrub Warbler: The name 'Streaked Scrub Warbler' was used by Sibley & Monroe (1990) to differentiates this species from a number of *Bradypterus* species inhabiting subsaharan Africa for which these authors used the group name 'scrub warbler'. Use of the name 'scrub warbler' for these *Bradypterus* species, which is not the usual practice in Africa, is an unsatisfactory development (creating the false impression of a relationship with *Scotocerca inquieta*) and should be avoided. All seven species already have unique English names, so the addition of 'scrub' is unnecessary. If required, 'bush warbler' can be used instead of 'scrub warbler', as in the Asian *Bradypterus*.

Chinese Hill Warbler: Both this name and 'White-browed Chinese Warbler' are in current use and unique, but only the westernmost subspecies has a white brow while this species is typical of dry hill country across northern China.

Styan's Grasshopper Warbler: Neither of the English names for *L. pleskei* is widely used, largely because this form is so often treated as conspecific with Middendorff's Grasshopper Warbler *L. ochotensis* (see 'Taxonomic notes'). Both names are unique, but 'Styan's Grasshopper Warbler' is used much more often than 'Pleske's Grasshopper Warbler' and should thus have preference. For what it is worth, Pleske had no direct connection with the species, whereas Styan worked closely with La Touche in eastern

China and the bird was named *Locustella styani* in his honour by La Touche in 1905 before it became apparent that this form had already been described (as *L. pleskei*) by Taczanowski in 1889. More importantly, from La Touche (1930) to Chalmers (1986) and Viney & Phillipps (1994), virtually every English language book on the birds of eastern Asia that treated this form as a full species has used 'Styan's Grasshopper Warbler'.

River Warbler: Creating new English names that falsely suggest close relationships across family boundaries is not good practice and so, as the problem species in the New World is not exactly a 'household name', I support the call made by Inskipp & Sharrock (1992) to have the Neotropical species *Basileuterus rivularis* renamed 'Stream Warbler'. The name for the New World species has been in use for a much shorter period and so should be the one to change, especially as the proposed new name is highly appropriate. If it is felt necessary to modify the name 'River Warbler' for the Palearctic *Locustella fluviatilis* then 'Eurasian River Warbler' (as used by Sibley & Monroe 1990) is inappropriate for a bird with an almost entirely European breeding distribution and 'European River Warbler' should be adopted instead.

Japanese Swamp Warbler: As very good grounds for not including this species in *Megalurus* have recently been advanced (see entry for *Locustella pryeri* in 'Taxonomic notes'), there is no need to adopt the newly-coined 'Marsh Grassbird' (used by Sibley & Monroe 1990). Nonetheless, I advocate that 'swamp' be substituted for 'marsh' in the English name for *Locustella pryeri*. This species has sometimes been called 'Streak-backed Swamp Warbler' (Cheng 1987) or 'Chinese Swamp Warbler' in the past and this simple change obviates the need to add a modifier, such as 'European', to the well-known name 'Marsh Warbler' for *Acrocephalus palustris*. The proposal to change the English name for this bird to 'Marsh Grassbird', in an attempt to 'standardize' the names for all *Megalurus* species, only for it to become evident shortly afterwards that the species should not be placed in this genus at all, is a classic example of the dangers inherent in trying to impose uniformity on English bird names.

Moustached Warbler: There is no need to add the modifier 'European' to the name for this species if the subsaharan species *Melocichla mentalis* is referred to as 'Moustached Grass Warbler' (the name used by Sibley & Monroe 1990) rather than the more traditional 'African Marsh Warbler', a name which has often been used for *Acrocephalus baeticatus*.

Sedge Warbler: There is no need to add the modifier 'European' to the name for this species as long as the subsaharan species *Bradypterus baboecala* is referred to as 'Little Rush Warbler' (the more widely used name) rather than 'African Sedge Warbler'.

Speckled Reed Warbler: The existing name is not especially accurate, as the mantle markings are streaks rather than speckles, but some of the crown markings do look like 'speckles' and this is probably how the species attained its English name. Minor imprecisions or ambiguities in an English name should not be considered good cause for revisions (otherwise numerous Palearctic bird names would have to change), so I have not adopted the newly-coined 'Streaked Reed Warbler' (used by Sibley & Monroe 1990).

Cape Verde Warbler: This species does not occur in swamps, so the name 'Cape Verde Swamp Warbler' used by Sibley & Monroe (1990) represents a movement in the wrong direction. Shortening the existing, and almost as inaccurate, 'Cape Verde Cane Warbler' to 'Cape Verde Warbler' is the best option.

European Reed Warbler: The modifier 'European' is more appropriate for this species than 'Eurasian' as the breeding range in Asia is limited, reaching only as far as Iran and parts of Turkestan. Other species with similarly restricted Asian ranges, or even wider ones, are given the epithet 'European' (e.g. European Honey Buzzard *Pernis apivorus*, European Bee-eater *Merops apiaster*, European Goldfinch *Carduelis carduelis*).

Ménétries's Warbler: In this international era the accents should be retained, contra Sibley & Monroe (1990).

Rüppell's Warbler: Likewise 'Rüppell's' should be spelt with an umlaut rather than 'Rueppell's' as per Sibley & Monroe (1990).

Arabian Warbler: This name is in much more widespread use and is both unique and appropriate, so it is unnecessary to change over to 'Red Sea Warbler' (used by Sibley & Monroe 1990).

Barred Warbler: The name 'European Barred Warbler' is sometimes used in Africa to avoid conflict with the names 'Southern Barred Warbler' for *Camaroptera fasciolata* (= *Calamonastes fasciolatus*) and 'Stierling's Barred Warbler' for *C. stierlingi*, but this problem is avoided if these species are referred to as 'Barred Wren Warbler' and 'Stierling's Wren Warbler' respectively (the names used by Sibley & Monroe 1990). (If the form *undosa* is treated as specifically distinct from Grey Wren Warbler *C. simplex* and *stierlingi* is treated as conspecific with *undosa*, then the name 'Miombo Wren Warbler' is suitable for the enlarged species.)

Desert Whitethroat: As regards the English name for the form *minula*, which is sometimes treated as a full species (see 'Taxonomic notes'), the name 'Desert Whitethroat' is greatly preferable to the newly-coined 'Small Whitethroat' (used by Sibley & Monroe 1993) as it well reflects the habitat of the species whereas the size difference compared to 'Lesser Whitethroat' is hardly noticeable.

Common Whitethroat: This name, which reflects the scientific name, has been used for the species in the past and is to be preferred to 'Greater Whitethroat'. *S. communis* is often more numerous than the Lesser Whitethroat *S. curruca* while the size difference is not so large as to make 'greater' a very appropriate description.

Blackcap: In southern Africa this species is called 'European Blackcap' to differentiate it from the name 'Bush Blackcap' for *Lioptilus nigricapillus*, a species usually placed among the Timaliidae (babblers) or sometimes the Pycnonotidae (bulbuls). As the latter species is not exactly a 'household name' it is preferable to modify its name rather than add the modifier 'European' to the English name for *Sylvia atricapillus* and thus imply a close relationship where none exists. The names 'Blackcap Mountain Babbler' (as suggested by Sibley & Monroe 1990) or, if placed in the Pycnonotidae, 'Blackcap Mountain Bulbul' would be appropriate.

Bright-green Warbler: As regards the English name for the form *nitidus*, which was formerly treated as a full species (see 'Taxonomic notes'), a modifier needs to be added to the traditional name 'Green Warbler' to avoid a clash with the name 'Black-throated Green Warbler' for *Dendroica virens*. The name 'Bright Green Warbler' (suggested by Inskipp & Sharrock 1992) is preferable to the newly-coined 'Yellowish-breasted Warbler' (used by Sibley & Monroe 1990) as this form does not always have a yellowish breast but is always distinctly green-looking above compared to most other *Phylloscopus*, but for clarity it is preferable to hyphenate 'bright' and 'green' for the same reason that 'slaty' and blue' are linked in 'Slaty-blue Flycatcher'.

Pallas's Leaf Warbler: With the form *chloronotus* now being treated as a full species (see 'Taxonomic notes'), the name 'Lemon-rumped Warbler' (which has often been used for *P. proregulus* in Asia) can usefully be applied to *P. chloronotus*. The addition of 'leaf' prevents confusion with Pallas's Grasshopper Warbler *Locustella certhiola*, which has sometimes, confusingly, been called simply 'Pallas's Warbler'.

Lemon-rumped Warbler: This existing name is preferable to the newly-coined 'Pale-rumped Warbler' (used by Sibley & Monroe 1990) as it is more precise. See also Pallas's Leaf Warbler.

Yellow-browed Warbler: Although this name is not perfect, since even fresh-plumaged individuals only have a creamy-yellow supercilium, it is much better than the ugly name 'Inornate Warbler', which is hardly appropriate for a well-marked *Phylloscopus* with a prominent supercilium and two wing bars!

Hume's Leaf Warbler: The existing name 'Hume's Yellow-browed Warbler' is unsuitable when the form *humei* is treated as a full species, rather than as a race of *P. inornatus* (see 'Taxonomic notes'), but shortening the name to 'Hume's Warbler' simply invites confusion with the English name 'Hume's (Lesser) Whitethroat' for *Sylvia (communis) althaea*. The newly-coined 'Buff-browed Warbler' (used by Sibley & Monroe 1990) is instantly forgettable (it could be applied to any one of a host of warbler species) and so I urge the adoption of 'Hume's Leaf Warbler', a name which is appropriate, retains much of the existing English name and is unambiguous.

Bonelli's Warbler: In the event of the form *orientalis* (Eastern Bonelli's Warbler) being treated as a full species (see 'Taxonomic notes'), it becomes necessary to change the English name for the residual *P. bonelli* to 'Western Bonelli's Warbler' or else find a new name for *orientalis*.

Plain Leaf Warbler: This name is more appropriate than 'Plain Willow Warbler' as the species has no connection either with willows or the Willow Warbler *P. trochilus*.

Chiffchaff: This name requires no 'modifier' unless the form *sindianus* (Mountain Chiffchaff) or the form *lorenzii* (Caucasian Chiffchaff) are treated as full species (see 'Taxonomic notes'). In this case, in view of its much wider distribution and the fact that *P. sindianus* (when it includes *lorenzii*) also has a Eurasian range, the name 'Common Chiffchaff' is more appropriate than 'Eurasian Chiffchaff'.

Goldcrest: If the form *teneriffae* is treated as a full species (see 'Taxonomic notes') there is no need to add the modifier 'common' to the name for *R. regulus* provided the English name 'Canary Islands Kinglet' is used in preference to 'Tenerife Goldcrest' for *teneriffae* (see next entry).

Canary Islands Kinglet: A better name for the form *teneriffae* than 'Tenerife Goldcrest' (used by Sibley & Monroe 1990) as it occurs on several islands. In addition, since it is uncertain whether the relationship of *teneriffae* with Goldcrest *R. regulus* is closer than that with Firecrest *R. ignicapillus*, use of 'goldcrest' in its English name is better avoided.

Severtzov's Tit-warbler: Both 'Severtzov's Tit-warbler' and 'Stoliczka's Tit-warbler' are frequently used names, but Severtzov described the species first, in 1872, and so 'Severtzov's Tit-warbler' has a marginally better claim to become the standard. The less often used 'White-browed Tit-warbler' is hardly apt as the supercilium is actually creamy-buff.

MUSCICAPIDAE

Dark-sided Flycatcher: Now the most widely used name for the species and one which points up a key plumage feature, although 'Sooty Flycatcher' and 'Siberian Flycatcher' are not inappropriate.

Grey-streaked Flycatcher: The more widely used name and more accurate than 'Grey-spotted Flycatcher'.

Rusty-tailed Flycatcher: A minor change from 'rufous-tailed' to 'rusty-tailed' prevents conflict with the name 'Rufous-tailed Flycatcher' for *Myiarchus validus* of Jamaica. Neither species is especially well-known, so in this instance a minor revision to the name of one of them is preferable to adding modifiers such as 'Asian' and 'Jamaican' which might imply a non-existent relationship.

Red-breasted Flycatcher: Although this name is less accurate, it is much better known than 'Red-throated Flycatcher' (in use only in Southeast Asia). Since there is a strong likelihood that the eastern form *albicilla* will be treated as a full species (see 'Taxonomic notes'), the name 'Red-throated Flycatcher' should be kept available for that eventuality.

European Pied Flycatcher: The addition of 'European' is necessary to differentiate this species from Little Pied Flycatcher *F. westermanni*.

Grey-headed Flycatcher: The addition of 'Canary' is not necessary if this species is placed in the Muscicapidae (as done by Sibley & Monroe 1993, but not 1990).

TIMALIIDAE

Rufous-throated Wren-babbler: This name is of recent origin, but the old name 'Tailed Wren-babbler' is so unsatisfactory (all wren-babblers have tails) that adoption of a new name in this instance is clearly desirable.

Bearded Reedling: It is now generally accepted that this species is closely related to the parrotbills. Nonetheless, it lacks the deep, parrot-shaped bill of the *Paradoxornis* species and in consequence I prefer 'Bearded Reedling' (as used, for example, by Dresser 1902) to the newly-coined 'Bearded Parrotbill' (used by Sibley & Monroe 1990). The old Norfolk name 'reedling' well describes the habitat of the species and retaining 'bearded' provides a useful link with the traditional name 'Bearded Tit'. Admittedly 'bearded' is inaccurate: 'moustached' would be more precise, but use of this term would mean abandoning all elements of the traditional name. I accept that I am going against a general principle of this checklist in not retaining the well-established name 'Bearded Tit', but this is a most exceptional case (a single member of a very large family carrying a misleading group name) where I consider a name revision particularly helpful.

Grey-hooded Parrotbill: Of the existing names, only 'Crested Parrotbill' is at all well-known today (due to its use in Meyer de Schauensee 1984, the only English language guide to the birds of China). Unfortunately this name, which superceded both 'Zappey's Parrotbill' and 'Dusky Parrotbill', was an unsatisfactory replacement (the slight crest is no more obvious than on several other parrotbills). Rather than try to restore one of the old, largely disused names, in this instance I prefer to adopt the newly-coined and appropriate 'Grey-hooded Parrotbill' (used by Sibley & Monroe 1990).

Przevalski's Parrotbill: The existing name is unique and appropriate, honouring the great ornithologist-explorer of the Tibetan plateau and its surroundings, so it is unnecessary to adopt the newly-coined 'Rusty-throated Parrotbill' (used by Sibley & Monroe 1990).

Reed Parrotbill: This name, which has been in use for a decade or more (e.g. Flint *et al.* 1984), refers to the characteristic habitat of the species and is preferable to 'Chinese Parrotbill' (also a relatively recent invention) as so many other parrotbills occur in that country, several being endemic to it. 'Yangtze Parrotbill' and 'Heude's Parrotbill' have been used in the past, but do not merit restoration at the expense of an apt new name like 'Reed Parrotbill'.

Arabian Babbler: The name 'Brown Babbler' should be avoided for this species as it clashes with the name 'Brown Babbler' for the subsaharan *T. plebejus*. In any case it is far less precise, as most *Turdoides* species are brown.

Fulvous Babbler: Applying the name 'Fulvous Chatterer' to this species (as per Sibley & Monroe 1990) flies in the face of current usage and is unnecessary.

Kozlov's Babax: The existing name is unique and appropriate, commemorating one of the great pioneers of Tibetan ornithology, so it is unnecessary to adopt the newly-coined 'Tibetan Babax' (used by Sibley & Monroe 1990).

Père David's Laughingthrush: The existing name is unique and appropriate, celebrating one of the greatest names in Chinese ornithology and the discoverer of the species, so it is unnecessary to adopt the newly-coined and distinctly uninspiring 'Plain Laughingthrush' (used by Sibley & Monroe 1990).

Sukatschev's Laughingthrush: The existing name is unique and reflects the scientific name, so it is unnecessary to adopt the newly-coined 'Snowy-cheeked Laughingthrush' (used by Sibley & Monroe 1990).

Hwamei: This is one of the best-known birds in China, often kept as a cage-bird because of its rich and varied songs, and known by this local name to every English-speaking ornithologist with an interest in the birds of the country. 'Hwamei' is more commonly used than 'Hwamey'.

Prince Henri's Laughingthrush: The existing name is unique and appropriate, honouring the discoverer of the species, so it is unnecessary to adopt the newly-coined 'Brown-cheeked Laughingthrush' (used by Sibley & Monroe 1990).

Emei Shan Liocichla: This species is restricted to Emei Shan and nearby areas (rather than a large part of Szechwan, or 'Sichuan' as it is now spelt). The modern spelling is 'Emei' rather than 'Omei'.

Black-capped Sibia: The existing name is unique and so it is unnecessary to adopt the newly-coined 'Rufous Sibia' (used by Sibley & Monroe 1990). Unfortunately both these names are quite similar to those for other sibias: i.e. Black-headed Sibia *H. melanoleuca* and Rufous-backed Sibia *H. annectens*.

AEGITHALIDAE

Sooty Tit: The existing name is unique and appropriate, so it is unnecessary to adopt the newly-coined name 'White-necklaced Tit' (used by Sibley & Monroe 1990).

PARIDAE

Black-bibbed Tit: This is the name normally used for the distinctive form *hypermelaena* and, unlike 'Black-bibbed Marsh Tit' (used by Sibley & Monroe 1990), has the advantage of not needing modification if *hypermelaena* is treated as a full species (see 'Taxonomic notes').

Caspian Tit: Regarding the English names for the form *hyrcanus*, which is sometimes treated as a full species (see 'Taxonomic notes'), both are of recent invention but 'Caspian Tit' is much more meaningful to most people than 'Hyrcanian Tit' (a name which refers to the region on the Caspian that long ago was known as Hyrcania).

Père David's Tit: The existing name is unique and appropriate, celebrating one of the greatest names in Chinese ornithology and a pioneer explorer of the forests of western China, so it is unnecessary to adopt the newly-coined 'Rusty-breasted Tit' (used by Sibley & Monroe 1990).

Rufous-naped Tit: This name, although reflecting the scientific name, is not ideal as the rufous patch at the base of the nape is inconspicuous. The newly-coined 'Dark-grey Tit' (used by Sibley & Monroe 1990), a name that could equally well be applied to Rufous-vented Tit *P. rubidiventris*, is no better, however, so I see no advantage in a change. The name 'Simla Black Tit' is geographically restricted for such a wide-ranging species and so, in spite of its drawbacks, 'Rufous-naped Tit' is to be preferred.

Spot-winged Tit: Many Asian tits have black crests and a number are dark and crested, so both 'Crested Black Tit' and the newly-coined 'Black-crested Tit' (used by Sibley & Monroe 1990) are unsatisfactory names. The latter also suffers from the same problem that afflicts the name 'Grey-crested Tit' for *P. dichrous*, which is frequently misinterpreted as 'Grey Crested-Tit'. The name 'Spot-winged Tit' has been in use (in the form 'Spot-winged Black Tit') for a long time and at least points to a feature shared, among this group of similar-looking species, only with Coal Tit *P. ater*.

Cinereous Tit: If the form *cinereus* is treated as a full species (see 'Taxonomic notes'), use of the name 'Cinereous Tit' rather than 'Grey Tit' removes the need to amend the latter to 'Asian Grey Tit' in order to avoid a clash with the names 'Southern Grey Tit' for *P. afer* and 'Northern Grey Tit' for *P. griseiventris* of subsaharan Africa. (In Sibley & Monroe 1990, *P. afer* is called simply 'Grey Tit', adding a further complication.)

SITTIDAE

Chinese Nuthatch: The existing name is unique and appropriate (for a bird with an almost exclusively north Chinese distribution), so it is unnecessary to adopt the newly-coined 'Snowy-browed Nuthatch' used by Sibley & Monroe (1990). The supercilium frequently appears indistinct and off-white in this species.

Krüper's Nuthatch: In this international era 'Krüper's' should be spelt with an umlaut rather than 'Krueper's' as per Sibley & Monroe (1990).

Algerian Nuthatch: This is the name the species is almost invariably known by and, since it is appropriate enough for the only nuthatch species to be found in the country, it is unnecessary to adopt the name 'Kabylie Nuthatch' as used by Sibley & Monroe (1990), especially as not all the known sites are in these mountains.

Eurasian Nuthatch: This name is already in frequent use, mainly in Asia, and well describes the distribution of a species that occurs from the British Isles to Kamchatka and Japan, so is preferable to the infrequently used and less precise 'Common Nuthatch'. The recently proposed 'Wood Nuthatch' has to compete with a better established and more informative name (after all, most nuthatches inhabit woodland).

Eastern Rock Nuthatch: A marginally preferable name to 'Great Rock Nuthatch' as, while the ranges do partly overlap, the size difference is often not very marked.

REMIZIDAE

Eurasian Penduline Tit: If the forms *coronatus* (White-crowned Penduline Tit) and *consobrinus* (Chinese Penduline Tit) are treated as full species (see 'Taxonomic notes') then the residual *R. pendulinus* has a range which does not extend far into Asia and the name 'Eurasian Penduline Tit' is then best replaced by 'European Penduline Tit'. Note: Sibley & Monroe (1990) used the name 'Eurasian Penduline Tit' for *R. pendulinus* in spite of treating *coronatus* and *consobrinus* as full species.

NECTARINIIDAE

Palestine Sunbird: Use of the name 'Orange-tufted Sunbird' for this species should be avoided to prevent conflict with the name 'Orange-tufted Sunbird' for *N. bouvieri* of subsaharan Africa.

Mrs Gould's Sunbird: This species is named in honour of John Gould's wife Elizabeth, who herself laboured mightily in the cause of ornithology. While it is perfectly true that the ending of the scientific name shows that a female Gould is involved, this fact would not be immediately obvious to many people. We keep 'Lady Amherst's Pheasant', so why make this English name ambiguous?

DICAEIDAE

Buff-bellied Flowerpecker: This name has been widely used in Asia for many years and is preferable to 'Fire-breasted Flowerpecker' as several populations lack scarlet on the breast.

ZOSTEROPIDAE

Abyssinian White-eye: Of the two names in current use, 'Abyssinian White-eye' (a name that refers to a large part of the distribution of the species, and reflects the scientific name) is more appropriate than 'White-breasted White-eye' as the southern populations of this species are completely yellow below. The former was used by Dowsett & Forbes-Watson (1993).

LANIIDAE

Black-crowned Tchagra: Members of the predominantly subsaharan genus *Tchagra* are nowadays more usually known as 'tchagras' rather than 'bush shrikes'. Of the names in current use, 'Black-crowned' is more accurate than 'Black-headed'.

Rosy-patched Bush Shrike: All other bush shrikes are nowadays known as 'tchagras' or 'bush shrikes' and, as they are now often treated as members of a separate family, Malaconotidae, the name 'Rosy-patched Bush Shrike' is preferable to 'Rosy-patched Shrike'. When they are treated as a separate family the name 'bush shrike' is sometimes compounded to 'bushshrike'.

Isabelline Shrike: This name is much better established than 'Red-tailed Shrike' and, since it is unique (and presumably an appropriate description of the upperpart coloration of some races if one is familiar with the story of Queen Isabella's underwear), a change of name is unnecessary. Furthermore, should *phoenicuroides* be treated as a full species in the future (see 'Taxonomic notes'), the English name for *L. isabellinus* would have to revert to 'Isabelline Shrike' and there would have been serious disruption for no good reason.

Great Grey Shrike: The name 'Northern Shrike' may be satisfactory in a North American context but its use on a world scale would be a retrograde step as it removes the useful linkage between this species and the closely similar Lesser Grey Shrike *L. minor* and Chinese Grey Shrike *L. sphenocercus*, as well as being inappropriate for a species that breeds southwards as far as the Sahel and India. If *meridionalis* Southern Grey Shrike is treated as a full species (see 'Taxonomic notes') and the English name for *L. excubitor* had to change (which is debatable), the name 'Northern Grey Shrike' would be more appropriate than plain 'Northern Shrike'.

DICRURIDAE

Hair-crested Drongo: This is the name that should be applied to the species now that *bracteatus* of Australasia and the Philippines is treated as a full species under the name 'Spangled Drongo'.

CORVIDAE

Lanceolated Jay: Of the two names in widespread use, only 'Lanceolated Jay', which reflects the scientific name and a noticeable plumage feature, is appropriate. The species has a black head, not just a black throat, and in addition the name 'Black-throated Jay' is also used for *Cyanolyca pumilo* of Central America. Since one of the existing names is adequate it is unnecessary to adopt the newly-coined 'Black-headed Jay' (used by Sibley & Monroe 1990).

Common Magpie: The name 'Black-billed Magpie' is only appropriate in a North American context (where it contrasts with 'Yellow-billed Magpie' for *P. nuttalli*). The black bill is just about the least conspicuous feature of this strikingly pied, long-tailed bird and the name becomes meaningless in a Palearctic context where the only other widespread magpie also has a black bill! For much the most widespread magpie in the world, with a distribution extending from North Africa right across Eurasia and well into North America, 'Common Magpie' is the most appropriate name.

Henderson's Ground Jay: All the current names for the 'ground jays' are unique and most honour their discoverers, so a completely unnecessary purge has been carried out by Sibley & Monroe (1990), who use newly-coined names for every species!

Biddulph's Ground Jay: See Henderson's Ground Jay.

Pander's Ground Jay: See Henderson's Ground Jay.

Pleske's Ground Jay: See Henderson's Ground Jay.

Hume's Ground Jay: See Henderson's Ground Jay.

Spotted Nutcracker: A modifier needs to be added to the traditional name 'Nutcracker' to differentiate it from the name 'Clark's Nutcracker' for *N. columbiana*. Although the name 'Eurasian Nutcracker' is already in use in Asia, the newly-coined 'Spotted Nutcracker' is so appropriate for this species that it has already been widely adopted.

Alpine Chough: This name is far better established than 'Yellow-billed Chough', a name only in use in a few parts of Asia. Although the latter name is appropriate enough, I do not believe it is desirable to replace very well-known names unless there is some pressing need. 'Alpine Chough' is highly appropriate as an English name for this species, referring to its 'alpine' habitat requirement and not just to the Alps as such.

Western Jackdaw: A modifier must be added to the traditional name 'Jackdaw' to differentiate it from the name 'Daurian Jackdaw' for *C. dauuricus* of eastern Asia. Use of the term 'Eurasian' for the western representative of a pair of species that share a group name is generally unsatisfactory (except in those few cases, like 'Eurasian Curlew', where the 'western' representative occurs very widely in eastern Asia as well as further west: this does not apply to *C. monedula*, which does not extend beyond western Siberia, the Tien Shan and Kashmir).

STURNIDAE

Tristram's Starling: While loath to see the demise of 'Tristram's Grackle', I accept that other members of the genus *Onychognathus* are all called 'starlings' and that retaining 'grackle' for just this one species invites confusion with the many members of the New World family Icteridae that carry this name.

Purple-backed Starling: This is the English name by which the species is now most often called in its area of occurrence in east Asia. Although the plumage feature is shared with Chestnut-cheeked Starling *S. philippensis*, the less often used 'Daurian Starling' only refers to the western periphery of the species' breeding range and so is no more appropriate. The more widely used name should have precedence.

Common Starling: Even before its introduction to many other parts of the world, the range of this species extended far beyond the bounds of Europe.

Rose-coloured Starling: Changing this well-established name to 'Rosy Starling' is surely unnecessary tinkering.

PASSERIDAE

Sind Jungle Sparrow: Shortening this rather pleasing English name, which refers to the *Acacia* 'jungle' of the Indus valley which this species typically inhabits, to 'Sind Sparrow' (as used by Sibley & Monroe 1990) is unnecessary.

Iago Sparrow: Now that taxonomic changes have resulted in *P. iagoensis* being once more restricted to the Cape Verde Islands, either 'Iago Sparrow' or 'Cape Verde Sparrow' are the most appropriate English names. Sibley & Monroe (1990) originally adopted the latter, but subsequently (1993) changed to 'Iago Sparrow'. Both the English and scientific names refer to the island of São Tiago (St James) where the species was first discovered. Used by Summers-Smith (1988), the name 'Iago Sparrow' was recently adopted by Cramp & Perrins (1994a) for *The Birds of the Western Palearctic* and, since 'Cape Verde' is always a rather ambiguous title (as Cape Verde itself is situated in Senegal), 'Iago Sparrow' is to be preferred.

Eurasian Tree Sparrow: The addition of 'Eurasian' is necessary to prevent conflict with the name 'American Tree Sparrow' for *Spizella arborea*. These names may falsely suggest a close relationship between two species which in reality are members of separate families, but the name 'tree sparrow' is so well entrenched on both sides of the Atlantic that no one looks likely to succeed in making a change of name for either species stick.

Pale Rockfinch: The existing name 'Pale Rock Sparrow' conflicts with the well-known name 'Rock Sparrow' for *Petronia petronia*. If this unusual species, which has little in common with typical *Petronia*, is placed in its own genus *Carpospiza* (see 'Taxonomic notes') then the newly-coined 'Pale Rockfinch' (used by Sibley & Monroe 1990) certainly points up its distinctive character. (The name is not perfect, however, as the species by no means always shows an affinity for rocks.) If the species is retained in *Petronia* then the name problem can be solved by use of 'Pale Petronia' or 'Pale Sparrow'.

Chestnut-shouldered Petronia: Unfortunately the established name 'Yellow-throated Sparrow' clashes with the equally well-established name 'Yellow-throated Petronia' (or 'Yellow-throated Sparrow') for *P. superciliaris* of subsaharan Africa. In this particular instance, faced with a name conflict with the African species and also a misleading description (the yellow patch is on the upper breast, not the throat), adopting 'Chestnut-shouldered Petronia' (a name which derives from 'Chestnut-shouldered Rock Sparrow' and describes a noticeable plumage feature) seems preferable to ending up with the very long-winded 'Asian Yellow-throated Petronia' and 'African Yellow-throated Petronia'.

Rock Sparrow: Replacing the very well-established English name for this species with 'Rock Petronia' might be tidier, but is certainly not a necessary change. Use of the name 'petronia' has (except for Sibley & Monroe 1990) been restricted to the subsaharan species.

Theresa's Snowfinch: The existing name is unique and reflects the scientific name, so it is unnecessary to adopt the newly-coined 'Afghan Snowfinch' (used by Sibley & Monroe 1990).

Blanford's Snowfinch: The existing name is unique and appropriate, honouring the ornithologist who first described the species in 1871, so it is unnecessary to adopt the newly-coined 'Plain-backed Snowfinch' (used by Sibley & Monroe 1990). The back in this species is only weakly streaked.

Père David's Snowfinch: The existing name is unique and appropriate, celebrating one of the greatest names in Chinese ornithology and the discoverer of the species, so it is unnecessary to adopt the newly-coined 'Small Snowfinch' (used by Sibley & Monroe 1990).

Adams's Snowfinch: This existing name is both unique and appropriate, celebrating the ornithologist who first described the species in 1859, so it is unnecessary to adopt the newly-coined name 'Black-winged Snowfinch' used by Sibley & Monroe (1990). The latter name is not particularly accurate as the wing is a mixture of blackish, brown and white. The name 'Tibetan Snowfinch' is also unsatisfactory as a series of snowfinches occur widely on the Tibetan plateau and this name has also been applied to the form M. *nivalis henrici*, which is occasionally treated as a full species (see 'Taxonomic notes').

White-winged Snowfinch: A modifier needs to be added to the traditional name 'Snowfinch' to differentiate this species from the other snowfinches in Asia. 'White-winged Snowfinch' is more pleasing to my mind than 'Eurasian Snowfinch', although the latter is also appropriate.

Prince Henri's Snowfinch: Use of the English name 'Tibetan Snowfinch' for the form *henrici* (occasionally regarded as a full species: see 'Taxonomic notes'), as in Cramp & Perrins (1994a), should be avoided as this name has often been used for M. *adamsi*. 'Prince Henri's Snowfinch' is a suitable and unambiguous name.

PLOCEIDAE

Rüppell's Weaver: In this international age 'Rüppell's' should be spelt with an umlaut rather than 'Rueppell's' as per Sibley & Monroe (1990).

ESTRILDIDAE

Red-billed Firefinch: This is most widely used name for this widespread African species. The name 'Senegal Firefinch' is primarily in use in West Africa.

Indian Silverbill: This is a better name for this primarily Indian subcontinent species than the newly-coined 'White-throated Silverbill' (used by Sibley & Monroe 1990). The latter name appears to derive directly from 'White-throated Munia', the name in use in the Indian subcontinent, but in this context 'white-throated' refers to the absence of a dark throat in this 'munia' (which is all whitish below) compared to most other Indian munias. Although African Silverbill L. *cantans* does have a dusky tinge on the throat, it often appears an overall whitish below.

Cut-throat: Both names are in widespread use, but 'Cut-throat' is preferable to 'Cut-throat Finch' for a species that is not a finch as such.

FRINGILLIDAE

Common Chaffinch: A modifier needs to be added to the traditional name 'Chaffinch' for F. *coelebs* to differentiate it from the Blue Chaffinch F. *teydea*.

Blue Chaffinch: The ugly, newly-coined 'Teydefinch' (used by Sibley & Monroe, 1990) and 'Teydean Finch' should be strongly resisted. This species,which is closely related to the Common Chaffinch F. *coelebs*, is not restricted to Mount Teyde (or Teide) or even Tenerife, occurring on Gran Canaria in addition.. The name 'Canary Islands Chaffinch' is rather unsatisfactory when one considers that F. *teydea* is neither the most widespread nor the most abundant chaffinch in the islands. The other widely used name, 'Blue Chaffinch', suffers from none of these drawbacks.

Red-fronted Serin: The existing name is unique and appropriate enough (the forehead patch is orange-scarlet), so I cannot see any good reason to adopt the newly-coined 'Fire-fronted Serin' (used by Sibley & Monroe 1990). Tinkering with well-established names to try to produce marginal descriptive improvements, rather than resolve significant nomenclatural problems, should be resisted.

Syrian Serin: This name is currently more widely used than 'Tristram's Serin' and reflects the scientific name, but both names are appropriate.

Atlantic Canary: A modifier is necessary to differentiate this species from the many other 'canaries' in subsaharan Africa. Although not the only surviving canary found naturally on islands (the other is the Príncipe Seedeater *S. rufobrunneus*), this is the only one to occur on several island groups (all in the eastern Atlantic, and frequently referred to as 'The Atlantic Islands'). The recently proposed 'Island Canary' gives no indication of which islands this species might inhabit and so I propose 'Atlantic Canary' as a more precise alternative.

Arabian Serin: The existing name is unique and appropriate, so it is unnecessary to adopt the newly-coined 'Olive-rumped Serin' (used by Sibley & Monroe 1990) which removes the helpful geographical link.

Spectacled Finch: This newly-coined name (used in Sibley & Monroe 1990 and Inskipp & Inskipp 1991) is so much more accurate than the downright misleading 'Red-browed Finch' that a change of name can be justified.

Grey-capped Greenfinch: Perhaps more widely used in recent years, but 'Oriental Greenfinch' is also appropriate.

Tibetan Siskin: This is the traditional name, the name having been amended to 'Tibetan Serin' in recent times to reflect the species' placement in *Serinus* rather than *Carduelis*. I consider this treatment to be mistaken (see 'Taxonomic notes').

Common Linnet: This is the more appropriate name, as this species only extends eastwards as far as Turkestan (and so is hardly 'Eurasian' in the sense of spreading right across the land mass) yet is still much more widespread and familiar than the other linnet species.

Arctic Redpoll: The Old World name 'Arctic Redpoll', which well describes the distribution of the species, has the edge on the North American 'Hoary Redpoll' ('hoary' means greyish-white or white) in view of the similarity in coloration between some populations of this species and the northern populations of the Common Redpoll *C. flammea*.

Two-barred Crossbill: Likewise this Old World name is more appropriate for the species than the North American 'White-winged Crossbill' when the only white in the wing is the two wing bars.

Common Crossbill: Not all races of *L. curvirostra* have red males, while the males of all other crossbill species are red. This is generally the commonest species, so the Old World name 'Common Crossbill' is preferable to the North American 'Red Crossbill'. In any event, it looks possible that North American populations will in future be treated as a series of distinct species, separate from *L. curvirostra*.

Brandt's Mountain Finch: The existing name is unique and so, especially as this species has at most a blackish-brown head in summer and from autumn onwards has the black feather bases largely obscured by buff-brown fringes, it is unnecessary to adopt the newly-coined 'Black-headed Mountain Finch' (used by Sibley & Monroe 1990),

Asian Rosy Finch: This name is appropriate if *tephrocotis* (Grey-crowned Rosy Finch) and the other related forms restricted to North America are treated as full species (see 'Taxonomic notes'). When all are lumped in *L. arctoa* the species is simply called 'Rosy Finch'.

Blanford's Rosefinch: Replacing this unique and appropriate name, which celebrates the ornithologist who first described the species in 1872, with 'Crimson Rosefinch' would be a retrograde step as many rosefinch species are equally 'crimson'.

Common Rosefinch: This is the name almost always used in Asia (where all the other rosefinches are found) and, since a number of *Carpodacus* are 'scarlet' but this is by far the most widespread species, it is more appropriate than the largely British 'Scarlet Rosefinch'.

Sinai Rosefinch: This name is unique, well-established and appropriate enough (reflecting both the scientific name and the best-known part of the distribution), so it is unnecessary to adopt the obscure name 'Pale Rosefinch' (used by Sibley & Monroe 1990).

Red-breasted Rosefinch: The existing name is unique, so it is unnecessary to adopt the newly-coined 'Red-fronted Rosefinch' (used by Sibley & Monroe 1990). Many bird names refer to features that are not unique to the species in question and this in itself is certainly not sufficient justification for replacing them with new names.

Roborovski's Rosefinch: The existing name is unique and appropriate, celebrating a brave pioneer of the ornithological exploration of the Tibetan plateau, so it is unnecessary to adopt the newly-coined 'Tibetan Rosefinch' (used by Sibley & Monroe 1990).

Przevalski's Rosefinch: The existing name is both unique and appropriate, celebrating the great ornithologist-explorer of the Tibetan plateau who first described this species in 1876, so it is unnecessary to adopt the newly-coined 'Pink-tailed Rosefinch'. Sibley & Monroe (1990) place this species amongst the Emberizidae under the name 'Pink-tailed Bunting'. If this placement is justified, which is in doubt (see 'Taxonomic notes'), then the name 'Przevalski's Bunting' should be used.

Eurasian Bullfinch: With a range that extends from the British Isles to Kamchatka, the name 'Eurasian Bullfinch' is highly appropriate and preferable to 'Common Bullfinch' as the species is only 'common' in the sense that it occurs more widely. It does not normally come into contact with other bullfinch species.

Grey-breasted Bullfinch: The form *griseiventris*, which is sometimes treated as a full species (see 'Taxonomic notes') is usually known as 'Grey-bellied Bullfinch'. The less frequently used 'Japanese Bullfinch' has the disadvantage of only referring to a small part of the range.

Grey-bellied Bullfinch: Regarding the English name for the form *cineracea*, which is sometimes treated as a full species (or grouped with *griseiventris*, see 'Taxonomic notes'), the names 'Grey Bullfinch' or 'Grey-breasted Bullfinch' are usually used for this form and, as both are unique and appropriate, it is unnecessary to adopt the newly-coined 'Baikal Bullfinch' (used by Sibley & Monroe 1990). Of the two current names, 'Grey Bullfinch' is marginally superior as a description for this distinctive form.

EMBERIZIDAE

Lapland Longspur: With all four *Calcarius* species occurring in North America, where they are all called 'longspurs', it would be flying in the face of logic to suggest that the name 'Lapland Bunting' should be used on a worldwide basis for this sole circumpolar species, or that North American ornithologists should change the names for the other species to 'bunting'.

Slaty Bunting: The male is slate-coloured rather than blue and the species only winters in Fukien (now spelt Fujian), so 'Slaty Bunting' is the most appropriate name.

Japanese Yellow Bunting: It is helpful to retain 'Japanese' in the name for this species, which breeds only in Japan, as it is just one of several buntings which are conspicuously yellow in coloration. The name 'Yellow Bunting' has occasionally been used instead of 'Yellowhammer' for *E. citrinella*.

Kozlov's Bunting: The existing name is unique and appropriate, celebrating a brave pioneer of the ornithological exploration of the Tibetan plateau, so it is unnecessary to adopt the newly-coined 'Tibetan Bunting' (used by Sibley & Monroe 1990).

White-capped Bunting: The existing name is unique, well-established and fairly appropriate (the crown is greyish-white), so it is unnecessary to adopt the newly-coined 'Chestnut-breasted Bunting' (used by Sibley & Monroe 1990).

Jankowski's Bunting: The existing name is unique and appropriate, honouring the ornithologist who discovered the species in 1886, so it is unnecessary to adopt the newly-coined 'Rufous-backed Bunting' (used by Sibley & Monroe 1990).

Common Reed Bunting: If the word 'reed' is retained in the English names for *E. pallasi* and *E. yessoensis* then it is necessary to add the modifier 'common' to the English name for *E. schoeniclus*. See Pallas's Reed Bunting.

Pallas's Reed Bunting: It is helpful to retain the word 'reed' in the names for the three closely similar, frequently reed-haunting species *E. schoeniclus*, *E. pallasi* and *E. yessoensis*.

Japanese Reed Bunting: The existing name is unique and places the species both geographically (although it also breeds in mainland northeast Asia) and by habitat, so it is unnecessary to adopt the newly-coined 'Ochre-rumped Bunting' (used by Sibley & Monroe 1990). See Pallas's Reed Bunting.

NOTES ON DISTRIBUTIONAL STATUS

PROCELLARIIDAE

Pterodroma mollis Soft-plumaged Petrel: if the forms *feae* (Fea's Petrel) and *madeira* (Zino's Petrel) are treated as specifically distinct, it is possible that *P. mollis* (*sensu stricto*) may not actually have occurred in the Palearctic. Although the latter has been reported from Madeira (Jepson & Zonfrillo 1988), identification problems in the *mollis* group cloud the issue (see Zonfrillo 1994) and the complete range of plumage variation shown by *P. feae* remains uncertain. *P. mollis* is retained here pending further developments.

Pterodroma nigripennis Black-winged Petrel: occurs in large numbers, albeit far offshore, in the seas southeast of Japan (Brazil 1991).

Bulweria fallax Jouanin's Petrel: breeding grounds unknown, but thought to be in coastal southeastern Arabia (?including the Kuria Muria Islands, Oman), where the species is common offshore from March-September.

HYDROBATIDAE

Fregetta tropica Black-bellied Storm-petrel: a regular visitor to waters off Oman (Gallagher & Woodcock 1980).

ARDEIDAE

Dupetor flavicollis Black Bittern: a vagrant to Japan (Brazil 1991) and central Gansu (see map in Cheng 1987). The range in China extends northwards to southern Shaanxi, just outside our limits.

Gorsachius melanolophus Malayan Night Heron: resident in the southern Nansei (or Ryukyu) Islands (Brazil 1991).

Egretta ardesiaca Black Heron: single vagrants recorded from Eilat, Israel in October 1982 (Shirihai in press) and from Boa Vista, Cape Verde Islands in March 1985 by S. C. Madge and the author (C. J. Hazevoet in press, *Birds of the Cape Verde Islands*).

Ardea melanocephala Black-headed Heron: a vagrant to Yemen, Oman and Israel (Hollom *et al.* 1988, Shirihai in press).

CICONIIDAE

Mycteria leucocephala Painted Stork: a vagrant to Hebei, north China (Cheng 1987). Also recorded in southeastern Baluchistan, just outside our limits.

Ciconia episcopus Woolly-necked Stork: a vagrant to Iran (Hollom *et al.* 1988).

THRESKIORNITHIDAE

Nipponia nippon Crested Ibis: the only known surviving population is found in China in the Yangxian area in the upper Han Shui valley in southern Shaanxi, just outside our limits.

ANATIDAE

Dendrocygna javanica Lesser Whistling Duck: used to breed in the southern Nansei (or Ryukyu) Islands. Now only a vagrant to Japan (Brazil 1991). Also a vagrant to Israel (Shirihai in press).

Cygnus atratus Black Swan: now breeds ferally in Slovakia (see Cramp & Perrins 1994b).

Cygnus buccinator Trumpeter Swan: a single individual was recorded at Anadyr, Chukotka district (northeast Siberia), on 16 June 1991 (M. Van Beirs *in litt.*).

Anser rossii Ross's Goose: recorded on Wrangel Island, northeastern Siberia (Stepanyan 1990) and unlikely to be other than a genuine vagrant in this location. Vagrant also to the Netherlands (and accepted on the national list), but as usual with wildfowl the possibility of escapes can never be ruled out.

Sarkidiornis melanotos Comb Duck: recorded as a vagrant to Oman (Oman Bird Record Committee 1994) and also recorded from Japan, where origin uncertain (Brazil 1991).

Anas erythrorhyncha Red-billed Teal: the sole Palearctic record, from Israel in June-July 1958, is considered to relate to a genuine vagrant (Shirihai in press), but with wildfowl the possibility of escapes is always a problem.

Anas smithii Cape Shoveler: recorded once from Morocco in 1978 (Duff 1979), but in view of the lack of acceptable records anywhere between here and south-central Africa, these two individuals may have been escapes and so only tentatively included here.

ACCIPITRIDAE

Chelictinia riocourii African Swallow-tailed Kite: a vagrant to Yemen (Hollom *et al.* 1988).

Haliastur indus Brahminy Kite: has wandered to Lhasa in southern Tibet (Vaurie 1972).

Sarcogyps calvus Red-headed Vulture: has wandered to 3050m in Nepal (Inskipp & Inskipp 1991).

Accipiter virgatus Besra: recorded up to 3000m in the western Himalayas (Ripley 1982) and occasionally reported up to 3440m in Nepal (Inskipp & Inskipp 1991). The range in China extends northwards to southern Shaanxi, just outside our limits. Not recorded above about 1900m on Emei Shan in central Sichuan (Cheng *et al.* 1963), which is just below our limits.

Ictinaetus malayensis Black Eagle: regularly recorded up to 3100m and exceptionally to 4000m in Nepal (Inskipp & Inskipp 1991).

PHASIANIDAE

Coturnix delegorguei Harlequin Quail: may breed in southwestern Arabia according to Hollom *et al.* (1988) and sometimes found to be quite common there in suitable habitat (N. J. Redman *in litt.*).

Bambusicola thoracica Chinese Bamboo Partridge: a long-established introduction in Japan. The range in China extends northwards to southeastern Gansu and southern Shaanxi, just outside our limits. This is a species of lower altitudes, not found above about 1200m on Emei Shan in central Sichuan (Cheng *et al.* 1963, pers. obs.).

Tragopan blythii Blyth's Tragopan: said to occur up to 3500m in the eastern Himalayas (Ripley 1982). This may be an exaggeration (C. Robson *in litt.*), but presumed to occur within our limits (i.e. 2800m or above) in the eastern Himalayas and northernmost Burma.

Catreus wallichii Cheer Pheasant: recorded up to 2700m in the western Himalayas in general (Ripley 1982) and up to 3050m in Nepal (Inskipp & Inskipp 1991).

RALLIDAE

Gallirallus striatus Slaty-breasted Rail: a single vagrant at 2400m at Jiuzhaigou, northern Sichuan in May 1994 (pers. obs.).

Porzana bicolor Black-tailed Crake: recorded up to 2800m in the eastern Himalayas (Ripley 1982), so just reaches our limits.

Amaurornis akool Brown Crake: not usually recorded above about 800m, but has wandered to 3290m in Nepal (Inskipp & Inskipp 1991).

Amaurornis phoenicurus White-breasted Waterhen: this species has successfully colonized the southern Nansei (or Ryukyu) Islands since 1972 and is a vagrant northwards in east Asia to Hokkaido (Brazil 1991) and the Russian Far East (Stepanyan 1990).

Gallinula angulata Lesser Moorhen: a vagrant recorded from Oman in November 1991 (Oman Bird Record Committee 1994).

OTIDIDAE

Neotis nuba Nubian Bustard: recorded from the edge of the Tibesti (see Cramp & Simmons 1980), just within our limits. Occurs as far north as this elsewhere in the Saharan fringe (e.g. northern Mauritania: Lamarche 1988) and may well breed within our limits.

JACANIDAE

Hydrophasianus chirurgus Pheasant-tailed Jacana: this species normally occurs below 1500m in the Himalayas but has wandered to 3800m (Ripley 1982). Also a vagrant northwards in east Asia to Japan (Brazil 1991) and the Russian Far East (Stepanyan 1990). Vagrant to Yemen (Hollom *et al.* 1988) and a rare but regular visitor to Oman (Gallagher & Woodcock 1980).

GLAREOLIDAE

Pluvianus aegyptius Egyptian Plover: extinct in Egypt since the construction of the Aswan dams, but may still occur just within our limits along the Nile in northernmost Sudan (see Nikolaus 1987).

Glareola lactea Small Pratincole: included by Vaurie (1965a) and Voous (1977) as the species breeds along the Kabul River and its tributaries, but this area is a little outside our limits. Included here on the strength of its occurrence as a vagrant in several different parts of the Arabian Peninsula (Hollom *et al.* 1988) and in 1977 on the Caspian coast of Iran (D. A. Scott *in litt.*).

CHARADRIIDAE

Charadrius tricollaris Three-banded Plover: a vagrant recorded in Egypt in March 1993 (Anon 1993).

STERCORARIIDAE

Catharacta antarctica Southern Skua: a vagrant of this species recorded from Oman in October 1991 was presumed to have been of the form *lonnbergi* (Oman Bird Record Committee 1994).

STERNIDAE

Anous tenuirostris Lesser Noddy: a regular non-breeding visitor to waters off Oman (Gallagher & Woodcock 1980).

ALCIDAE

Ptychoramphus aleuticus Cassin's Auklet: a vagrant to Kamchatka and the Kuril Islands (Stepanyan 1990).

COLUMBIDAE

Columba arquatrix African Olive Pigeon: this species has been recorded in southwestern Arabia (Hollom *et al.* 1988) and is thought to be resident there.

Columba pulchricollis Ashy Wood Pigeon: recorded up to 3200m in the Himalayas (Ripley 1982).

Streptopelia decipiens African Mourning Dove: found along the Nile valley as far as northernmost Sudan (Nikolaus 1987), just within our limits, and is likely to be resident there.

Treron sphenura Wedge-tailed Green Pigeon: stated to occur up to about 4270m in northern Yunnan and up to about about 3050m in southern Sichuan by Vaurie (1965a), but the old altitudinal data from northern Yunnan and adjacent Sichuan that Vaurie had to work with is now considered highly dubious and has generally been discounted during work on the Birdlife International biodiversity project for continental Asia (C. Robson *in litt.*). Has occurred once at 2800m in Nepal (Inskipp & Inskipp 1991), but mainly recorded under 2000m, so probably only an altitudinal wanderer within our limits.

PSITTACIDAE

Psittacula eupatria Alexandrine Parakeet: a feral population exists in Bushire in southern Iran (Hollom *et al.* 1988) and the species is increasingly being observed in a feral state in the Arabian Peninsula (see, for example, *Phoenix* 9, 1992) and may be becoming established.

Psittacula krameri Rose-ringed Parakeet: found throughout the year at Quetta in northern Baluchistan (Roberts 1991), just within our limits, and probably of natural occurrence there. Populations elsewhere in the Palearctic are known to be, or presumed to be, introduced.

Psittacula himalayana Slaty-headed Parakeet: regularly recorded up to 2438m in the Himalayas in Pakistan (Roberts 1991), well within our limits, and up to 2500m in the Himalayas as a whole (Ripley 1982). Noted exceptionally at 3260m in Nepal (Inskipp & Inskipp 1991).

Psittacula finschii Grey-headed Parakeet: stated to occur up to about 3660m or more in northern Yunnan according to Vaurie (1965a). This may be an exaggeration (see entry for *Treron sphenurus* Wedge-tailed Pigeon), but certainly reaches about 3000m in the Lijiang range (pers. obs.), which is well within our limits.

CUCULIDAE

Clamator coromandus Chestnut-winged Cuckoo: the range in China extends northwards to Wushan in the Huang Ho drainage of southern Gansu, just within our limits. Also a vagrant to Japan (Brazil 1991).

Hierococcyx varius Common Hawk Cuckoo: a vagrant recorded from Oman in November 1988 (Oman Bird Record Committee 1994).

Eudynamys scolopacea Common Koel: a vagrant to Iran and Oman (Hollom *et al.* 1988). The range in China extends northwards to southeastern Gansu and southern Shaanxi, just outside our limits.

Centropus superciliosus White-browed Coucal: resident in southwestern Arabia (Hollom *et al.* 1988).

STRIGIDAE

Otus spilocephalus Mountain Scops Owl: found up to 2700m in the Himalayas as a whole (Ripley 1982) and reaches 3000m in Pakistan (Roberts 1991).

Otus senegalensis African Scops Owl: resident in southwestern Arabia (Hollom *et al.* 1988).

Glaucidium cuculoides Asian Barred Owlet: the range in China extends northwards to Wushan in the Huang Ho drainage of southern Gansu, just within our limits, and the species has wandered to the Shandong Peninsula (Cheng 1987).

Strix leptogrammica Brown Wood Owl: mostly recorded up to 2500m in the Himalayas, just reaching our limits in the west, but has been found at about 3900m in Sikkim (Ripley 1982).

CAPRIMULGIDAE

Caprimulgus poliocephalus Mountain Nightjar: recently discovered to be resident in southwestern Arabia (Stagg 1992, Symens *et al.* 1994).

TROCHILIDAE

Selasphorus rufous Rufous Hummingbird: a vagrant to Ratmanova (or Big Diomede) Island in the Bering Strait (Stepanyan 1990), just within our limits. Several unidentified hummingbirds have been recorded on St Lawrence island (Kessel & Gibson 1978), just outside our limits.

TROGONIDAE

Harpactes wardi Ward's Trogon: recorded from 1500m up to 3000m in the eastern Himalayas (Ripley 1982), thus reaching our limits. Also found up to about 2745m in the Myitkyina region of northern Burma (Smythies 1986), just outside our limits.

ALCEDINIDAE

Halcyon chloris Collared Kingfisher: an isolated population (the endemic subspecies *kalbaensis*) occurs in northern Oman and the adjacent United Arab Emirates (Gallagher & Woodcock 1980, Richardson 1990).

Halcyon cinnamomina Micronesian Kingfisher: the form *miyakoensis* Miyako Kingfisher, the only one recorded from the Palearctic, is known from just a single specimen from the island of Miyako in the southern Nansei (or Ryukyu) Islands. Vaurie (1965a) speculated that this specimen might even have originated from elsewhere.

Alcedo cristata Malachite Kingfisher: Recorded rarely from southwestern Arabia (Hollom *et al.* 1988), but it may even breed (see Kirwan 1993).

CORACIIDAE

Coracias caudata Lilac-breasted Roller: a vagrant to Yemen (Hollom *et al.* 1988).

Coracias noevia Rufous-crowned Roller: a vagrant to Yemen (Hollom *et al.* 1988).

CAPITONIDAE

Megalaima virens Great Barbet: recorded up to 3000m in the Himalayas as a whole (Ripley 1982) and up to 2600m in Pakistan (Roberts 1991).

INDICATORIDAE

Indicator xanthonotus Yellow-rumped Honeyguide: recorded up to 3500m in the Himalayas (Ripley 1982).

PICIDAE

Picumnus innominatus Speckled Piculet: this species is not usually recorded above 2000m in the Himalayas and eastern Afghanistan, but reaches 2700m in the Sutlej Valley in the western Himalayas (Ripley 1982) and has reached 2100m in Pakistan (Roberts 1991).

Blythipicus pyrrhotis Bay Woodpecker: this species occurs up to 2400m on Emei Shan in central Sichuan (Cheng *et al.* 1963), well within our limits. It also reaches about 2500m in Nepal (Inskipp & Inskipp 1991), but this is below our limits.

ALAUDIDAE

Eremopterix signata Chestnut-headed Sparrow-lark: a male recorded at Eilat, Israel in May 1993 (Shirihai in press), a remarkable case of vagrancy.

HIRUNDINIDAE

Hirundo aethiopica Ethiopian Swallow: a vagrant individual was trapped in Israel in March 1991 (Bear 1991).

Hirundo abyssinica Lesser Striped Swallow: a vagrant recorded from Oman in December 1986 (Oman Bird Records Committee 1994).

MOTACILLIDAE

Anthus rufulus Paddyfield Pipit: the race *waitei* has wandered exceptionally to 3000m in the western Himalayas (Ali & Ripley 1973).

Anthus sylvanus Upland Pipit: recorded up to 3000m in the Himalayas as a whole (Ripley 1982) and up to 2900m in Nepal (Inskipp & Inskipp 1991).

Tmetothylacus tenellus Golden Pipit: a vagrant to Oman (Hollom *et al.* 1988).

CAMPEPHAGIDAE

Pericrocotus solaris Grey-chinned Minivet: recorded up to 3000m in the eastern Himalayas according to Ripley (1982) and observed at about 3250m in Darjeeling district in March 1989 (N. J. Redman *in litt.*), so reaches our limits. Not usually recorded above about 2100m in the Himalayas, so treated here as an altitudinal wanderer.

Pericrocotus cinnamomeus Small Minivet: this species is resident in southeastern Baluchistan, within the area covered by Voous (1977) but just outside our limits. Included here on the strength of wanderers recorded at Quetta in northern Baluchistan (Vaurie 1965a, Ali & Ripley 1971).

PYCNONOTIDAE

Spizixos canifrons Crested Finchbill: occurs up to about 3965m in northern Yunnan according to Vaurie (1959a), but this may well be an exaggeration (see entry for *Treron sphenurus* Wedge-tailed Pigeon). The species is said to reach about 3050m at Muli in southern Sichuan (Meyer de Schauensee 1984), which is well within our limits.

Spizixos semitorques Collared Finchbill: included by Vaurie (1959a) and Voous (1977), but altitudinal information is rather sparse. Found up to 2100m near Jiuzhaigou in northern Sichuan (pers. obs.), just within our limits.

Pycnonotus cafer Red-vented Bulbul: now an established introduction in several parts of the Arabian Peninsula (Hollom *et al.* 1988).

TURDIDAE

Brachypteryx hyperythra Rusty-bellied Shortwing: recorded up to 2900m in the eastern Himalayas in winter (Ripley 1982), just within our limits, and may occur higher in summer.

Cinclidium leucurum White-tailed Robin: occurs up to 2100m on Emei Shan in central Sichuan (Cheng *et al.* 1963, pers. obs.), just within our limits. Also noted up to 2745m in Nepal, just outside our limits.

Cochoa purpurea Purple Cochoa: recorded up to 3000m in the Himalayas (Ripley 1982) and up to about 2200m on Emei Shan in central Sichuan (Cheng *et al.* 1963).

Cercomela familiaris Familiar Chat: a vagrant to Yemen (Hollom *et al.* 1988).

Saxicola macrorhyncha Stoliczka's Bushchat: the sole records from within our limits are two specimen records from southern Afghanistan in 1881 (Whistler 1945a), far from the usual range of the species in and around the Thar Desert of northwest India. Status uncertain, but probably only a vagrant.

Saxicoloides fulicata Indian Robin: the breeding range extends to the west of Ras Ormara in western Baluchistan (see map in Roberts 1992).

Copsychus saularis Oriental Magpie Robin: has wandered to 3050m in Nepal (Inskipp & Inskipp 1991). The range in China extends northwards to southeastern Gansu and southern Shaanxi, just outside our limits.

Zoothera monticola Long-billed Thrush: recorded up to 3850m in Nepal (Inskipp & Inskipp 1991).

Zoothera wardii Pied Thrush: recorded up to about 3000m in Nepal (Inskipp & Inskipp 1991), but mainly recorded below 2500m and so perhaps only a wanderer within our limits.

Turdus boulboul Grey-winged Blackbird: not usually recorded above 2745m in the Himalayas, but found up to 3300m in Nepal (Ripley 1982, Inskipp & Inskipp 1991).

Enicurus leschenaulti White-crowned Forktail: the range in China extends northwards to southwestern Gansu, Wushan in southern Gansu and Liupan Shan in southern Ningxia (Cheng 1987), all of which are within our limits. Usually found at low or moderate altitudes, but in central and northern Sichuan occasionally wanders up to about 2400m (pers. obs.).

SYLVIIDAE

Prinia inornata Plain Prinia: included by Vaurie (1959a) and Voous (1977) on the strength of its occurrence in the mountains of Sichuan, but the species only occurs at low altitudes in the deep valleys of Sichuan and does not reach Palearctic limits. Included here on the strength of its occurrence as a vagrant in the southern Nansei (or Ryukyu) Islands (Brazil 1991).

Prinia atrogularis Hill Prinia: occurs up to 2745m or more in southeast Tibet and southern Sichuan according to Vaurie (1959a), although the species has not been recorded above 2500m in the eastern Himalayas (Ripley 1982, Inskipp & Inskipp 1991).

Acrocephalus baeticatus African Reed Warbler: recently discovered breeding on the Red Sea coast of Saudi Arabia and also recorded from Yemen (Ash *et al.* 1989).

Seicercus xanthoschistos Grey-hooded Warbler: recorded up to about 2100m in Pakistan (Roberts 1992) and about 2700m elsewhere in the Himalayas (Ripley 1982).

Seicercus poliogenys Grey-cheeked Warbler: recorded up to 3000m in the eastern Himalayas in general (Ripley 1982) and up to 3200m in Nepal (Inskipp & Inskipp 1991).

Seicercus castaniceps Chestnut-crowned Warbler: recorded once at about 3000m on Emei Shan in central Sichuan (pers. obs.), although probably only a wanderer at such altitude. Also reaches 2750m in Nepal (Inskipp & Inskipp 1991), just outside our limits.

Phylloscopus sichuanensis Chinese Leaf Warbler: a newly described species from west-central and north-central China (Alström *et al.* 1992), reaching at least 2800m in Jiuzhaigou in northern Sichuan (pers. obs.).

Phylloscopus davisoni White-tailed Leaf Warbler: found up to 2100m on Emei Shan in central Sichuan (P. Alström *in litt.*), so just reaches our limits.

MUSCICAPIDAE

Niltava grandis Large Niltava: recorded up to 2850m in Nepal (Inskipp & Inskipp 1991), so just reaches our limits.

Niltava davidi Fujian Niltava: found up to at least 2200m on Emei Shan in central Sichuan (Cheng *et al.* 1963).

Niltava vivida Vivid Niltava: found up to at least 2000m on Emei Shan in central Sichuan (pers. obs.), where it just reaches our limits. Has been recorded from the Lhasa region according to Cheng (1987), where it can only be a vagrant. In the eastern Himalayas recorded up to about 2700m (Ripley 1982), just below our limits.

Cyornis banyumas Hill Blue Flycatcher: recorded up to 3350m in Nepal (Inskipp & Inskipp 1991).
Muscicapella hodgsoni Pygmy Blue Flycatcher: recorded up to 3500m in Nepal (Inskipp & Inskipp 1991).
Ficedula sapphira Sapphire Flycatcher: recorded up to 2800m in Nepal (Inskipp & Inskipp 1991), so just reaches our limits.
Ficedula superciliaris Ultramarine Flycatcher: recorded up to 3200m in the Himalayas (Ripley 1982, Inskipp & Inskipp 1991).
Ficedula westermanni Little Pied Flycatcher: recorded up to 3000m in Nepal (Inskipp & Inskipp 1991).
Ficedula hyperythra Snowy-browed Flycatcher: recorded up to 3000m in the Himalayas (Ripley 1982, Inskipp & Inskipp 1991).
Ficedula monileger White-gorgeted Flycatcher: has been observed at about 3000m in Nepal (Inskipp & Inskipp 1991), although probably only a wanderer within our limits as otherwise not found above 2300m in the Himalayas.

RHIPIDURIDAE

Rhipidura albicollis White-throated Fantail: recorded up to 2000m in the western Himalayas, exceptionally higher, and up to 2700m in the east (Ripley 1982). Exceptionally reaches 3050m in northern Burma and higher altitudes in Yunnan according to Smythies (1986). Presumably only a wanderer within our limits.

TIMALIIDAE

Pomatorhinus erythrogenys Rusty-cheeked Scimitar Babbler: recorded up to 2100m in Pakistan (Roberts 1992), so just occurs within our limits. Further to the east does not occur above 2440m (Ripley 1982, Inskipp & Inskipp 1991). Note: the distribution of this species is erroneously restricted to Burma and northwest Thailand by Sibley & Monroe (1990); in fact it also extends to all but the extreme northeastern Himalayas. Likewise the range given for *P. erythrocnemis* Spot-breasted Scimitar Babbler in the Himalayas is erroneous: it should be limited to the easternmost part only.
Pomatorhinus ferruginosus Coral-billed Scimitar Babbler: recorded up to 3800m in the eastern Himalayas (Ali 1962, Ripley 1982).
Xiphirhynchus superciliaris Slender-billed Scimitar Babbler: recorded up to 3050m in Nepal (Inskipp & Inskipp 1991) and up to 3400m elsewhere in the eastern Himalayas (Ali 1962, Ripley 1982).
Pnoepyga immaculata Nepal Wren-babbler: recorded up to 3100m in Nepal (Martens & Eck 1991).
Spelaeornis caudatus Rufous-throated Wren-babbler: recorded up to 3100m in the eastern Himalayas (Ali 1962, Ripley 1982).
Spelaeornis troglodytoides Bar-winged Wren-babbler: recorded up to 3300m in the eastern Himalayas (Ripley 1982).
Paradoxornis guttaticollis Spot-breasted Parrotbill: the range in China extends northwards to southern Gansu and southern Shaanxi, and the species has been recorded up to about 2250m on Emei Shan in central Sichuan (Cheng *et al.* 1963).
Paradoxornis brunneus Brown-winged Parrotbill: occurs up to about 3965m in northern Yunnan according to Vaurie (1959a). This may well be an exaggeration (see entry for *Treron sphenurus* Wedge-tailed Green Pigeon), but definitely found up to at least 2895m in northern Yunnan (C. Robson *in litt.*), which is well within our limits.
Garrulax perspicillatus Masked Laughingthrush: the range in China extends northwards to southern Shanxi, just within our limits. Has been recorded also from the Shandong peninsula (Cheng 1987), where status uncertain.
Garrulax cineraceus Moustached Laughingthrush: the range in China extends northwards to Shanxi, well within our geographical limits, and near Jiuzhaigou in northern Sichuan it reaches at least 2200m (pers. obs.).

Garrulax rufogularis Rufous-chinned Laughingthrush: recorded in winter at 3500m in Sikkim (Ripley 1982), although as it normally occurs no higher than 2135m it is probably only a wanderer within our limits.

Garrulax canorus Hwamei: this species reaches Minxian in the Huang Ho drainage of southern Gansu, just within our limits. Altitudinal data is rather lacking for this species, but it is typically a bird of the lowlands and foothills and so may not reach our limits further south in Sichuan or Yunnan.

Garrulax squamatus Blue-winged Laughingthrush: recorded up to about 3600m in winter in Sikkim (Ali 1962), although it usually occurs no higher than 2400m in the eastern Himalayas and so is probably only a wanderer within our limits.

Liocichla omeiensis Emei Shan Liocichla: recorded up to about 2400m on Emei Shan in central Sichuan (Cheng *et al*. 1963).

Leiothrix lutea Red-billed Leiothrix: recorded up to about 3000m on Emei Shan in central Sichuan (pers. obs.), well within our limits. In the Himalayas found up to 2400m in the west and 2745m in the east (Ripley 1982, Inskipp & Inskipp 1991), just below our limits.

Pteruthius rufiventer Black-headed Shrike-babbler: recorded up to 3230m in Nepal (Inskipp & Inskipp 1991), although it usually occurs no higher than 2700m and so is probably only a wanderer within our limits.

Actinodura waldeni Streak-throated Barwing: recorded up to 3300m in the eastern Himalayas (Ripley 1982).

Alcippe castaneceps Rufous-winged Fulvetta: Recorded up to 3000m in the eastern Himalayas in general (Ripley 1982) and up to about 3500m in Nepal (Inskipp & Inskipp 1991).

Heterophasia pulchella Beautiful Sibia: recorded up to 3000m in southeastern Tibet and Yunnan (Cheng 1987).

Yuhina flavicollis Whiskered Yuhina: recorded up to 3000m in the Himalayas in general (Ripley 1982) and up to about 3100m in Nepal (Inskipp & Inskipp 1991).

PARIDAE

Parus xanthogenys Black-lored Tit: exceptionally recorded up to 2925m in Nepal (Inskipp & Inskipp 1991), where probably only a wanderer.

Parus spilonotus Yellow-cheeked Tit: exceptionally recorded up to 3700m in the eastern Himalayas in winter (Ali 1962, Ripley 1982), but usually found below 2440m and so presumably only a wanderer within our limits.

DICAEIDAE

Dicaeum agile Thick-billed Flowerpecker: has wandered to 3000m in Garhwal in the western Himalayas (Ripley 1982).

ZOSTEROPIDAE

Zosterops palpebrosus Oriental White-eye: recorded regularly up to 2400m in the Himalayas in Pakistan (Roberts 1992), well within our limits., and exceptionally noted in the Himalayas at 3000m (Ripley 1982).

ORIOLIDAE

Oriolus tenuirostris Slender-billed Oriole: this species is stated by Vaurie (1959a) to occur up to about 4270m in northern Yunnan, but this is exceedingly unlikely (see entry for *Treron sphenurus* Wedge-tailed Green Pigeon regarding the dubious nature of some of the altitudinal data for this area). Nonetheless, definitely reaches 2745m in the Lijiang area of northern Yunnan (C. Robson *in litt.*), so occurs within our limits. In the Himalayas not found above 2100m (Ripley 1982).

STURNIDAE

Sturnus pagodarum Brahminy Starling: recorded (breeding) up to 2400m in the Himalayas in Pakistan (Roberts 1992) and has exceptionally reached 3000m in Lahul (Ripley 1982) and 3050m in Nepal (Inskipp & Inskipp 1991). Also occurs in eastern Afghanistan (mostly below our limits), and has wandered to the Kugitang mountains on the Turkmenistan/Tadjikistan border (Stepanyan 1990).

Sturnus sericeus Red-billed Starling: a vagrant to Japan (Brazil 1991). The range in China extends northwards to southern Shaanxi, just outside our limits.

Creatophora cinerea Wattled Starling: scarce and irregular visitor to Yemen and Oman (Hollom *et al.* 1988).

Acridotheres ginginianus Bank Myna: this introduced species is established in the United Arab Emirates (Richardson 1990). Has wandered to Kandahar in southern Afghanistan also (Whistler 1945b).

Acridotheres cristatellus Crested Myna: a small feral population is established in Japan, where the species has also occurred as a vagrant (Brazil 1991).

PLOCEIDAE

Ploceus manyar Streaked Weaver: now an established introduction in Egypt (Goodman & Meininger 1989) and increasingly being found in a feral state in the Arabian Peninsula (see, for example, *Phoenix* 9, 1992).

ESTRILDIDAE

Amandava amandava Red Avadavat: now an established introduction in Japan (Brazil 1991), Egypt (Goodman & Meininger 1989), Spain and Italy (Cramp & Simmons 1994a), and increasingly being found in a feral state in the Arabian Peninsula (see, for example, *Phoenix* 9, 1992). Has wandered to the Quetta region of northern Baluchistan (Roberts 1992).

Lonchura striata White-rumped Munia: now an established introduction on Okinawa (Brazil 1991). The range in China extends northwards to southern Shaanxi, just outside our limits.

Lonchura punctulata Scaly-breasted Munia: now an established introduction on Okinawa (Brazil 1991).

Lonchura malacca Chestnut Munia: now an established introduction in Japan (Brazil 1991).

Padda oryzivora Java Sparrow: now an established introduction in Japan (Brazil 1991).

Amadina fasciata Cut-throat: recorded in northernmost Sudan (Nikolaus 1987) just within our limits. Presumably a wanderer, as the usual range in Sudan is well to the south.

FRINGILLIDAE

Leucosticte sillemi Sillem's Mountain Finch: a newly described species from western Tibet (see Roselaar 1992, 1994).

EMBERIZIDAE

Spizella arborea American Tree Sparrow: a vagrant to the Chukotka peninsula and Wrangel Island in northeastern Siberia (Stepanyan 1990).

ICTERIDAE

Euphagus carolinensis Rusty Blackbird: a vagrant to the Chukotka peninsula in northeastern Siberia (Stepanyan 1990). Known to be a rare visitor to the adjacent Alaskan coast and to St Lawrence Island, so its occurrence within our limits is not surprising.

OMITTED SPECIES
(and subspecies)

PODICIPEDIDAE

Podiceps major Great Grebe: two old Spanish records are considered dubious (Cramp & Simmons 1977). The chances of this southern South American species reaching the Palearctic unaided must be remote.

DIOMEDEIDAE

Diomedea chrysostoma Grey-headed Albatross: old records from Iceland and Norway are considered dubious (Cramp & Simmons 1977).

Diomedea epomophora Royal Albatross: an old record from Morocco is considered dubious (Cramp & Simmons 1977).

PROCELLARIIDAE

Macronectes giganteus Southern Giant Petrel (or Antarctic Giant Petrel[1]): included by Voous (1977) on the strength of a vagrant recorded from the English Channel (see Cramp & Simmons 1977), but subsequently this record was only accepted as *Macronectes* sp. (i.e. not specifically identified) on the French list (Dubois & Yésou 1986).

Pterodroma arminjoniana Herald Petrel: Vaurie (1965a) thought that a specimen purchased in London in 1889 might have reached Britain unaided. The species has not, however, been admitted to the British & Irish List. Note: if the Pacific form *heraldica* is treated as specifically distinct (as by Sibley & Monroe 1990, but not 1993), *P. arminjoniana* is then renamed 'Trinidade Petrel'.

Pterodroma leucoptera Gould's Petrel (or Collared Petrel, or White-winged Petrel): included by Voous (1977), presumably on the strength of the 1889 record from Britain (see Vaurie 1965a), but this species has been removed from the British & Irish list (see British Ornithologists' Union Records Committee 1971). Note: the deleted British record referred to *brevipes* Collared Petrel, sometimes (including by Sibley & Monroe 1990) treated as specifically distinct.

Puffinus lherminieri lherminieri Audubon's Shearwater (nominate race): the record from Britain is considered unacceptable (see British Ornithologists' Union Records Committee 1978). Consequently, should both *persicus* Persian Shearwater and *bannermani* Bannerman's Shearwater be treated as specifically distinct (see 'Taxonomic Notes'), *P. lherminieri* would no longer qualify for inclusion in this checklist.

HYDROBATIDAE

Oceanodroma microsoma Least Storm-petrel: the record from Japan is considered suspect (Brazil 1991). Note: alternatively (as in Voous 1977) *Halocyptena microsoma*.

PHALACROCORACIDAE

Phalacrocorax melanoleucos Little Pied Cormorant: the record from Japan is not considered acceptable (Brazil 1991).

Phalacrocorax niger Little Cormorant (or Javanese Cormorant): included by Voous (1977), presumably on the strength of the three records of Aitchison (1889) from Afghanistan, but at the time Aitchison wrote *P. niger* (= *javanicus*) and *P. pygmeus* Pygmy Cormorant were considered conspecific and the author did not differentiate the records to subspecies. As these records are more likely to refer to the latter, which is (or was) a regular visitor to Afghanistan, it seems safer to omit *P. niger*.

PELECANIDAE

Pelecanus philippensis Spot-billed Pelican: as *P. crispus* Dalmatian Pelican was formerly treated as conspecific with *P. philippensis*, and as the old records from north China and Japan do not appear to have been allocated to subspecies, it is hard to say if any of the records of *P. philippensis* from the Palearctic actually refer to *philippensis sensu stricto*. Consequently it is safer to omit this species.

FREGATIDAE

Fregata andrewsi Christmas Frigatebird (or Christmas Island Frigatebird[1]): Brazil (1991) mentions an undocumented record from Japan involving a bird retrospectively identified from a photograph that appeared in a book (in which it was wrongly captioned as *F. ariel* Lesser Frigatebird). The origin of the photograph was not established, however, and so this record must be considered questionable.

CICONIIDAE

Anastomus oscitans Asian Openbill (or Asian Open-billed Stork): included by Voous (1977) following Vaurie (1965a) who mentioned that it had occurred in Baluchistan, but this may have been an error as no records from the region were mentioned by Roberts (1991).

Anastomus lamelligerus African Openbill (or African Open-billed Stork): Vaurie (1965a) refers to this species as breeding in northern Sudan, on the southern border of the Palearctic region, but there are no confirmed reports of the species from this area (see Nikolaus 1987).

ACCIPITRIDAE

Ichthyophaga humilis Lesser Fish Eagle (or Himalayan Grey-headed Fishing Eagle): reported as wandering to 3500m and 4250m in Nepal (Inskipp & Inskipp 1991), but these records are now considered unacceptable (T. P. Inskipp *in litt.*). Note: synonym *I. nana*.

Gyps indicus Long-billed Vulture: included by Voous (1977), but the maximum elevation reached by this species in the Himalayas is 1525m in Nepal (Inskipp & Inskipp 1991), well below our limits.

Buteo lineatus Red-shouldered Hawk: An old record from Scotland is not acceptable (Alexander & Fitter 1955).

PHASIANIDAE

Francolinus pintadeanus Chinese Francolin: reported as a vagrant from the Shandong peninsula (see Cheng 1987), but this sedentary species is highly unlikely to wander so far from the normal range unaided. The species is a common cage-bird in China, so the possibility of escapes is high.

Perdicula asiatica Jungle Bush Quail: included by Voous (1977) following Vaurie (1965a), who mentioned that it occurred in Kashmir. The highest altitude reached in the Himalayas is 1200m (Ripley 1982), well below our limits.

Arborophila rufogularis Rufous-throated Partridge (or Rufous-throated Hill Partridge): included by Voous (1977), but this is a species of evergreen forest and has not been recorded above about 2400m in the eastern Himalayas (Ripley 1982), which is below our limits.

Arborophila rufipectus Sichuan Partridge (or Szechwan Hill Partridge, or Boulton's Hill Partridge): included by Vaurie (1965a) and Voous (1977), but Cheng (1987) gives its altitudinal limits as 1300-1800m, which is below our limits.

Gallus gallus Red Junglefowl: included by Voous (1977), but the highest altitude reached in the Himalayas is no more than about 2000m (Ripley 1982) and there is no evidence that the species reaches anything like this altitude in the western Himalayas and thus occurs within our limits.

SCOLOPACIDAE

Calidris paramelanotos Cox's Sandpiper: the taxonomic status of this recently described 'species', which presumably originates from eastern Palearctic breeding grounds, remains contentious. It is increasingly thought to be a hybrid between *C. melanotos* Pectoral Sandpiper and *C. ferruginea* Curlew Sandpiper (Cox 1987, 1989, 1990), although other parents have also been suggested (see Sibley & Monroe 1993).

Gallinago gallinago delicata Common Snipe (North American race): the sole Palearctic records of this form, which is known as 'Wilson's Snipe', are from Britain and have been rejected (British Ornithologists' Union Records Committee 1993b, Knox 1993). Note: this form may be worthy of specific status (see Olsson 1987).

Arenaria melanocephala Black Turnstone: reported as a vagrant to Wrangel Island and Chaun Bay, northeastern Siberia and included by Stepanyan (1990), but doubt has been cast on these very old records (see Vaurie 1965a). As the species is not even known to reach northern Alaska (American Ornithologists' Union 1983), the occurrence of the species within our limits needs confirmation.

STERNIDAE

Sterna aurantia River Tern (or Indian River Tern): recorded as a wanderer from the vicinity of Kabul (Niethammer & Niethammer 1967), but this area lies below 2000m and so is just outside our limits.

Sterna antillarum Least Tern: individuals showing the characters of the species have been reported from Britain (Yates & Taffs 1990, Clifton 1992), but this species has not yet been admitted to the British & Irish list. Note: sometimes (including by Voous 1977) treated as conspecific with *S. albifrons* Little Tern, but see Massey (1976).

COLUMBIDAE

Macropygia unchall Bar-tailed Cuckoo Dove: recorded from the Baoxing (formerly Muping) area of Sichuan by Père David, but this record has been questioned (see Vaurie 1965a) and, even if correct, is likely to have been outside our altitudinal limits. In the Himalayas occasionally reaches about 2700m (Inskipp & Inskipp 1991), just outside our limits.

Ectopistes migratorius Passenger Pigeon: recorded from British Isles and France in 19th century but not admitted to any national list (see Cramp 1985).

Treron curvirostra Thick-billed Green Pigeon: reported at 2750m in Nepal (see Ripley 1982), but Inskipp & Inskipp (1991) did not accept this record and give a maximum altitude of only about 400m for this species. The maximum recorded altitude elsewhere in the Himalayas is about 1500m (Ripley 1982).

PSITTACIDAE

Melopsittacus undulatus Budgerigar: possibly now breeding in the wild in Japan (see Brazil 1991), but there is no evidence it is established.

CUCULIDAE

Chrysococcyx maculatus Asian Emerald Cuckoo: included by Voous (1977) following Vaurie (1965a) who mentioned that this species has occurred up to about 3355m at Muli in southern Sichuan. This is highly unlikely, however (see entry for *Treron sphenurus* Wedge-tailed Green Pigeon regarding the dubious nature of some altitudinal data from this area). In the Himalayas this species is not known to have occurred above about 1500m (Ripley 1982). Note: alternatively (as in Cheng 1987) *Chalcites maculatus*.

Cacomantis merulinus Plaintive Cuckoo: included by Voous (1977) following Vaurie (1965a) who mentions that this species has occurred up to about 3355m in northern Yunnan. This is highly unlikely, however (see entry for *Treron sphenurus* Wedge-tailed Green Pigeon regarding the dubious nature of some altitudinal data from this area). In the Himalayas this species is not known to have occurred above about 2000m (Ripley 1982). Note: alternatively (as in Cheng 1987) *Cuculus merulinus*.

STRIGIDAE

Otus leucotis White-faced Scops Owl: included by Vaurie (1965a), but this species does not occur north of the Adrar in Mauritania, the Aïr or the Nile valley near Atbara (Vaurie 1965a, Nikolaus 1987, Lamarche 1988), so does not reach our limits.

Ketupa flavipes Tawny Fish Owl: included by both Vaurie (1965a) and Voous (1977), but this species has only been found up to about 1500m in the Himalayas (Ali & Ripley 1981) and in China, where it extends north to southeastern Gansu and southern Shaanxi, there is similarly no evidence that it reaches our limits.

CAPRIMULGIDAE

Caprimulgus eximius Golden Nightjar: included by both Vaurie (1965a) and Voous (1977), but this species does not occur north of south-central Mauritania, the Aïr or the Nile valley near Merowe (Vaurie 1965a, Nikolaus 1987, Lamarche 1988), so does not reach our limits. An observation from Rio de Oro in the former Spanish Sahara (now Morocco) is not considered definite (Cramp *et al.* 1985).

APODIDAE

Collocalia maxima Black-nest Swiftlet: supposedly recorded from eastern Bhutan and Arunachal Pradesh at 2100-3900m by Ludlow (see Ripley 1982, Ali & Ripley 1983), but the specimens were examined by T. P. Inskipp and C. Inskipp and found to be misidentified *C. brevirostris* Himalayan Swiftlets (T. P. Inskipp *in litt.*).

PICIDAE

Picus chlorolophus Lesser Yellownape (or Lesser Yellow-naped Woodpecker): included by Voous (1977), but this species has not been recorded above 2135m in the Himalayas (Ripley 1982, Inskipp & Inskipp 1991) so does not reach our limits.

Picus flavinucha Greater Yellownape (or Large Yellow-naped Woodpecker): included by Voous (1977), perhaps on the strength of a record from the Tsangpo valley in southeast Tibet (Vaurie 1972), but the area where the observation was made is under 2000m and outside our limits. In the Himalayas this species has not been recorded above about 2400m (Ripley 1982).

Dinopium benghalense Black-rumped Flameback (or Black-rumped Goldenback, or Lesser Golden-backed Woodpecker): included by Voous (1977), but this species has not been recorded west of the Indus lowlands and has not been recorded above 1700m in the Himalayas (Ripley 1982) so does not reach our limits.

Dinopium shorii Himalayan Flameback (or Himalayan Goldenback, or Himalayan Golden-backed Woodpecker): said to have reached 2900m in Nepal in winter (see Ripley 1982), but this is almost certainly erroneous as the highest confirmed record from Nepal is only 275m (T. P. Inskipp *in litt.*). Elsewhere in the Himalayas recorded to 1800m according to Ripley (1982), but this also requires confirmation.

Dinopium javanense Common Flameback (or Common Goldenback, or Common Golden-backed Woodpecker): this species is described in Cheng (1987) as occurring in China only in Qinghai and Gansu provinces, but this is clearly a misprint as in reality the species is only known in China from southernmost Yunnan, well outside our limits.

Dendrocopus macei Fulvous-breasted Woodpecker: said to occur exceptionally at 2800m in Nepal by Ripley (1982), but as this record was actually slightly lower than this, at 2745m (see Inskipp & Inskipp 1991), this species just fails to reach our limits.

ALAUDIDAE

Ammomanes phoenicurus Rufous-tailed Lark: included by Voous (1977), but I was unable to find any published record from the geographical area he covers. This species has not been recorded west of the Punjab, or at any significant altitude (see Roberts 1992). Perhaps an error stemming from Bar-tailed Lark *A. cincturus* having previously been treated as conspecific with *phoenicurus*.

HIRUNDINIDAE

Hirundo fluvicola Indian Cliff Swallow (Streak-throated Swallow[1]): included by both Vaurie (1959a) and Voous (1977), based on a record from Kabul in Afghanistan. The Kabul area is situated at under 2000m and so is just outside our limits. Although included by Vaurie as if breeding in the area, this was not subsequently confirmed and the species may well be only a vagrant. Note: the existing English name is unique and appropriate enough (as this colonial species breeds mostly on riverside cliffs, overhangs and bridges), so there is no need to adopt the newly-coined (and forgettable) 'Streak-throated Swallow' (used by Sibley & Monroe 1990). See also the entry for American Cliff Swallow in the 'Notes on English names'.

MOTACILLIDAE

Motacilla maderaspatensis Large Pied Wagtail (or White-browed Wagtail[1]): included by Voous (1977) following Vaurie (1959a). The latter admitted that it is not a truly Palearctic bird, but stated that he wished to include it anyway as it is part of the *M. alba* White Wagtail complex. Not recorded above about 1700m in the Himalayas (Ripley 1982). Note: formerly sometimes (including by Cheng 1987) regarded as conspecific with *M. alba* White Wagtail, but now usually treated as a member of a superspecies.

CAMPEPHAGIDAE

Tephrodornis pondicerianus Common Wood-shrike: included by Voous (1977) following Vaurie (1959a) who mentioned that the species occurs in southeast Baluchistan, but this area is outside our limits. Has not been recorded above 1200m in the Himalayas (Ripley 1982). Note: this species is placed amongst the Vangini in Corvidae by Sibley & Monroe (1990).

Pericrocotus roseus Rosy Minivet: included by Voous (1977) following Vaurie (1959a), but Vaurie thought the Afghan records questionable and this species has not been recorded above about 1800m in the Himalayas (Ripley 1982).

Pericrocotus cantonensis Swinhoe's Minivet (or Brown-rumped Minivet[1]): the range in China extends northwards to southeastern Gansu and southern Shaanxi, but at rather low altitudes (reaching a maximum elevation of only about 1000m in central Sichuan; pers. obs.), so the species probably does not reach our limits. Note: sometimes (including by Cheng 1987) treated as conspecific with *P. roseus* Rosy Minivet, but *cantonensis* is morphologically distinct. There is an apparently stabilized hybrid population between the two, known as *stanfordi*, in one area of SE China, but there is no evidence of hybridization elsewhere where the two forms come into contact or overlap (Meyer de Schauensee 1984, Sibley & Monroe 1990).

PYCNONOTIDAE

Pycnonotus jocosus Red-whiskered Bulbul: often recorded in a feral state in the Arabian Peninsula (see, for example, Hollom *et al.* 1988 and *Phoenix* 9, 1992), but perhaps not yet established.

Pycnonotus xanthorrhous Brown-breasted Bulbul: included by Vaurie (1959a) and Voous (1977), this species is said by Vaurie to reach about 4270m in northern Yunnan, but this is exceedingly unlikely (see entry for *Treron sphenurus* Wedge-tailed Green Pigeon regarding the dubious nature of some altitudinal data from this area). This is a species of low and moderate altitudes, not usually found above 1000m in central and northern Sichuan for example, or above 2000m in northern Yunnan (pers. obs.).

Hypsipetes mcclellandii Mountain Bulbul (or Rufous-bellied Bulbul): included by Voous (1977), but this species is not known to occur above about 2700m even in the eastern Himalayas and is found below 1700m on Emei Shan in central Sichuan (Cheng *et al.* 1963), so does not quite reach our limits. Note: sometimes treated as conspecific with *P. virescens* Sunda Bulbul (or Sumatran Bulbul).

CHLOROPSEIDAE

Chloropsis hardwickii Orange-bellied Leafbird: included by Voous (1977), but this species is not recorded above about 2400m in most of the Himalayas and about 2600m in Nepal (Ripley 1982, Inskipp & Inskipp 1991), so fails to reach our limits in this area. There is no evidence it does so in southwestern China either. Note: Chloropseidae is merged in Irenidae by Sibley & Monroe (1990).

BOMBYCILLIDAE

Bombycilla cedrorum Cedar Waxwing: a record from Scotland in 1985 was not admitted to the British & Irish list (British Ornithologists' Union Records Committee 1993a).

TURDIDAE

Brachypteryx leucophrys Lesser Shortwing: stated to reach 3900m in the eastern Himalayas (Ripley 1982), but this is likely to be erroneous. The species has not been recorded above 2135m in Nepal (Inskipp & Inskipp 1991) and is not found above about 1600m on Emei Shan in central Sichuan (Cheng *et al.* 1963, pers. obs.).

Cinclidium frontale Blue-fronted Robin: although said to occur up to 3000m in the eastern Himalayas (Ali 1962), no recent records from this region or from southern Sichuan have exceeded 2300m (see Redman 1992), so may not reach our limits.

Enicurus schistaceus Slaty-backed Forktail: included by Voous (1977), but this species has not been recorded above 1675m from the Himalayas to Sichuan (Cheng *et al.* 1963, Ripley 1982, Inskipp & Inskipp 1991) so fails to reach our limits.

SYLVIIDAE

Acrocephalus orinus Large-billed Reed Warbler: included by Vaurie (1959a), this taxon is known from a single specimen from the Sutlej valley in the western Himalayas, but this was taken at Rampur which is well below our limits. Vaurie treated this form as specifically distinct, but it was treated as an isolated subspecies of *A. stentoreus* Clamorous Reed Warbler by Sibley & Monroe (1990) in spite of the considerable differences in size and structure (see Vaurie 1955b).

Abroscopus albogularis Rufous-faced Warbler (or White-throated Warbler): included by Voous (1977), but this species has not occurred above 1800m in the Himalayas (Ripley 1982) and, while the range of the species extends northwards in China to southern Gansu and southern Shaanxi, it is typically a bird of low or moderate altitudes (the altitudinal limit on Emei Shan in central Sichuan is no more than 1200m: Cheng *et al.* 1963, pers. obs.) and there is no evidence it reaches our limits. Note: alternatively (as in Cheng 1987) *Seicercus albogularis*.

Abroscopus schisticeps Black-faced Warbler: included by Voous (1977), but this species has not been recorded above about 2700m in the eastern Himalayas and so does not quite reach our limits. Note: alternatively (as in Cheng 1987) *Seicercus schisticeps*.

Phylloscopus ricketti Sulphur-breasted Warbler: included by Voous (1977), the range of this species in China extends northwards to southeastern Gansu and northeastern Sichuan, but at low to moderate altitudes. Only reaches a maximum elevation of about 1500m on Emei Shan in central Sichuan for example (Cheng *et al.* 1963, pers. obs.) and not known to reach our limits anywhere. Note: sometimes (including by Cheng 1987) treated as conspecific with *P. cantator* Yellow-vented Warbler, or occasionally as conspecific with *P. trivirgatus* Mountain Leaf Warbler.

Phylloscopus cantator Yellow-vented Warbler (or Yellow-faced Leaf Warbler, or Black-browed Leaf Warbler): included by Voous (1977), but this species only reaches a maximum elevation of 2000m in the eastern Himalayas (Ripley 1982) which is well below our limits.

Phylloscopus emeiensis Emei Leaf Warbler (or Emei Shan Warbler): a newly described species, rather similar in appearance to *P. reguloides* Blyth's Leaf Warbler but sympatric with it in Sichuan and with a completely different song (Alström, A. & Olsson, U. A new species of *Phylloscopus* warbler from Sichuan Province, China. *Ibis* in press.) Has not yet been recorded above 1900m (P. Alström pers. comm., pers. obs.) so does not quite reach our limits (at least according to present knowledge).

Regulus satrapa Golden-crowned Kinglet: an old record from Britain is not acceptable (Alexander & Fitter 1955). The species has been recorded on an eastbound ship in mid-Atlantic (Durand 1963).

MUSCICAPIDAE

Cyornis rubeculoides Blue-throated Flycatcher: included by both Vaurie (1959a) and Voous (1977), this species is said by Vaurie to reach about 3355m in northern Yunnan, but this is exceedingly unlikely (see entry for *Treron sphenurus* Wedge-tailed Green Pigeon regarding the dubious nature of some altitudinal data from this area). This is a species of low and moderate altitudes, not usually found above 1300m at Emei Shan in central Sichuan (Cheng *et al.* 1963, pers. obs.) and in the Himalayas it reaches a maximum of about 2100m (Ripley 1982, Inskipp & Inskipp 1991). Note: alternatively (as in Cheng 1987) *Niltava rubeculoides*. The form occurring in China (and thus the principal candidate for inclusion in a Palearctic list), *glaucicomans* Chinese Blue Flycatcher, differs in morphology (and also in vocalizations; pers. obs. in Sichuan) and may be worthy of specific status.

Muscicapa muttui Brown-breasted Flycatcher: included by Voous (1977), the range of this species in China extends northwards southeastern Gansu, but at rather low altitudes, only reaching a maximum elevation of about 1000m on Emei Shan in central Sichuan for example (Cheng *et al.* 1963, pers. obs.), so does not reach our limits.

TIMALIIDAE

Spelaeornis chocolatinus Long-tailed Wren-babbler: recorded up to about 1900m on Emei Shan in central Sichuan, just below our limits.

Paradoxornis alphonsianus Ashy-throated Parrotbill: included by both Vaurie (1959a) and Voous (1977) as part of *P. webbianus*, this species occurs in central Sichuan at rather low altitudes, only reaching a maximum elevation of about 1400m on Emei Shan (Cheng *et al.* 1963, pers. obs.), and so does not reach our limits. Note: sometimes spelt *P. alphonsiana*. Sometimes (including by Voous 1977 and Cheng 1987) treated as conspecific with *P. webbianus* Vinous-throated Parrotbill, but now usually treated as specifically distinct due to morphological differences and only limited hybridization where the ranges meet (Traylor 1967).

Garrulax pectoralis Greater Necklaced Laughingthrush (or Black-gorgeted Laughingthrush): included by Voous (1977), the range of this species in China extends northwards to southern Shaanxi and southeastern Gansu, but at rather low altitudes (only reaching a maximum elevation of about 1500m; pers. obs.). Cheng (1987) lists this species for 'Gansu (eastern part)', but while his map suggests the species occurs north of the Yangtze-Huang Ho divide and thus within our limits, this appears to be a misprint as there do not seem to be any observations in Gansu away from the extreme southeast, which is just outside our limits.

Garrulax maesi Grey Laughingthrush: included by Vaurie (1959a) and Voous (1977), this species was said by Vaurie to occur in 'high mountain forests', but in reality it is found at rather modest altitudes. Occurs in central Sichuan, but has not been recorded above about 1200m on Emei Shan (Cheng *et al.* 1963).

Garrulax caerulatus Grey-sided Laughingthrush: included by Voous (1977), perhaps because he treated *poecilorhynchus* Rusty Laughingthrush as conspecific (although this was not stated). Reaches a maximum altitude of 2700m in the eastern Himalayas in general (Ripley 1982) and 2745m in Nepal (Inskipp & Inskipp 1991), so just fails to reach our limits.

Garrulax poecilorhynchus Rusty Laughingthrush (or Scaly-headed Laughingthrush): included by Vaurie (1959a), the range of this species in China extends northwards to Emei Shan in central Sichuan, but only reaches a maximum elevation of about 1900m at the latter (Cheng *et al.* 1963) and so does not quite reach our limits. In northernmost Yunnan, the form *ricinus* is said by Vaurie to reach about 4575m, but this is exceedingly unlikely (see entry for *Treron sphenurus* Wedge-tailed Green Pigeon regarding the dubious nature of some of the altitudinal data for this area). Note: sometimes treated as conspecific with *G. caerulatus* Grey-sided Laughingthrush, but morphologically very different (Vaurie 1965b).

Garrulax sannio White-browed Laughingthrush: included by both Vaurie (1959a) and Voous (1977), the range of this species in China extends northwards to southern Gansu and southern Shaanxi. It is a bird of low or moderate altitudes, being found only below 1300m on Emei Shan in central Sichuan for example (Cheng *et al.* 1963, pers. obs.), so probably does not reach our limits.

Cutia nipalensis Cutia (or Nepal Cutia): included by Voous (1977), this species has been recorded up to 2500m in the eastern Himalayas in general (Ripley 1982) and up to about 2700m in Nepal (Inskipp & Inskipp 1991), just below our limits.

Pteruthius melanotis Black-eared Shrike-babbler (or Chestnut-eared Shrike-babbler): recorded up to 2700m in the eastern Himalayas (Ripley 1982), just below our limits.

Minla cyanouroptera Blue-winged Minla (or Blue-winged Siva): included by Voous (1977), this species has been recorded up to 2500m in the eastern Himalayas in general (Ripley 1982) and exceptionally up to 2750m in Nepal (Inskipp & Inskipp 1991), just below our limits.

Alcippe variegaticeps Gold-fronted Fulvetta: occurs up to 1900m on Emei Shan in central Sichuan (Cheng *et al.* 1963), just below our limits.

Alcippe cinerea Yellow-throated Fulvetta: included by Voous (1977), but this species has not been recorded above about 2100m in the Himalayas (Ripley 1982) which is well below our limits. Likewise there is no evidence it reaches our limits in southwestern China.

Alcippe brunnea Brown-capped Fulvetta (or Dusky Fulvetta[1]): included by Voous (1977), the range of this species extends westwards to Arunachal Pradesh and northwards through China to southern Shaanxi, but at low to moderate altitudes. It reaches a maximum elevation of about 2400m in northeastern India (Ripley 1982) and about 1650m on Emei Shan in central Sichuan (Cheng *et al.* 1963), well below our limits. The existing English name is unique and appropriate, so it is unnecessary to adopt the newly-coined name 'Dusky Fulvetta' (used by Sibley & Monroe 1990). Note: includes *dubia* Rusty-capped Fulvetta (or Olive-sided Fulvetta), sometimes (including by Cheng 1987 and Sibley & Monroe 1990) treated as specifically distinct. The ranges overlap extensively in southern China according to Cheng (1987). Note: the distribution given for *A. dubia* by Sibley & Monroe (1990) is incorrect: it should also include most of the range attributed to *A. brunnea* with the exception of north-central and SE China, Hainan and Taiwan.

Alcippe morrisonia Grey-cheeked Fulvetta: included by Voous (1977), but not found above about 1500m on Emei Shan in central Sichuan (Cheng *et al.* 1963, pers. obs.) and, although it extends higher up the mountains further south, apparently does not reach our limits in northern Yunnan or southern Sichuan either.

Yuhina nigrimenta Black-chinned Yuhina: included by Voous (1977), this species has not been recorded above 1500m in the Himalayas (Ripley 1982, Inskipp & Inskipp 1991). It has, however, been recorded up to about 1900m on Emei Shan in central Sichuan (Cheng *et al.* 1963), just below our limits.

SITTIDAE

Sitta castanea Chestnut-bellied Nuthatch: included by Voous (1977) because he treats *cashmirensis* Kashmir Nuthatch as conspecific. *S. castanea* (*sensu stricto*) has not been recorded above 1830m in the Himalayas (Ripley 1982, Inskipp & Inskipp 1991), which is well below our limits. Note: sometimes treated as conspecific with *S. europaea* Eurasian Nuthatch, but shows marked sexual dimorphism and other morphological differences (Vaurie 1950b, 1959a) and so often treated as an allospecies (e.g. Sibley & Monroe 1990).

REMIZIDAE

Remiz punctifrons Sennar Penduline Tit (or Sudan Penduline Tit): included by Vaurie (1959a) as this species occurs in the Aïr and Ennedi, but these areas are outside our limits.

NECTARINIIDAE

Nectarinia pulchella Beautiful Sunbird: included by Vaurie (1959a) as this species occurs in the Aïr and Ennedi (also the Adrar in northern Mauritania: Lamarche 1988), but these areas are outside our limits.

ORIOLIDAE

Oriolus traillii Maroon Oriole: included by Voous (1977), this species is said to reach 3950m in Yunnan by Meyer de Schauensee (1984), but this is very likely to be erroneous (see entry for *Treron sphenurus* Wedge-tailed Green Pigeon regarding the dubious nature of some of the altitudinal data for this area). In the Himalayas this species has not been recorded above 2440m (Ripley 1982, Inskipp & Inskipp 1991) and so does not reach our limits.

CORVIDAE

Dendrocitta formosae Grey Treepie: included by Voous (1977), this species is not usually recorded above 2100m in the Himalayas, reaching no more than 1060m in Pakistan (Roberts 1992) and only rarely reaching 2600m in Nepal (Inskipp & Inskipp 1991). On Emei Shan in central Sichuan it is not found above about 1300m (Cheng *et al.* 1963, pers. obs.). There is no evidence it reaches our limits anywhere.

Corvus macrorhynchos levaillantii Jungle Crow (or Thick-billed Crow): included by Voous (1977), but although this form reaches 2200m or more in Nepal (T. P. Inskipp *in litt.*) it does not appear to reach our limits anywhere. Note: Sibley & Monroe (1990) treat this form as specifically distinct. There are some differences in morphology and vocalizations (Madge & Burn 1993).

STURNIDAE

Sturnus malabaricus Chestnut-tailed Starling (or Grey-headed Myna): Cheng (1987) lists the species as resident in Tibet at 'Qomolangma Peak foot-region' (= Mt. Everest region). The occurrence of the species, even as a wanderer, in the Everest region would be remarkable enough and, since the map in Cheng makes no reference to the Everest area, but instead shows the species occurring near Namchabarwa peak in southeast Tibet, where deep valleys provide easy access to the lowlands of northeast India, the text reference is presumably in error.

PASSERIDAE

Passer griseus Northern Grey-headed Sparrow (or Grey-headed Sparrow): included by Vaurie (1959a), as this species occurs in the Aïr and Ennedi, but these areas are outside our limits.

PLOCEIDAE

Ploceus cucullatus Village Weaver: six individuals collected in May 1924 on São Tiago, Cape Verde Islands are presumed to have been escapes (Bannerman & Bannerman 1968).

Ploceus philippinus Baya Weaver: increasingly being recorded in a feral state in the Arabian Peninsula (see *Phoenix* 9, 1992), but may not yet be established.

Quelea quelea Red-billed Quelea: a large flock on Tenerife in November 1965 was treated as an accidental record by Fernandez-Cruz *et al.* (1985), but the likelihood of the birds being escapes was not addressed.

ESTRILDIDAE

Uraeginthus bengalus Red-cheeked Cordon-bleu: included by Voous (1977) on the basis of the introduced population in Egypt, but this is now apparently extinct (Goodman & Meininger 1989).

FRINGILLIDAE

Serinus leucopygius White-rumped Seed-eater (or White-rumped Serin, or White-rumped Canary): included by Vaurie (1959a) as this species occurs in the Aïr, but this area is outside our limits.

Carduelis pinus Pine Siskin: one recorded on an eastbound ship in mid-Atlantic remained on board until 30°W (Durand 1963).

EMBERIZIDAE

Pipilo crissalis Californian Towhee: said to have been collected from the Chukotka peninsula in 1791 (see Dementiev & Gladkov 1954a), but this is highly unlikely as there is not even an Alaskan record of the species. It was not admitted to the avifauna of the USSR by Stepanyan (1990). Note: this form was formerly treated as conspecific with Canyon Towhee *P. fuscus*, with the English name 'Brown Towhee' then being used for the enlarged species.

Spizella pusilla Field Sparrow: of some recorded on an eastbound ship in mid-Atlantic, one remained on board until 15°W (Durand 1963).

Zonotrichia georgiana Swamp Sparrow: of some recorded on an eastbound ship in mid-Atlantic, at least one remained on board until 30°W (Durand 1963).

Melophus lathami Crested Bunting: included by Voous (1977), the range of this species extends westwards through the length of the Himalayas and north through China to northeastern Sichuan. A bird of the foothills, it has been recorded up to 1800m in the Himalayas in Pakistan (Roberts 1992) and 2440m in Nepal (Inskipp & Inskipp 1991), but there is no evidence that it reaches our limits.

Passerina ciris Painted Bunting: several records from Britain are not considered admissible to the British & Irish list (British Ornithologists' Union Records Committee 1994).

ICTERIDAE

Sturnella magna Eastern Meadowlark: four old records from Britain are generally considered to be escapes, although genuine vagrancy is a possibility (see Alexander & Fitter 1955).

Agelaius phoeniceus Red-winged Blackbird: some old records from Britain and one from Italy are considered to refer to escapes (Alexander & Fitter 1955).

Icterus wagleri Black-vented Oriole: one in Norway in 1975 is likely to have been an escape (Cramp & Perrins 1994b).

REFERENCES

Aitchison, J. E. T. 1889. The zoology of the Afghan Delimitation Commission. *Trans. Linn. Soc. Lond.* 5: 53-142.

Albrecht, J. S. M. 1984. Some notes on the identification, song and habitat of the Green Warbler in the Western Black Sea Coastlands of Turkey. *Sandgrouse* 6: 69-75.

Alexander, W. B. & Fitter, R. S. R. 1955. American land birds in Western Europe. *Brit. Birds* 48: 1-14.

Ali, S. 1962. *The Birds of Sikkim.* Oxford University Press, Bombay.

Ali, S. & Ripley, S. D. 1971. *Handbook of the Birds of India and Pakistan together with those of Nepal, Sikkim, Bhutan and Ceylon.* Volume 6. Oxford University Press, Bombay.

Ali, S. & Ripley, S. D. 1972. *Handbook of the Birds of India and Pakistan together with those of Nepal, Sikkim, Bhutan and Ceylon.* Volume 7. Oxford University Press, Bombay.

Ali, S. & Ripley, S. D. 1973a. *Handbook of the Birds of India and Pakistan together with those of Bangladesh, Nepal, Sikkim, Bhutan and Sri Lanka.* Volume 8. Oxford University Press, Bombay.

Ali, S. & Ripley, S. D. 1973b. *Handbook of the Birds of India and Pakistan together with those of Bangladesh, Nepal, Sikkim, Bhutan and Sri Lanka.* Volume 9. Oxford University Press, Bombay.

Ali, S. & Ripley, S. D. 1974. *Handbook of the Birds of India and Pakistan together with those of Bangladesh, Nepal, Sikkim, Bhutan and Sri Lanka.* Volume 10. Oxford University Press, Bombay.

Ali, S. & Ripley, S. D. 1978. *Handbook of the Birds of India and Pakistan together with those of Bangladesh, Nepal, Bhutan and Sri Lanka.* Volume 1, 2nd edition. Oxford University Press, Bombay.

Ali, S. & Ripley, S. D. 1980. *Handbook of the Birds of India and Pakistan together with those of Bangladesh, Nepal, Bhutan and Sri Lanka.* Volume 2, 2nd edition. Oxford University Press, Bombay.

Ali, S. & Ripley, S. D. 1981. *Handbook of the Birds of India and Pakistan together with those of Bangladesh, Nepal, Bhutan and Sri Lanka.* Volume 3, 2nd edition. Oxford University Press, Bombay.

Ali, S. & Ripley, S. D. 1983. *Handbook of the Birds of India and Pakistan together with those of Bangladesh, Nepal, Bhutan and Sri Lanka.* Volume 4, 2nd edition. Oxford University Press, Bombay.

Ali, S. & Ripley, S. D. 1987. *Handbook of the Birds of India and Pakistan together with those of Bangladesh, Nepal, Bhutan and Sri Lanka.* Volume 5, 2nd edition. Oxford University Press, Bombay.

Alström, P. & Mild, K. 1987. Some notes on the taxonomy of the Water Pipit complex. *Proc. 4th Int. Identification Meeting (Eilat)*: 47-48.

Alström, P. & Olsson, U. 1988. Taxonomy of Yellow-browed Warblers. *Brit. Birds* 81: 656-657.

Alström, P. & Olsson, U. 1990. Taxonomy of the *Phylloscopus proregulus* complex. *Bull. Brit. Orn. Club* 110: 38-43.

Alström, P. & Olsson, U. 1992. On the taxonomic status of *Phylloscopus affinis* and *Phylloscopus subaffinis*. *Bull. Brit. Orn. Club* 112: 111-125.

Alström, P., Olsson, U. & Colston, P. R. 1992. A new species of *Phylloscopus* warbler from central China. *Ibis* 134: 329-344.

Alström, P., Olsson, U. & Round, P. D. 1991. The taxonomic status of *Acrocephalus agricola tangorum*. *Forktail* 6: 3-13.

Alström, P., Olsson, U. & Round, P. D. 1994. Bestimmung der kleinen fernöstlichen Rohrsänger *Acrocephalus*. *Limicola* 8: 121-131.

Alström, A., Ripley, S. D. & Rasmussen, P. C. 1993. Re-evaluation of the taxonomic status of *Phylloscopus subaffinis arcanus*. *Bull. Brit. Orn. Club* 113: 207-209.

Amadon, D. 1974. Taxonomic notes on the serpent-eagles of the genus *Spilornis*. *Bull. Brit. Orn. Club* 94: 159-163.

Amadon, D. 1978. Remarks on the taxonomy of some Australasian raptors. *Emu* 78: 115-118.

Amadon, D. & Bull, J. 1988. Hawks and owls of the world. *Proc. World Found. Vertebr. Zool.* 3: 297-357.

Amadon, D. & Jewett, S. G. 1946. Notes on Philippine birds. *Auk* 63: 551-558.

American Ornithologists' Union. 1983. *Check-list of North American birds*. 6th edition. American Ornithologists' Union, New York.

Anon. 1993. Western Palearctic news. *Birding World* 6: 99-100.

Ash, J. S., Pearson, D. J., Nikolaus, G. & Colston, P. R. 1989. The mangrove reed warblers of the Red Sea and Gulf of Aden coasts, with description of a new subspecies of the African Reed Warbler *Acrocephalus baeticatus*. *Bull. Brit. Orn. Club* 109: 36-43.

Auezov, E. M. 1971. Taxonomic evaluation and systematic status of *Larus relictus*. (In Russian.) Zool. J. Acad. Sci. Moscow 50: 235-242.

Bannerman, D. A. & Bannerman, W. M. 1968. *History of the Birds of the Cape Verde Islands*. Birds of the Atlantic Islands, volume 4. Oliver & Boyd, Edinburgh.

Barth, E. K. 1975. Taxonomy of *Larus argentatus* and *Larus fuscus* in north-western Europe. *Ornis. Scand.* 6: 40-63.

Beaman, M. (ed.) 1978. *Bird Report no. 4*. Ornithological Society of Turkey, Sandy.

Beaman, M., Porter, R. F. & Vittery, A. (eds.) 1975. *Bird Report no. 3*. Ornithological Society of Turkey, Sandy.

Bear, A. 1991. Ethiopian Swallow *Hirundo aethiopica*: a new species for Israel and the Palearctic region. In Hebrew. *Torgos* 9: 41-42.

Belon, F. 1555. *L'Histoire de la Nature des Oyseaux*. France.

Biswas, B. 1950. On the shrike *Lanius tephronotus* (Vigors), with remarks on the *erythronotus* and *tricolor* groups of *Lanius schach* Linné, and their hybrids. *J. Bombay Nat. Hist. Soc.* 49: 444-455.

Bourne, W. R. P. 1983. The Soft-plumaged Petrel, the Gon-gon and the Freira, *Pterodroma mollis*, *P. feae* and *P. madeira*. *Bull. Brit. Orn. Club* 103: 52-58.

Bourne, W. R. P. 1989. The relationship between the Armenian and Heuglin's Gulls. *Abstracts 2nd Mediterranean Seabird Symp.* Mallorca, Spain, March 1989.

Bourne, W. R. P., Mackrill, E. J., Peterson, A. M. & Yésou, P. 1988. The Yelkouan Shearwater, *Puffinus (puffinus?) yelkouan*. *Brit. Birds* 81: 306-319.

Brazil, M. A. 1991. *The Birds of Japan*. Christopher Helm, London.

Brazil, M. A. & Ikenaga, H. 1987. The Amami Woodcock *Scolopax mira*: its identity and identification. *Forktail* 3: 3-16.

Bretagnolle, V., Carruthers, M., Cubitt, M., Bioret, F. & Cuillandre, J.-P. 1991. Six captures of a dark-rumped, fork-tailed storm-petrel in the northeastern Atlantic. *Ibis* 133: 351-356.

British Ornithologists' Union Records Committee. 1971. Fifth report. *Ibis* 113: 142-145.

British Ornithologists' Union Records Committee. 1978. Ninth report. *Ibis* 120: 409-411.

British Ornithologists' Union Records Committee. 1988. Suggested changes to the English names of some Western Palearctic birds. *Ibis* 130 (Supplement); *Brit. Birds* 81: 355-377.

British Ornithologists' Union Records Committee. 1993a. Eighteenth report. *Ibis* 135: 220-222.

British Ornithologists' Union Records Committee. 1993b. Nineteenth report. *Ibis* 135: 493-499.

British Ornithologists' Union Records Committee. 1994. Twentieth report. *Ibis* 136: 253-255.

Brooke, R. K. 1971a. Taxonomic notes on some lesser known *Apus* swifts. *Bull. Brit. Orn. Club* 91: 33-36.

Brooke, R. K. 1971b. Geographical variation in the Little Swift *Apus affinis* (Aves: Apodidae). *Durban Mus. Novit.* 9: 93-103.

Brown, L. H., Urban, E. K. & Newman, K. 1982. *The Birds of Africa*. Volume I. Academic Press, London.

Chalmers, M. L. 1986. *Annotated Checklist of the Birds of Hong Kong*. 4th edition. Hong Kong Bird Watching Society, Hong Kong.

Cheng Tso-hsin (= Zheng Zuo-xin). 1987. *A Synopsis of the Avifauna of China*. Science Press, Beijing.

Cheng Tso-hsin (= Zheng Zuo-xin), Tan Yao-kuang, Liang Chun-yu & Chang Chun-fan. 1963. Studies of birds of Mount Omei and their vertical distribution. (In Chinese.) *Acta Zoologica Sinica* 15(2): 317-335.

Christensen, S. J. 1974. Notes on the plumage of the female Cyprus Pied Wheatear. *Orn. Scand.* 5: 47-52.

Clark, W. S. 1992. The taxonomy of Steppe and Tawny Eagles, with criteria for separation of museum specimens and live eagles. *Bull. Brit. Orn. Club* 112: 150-157.

Clifton, J. 1992. Least Tern at Colne Pt. EWT Reserve—29th June to 1st July 1991. *Essex Bird Rep.* (1991): 120-121.

Condon, T. H. 1975. *Checklist of the Birds of Australia*. Part 1. Non-passerines. Royal Australian Ornithologists' Union, Melbourne.

Connors, P. G. 1983. Taxonomy, distribution and evolution of Golden Plovers (*Pluvialis dominica* and *Pluvialis fulva*). *Auk* 100: 607-620.

Connors, P. G., McCaffery, B. J. & Maron, J. L. 1993. Speciation in golden plovers, *Pluvialis dominica* and *Pluvialis fulva*: evidence from the breeding grounds. *Auk* 110: 9-20.

Coward, T. A. 1920. *The Birds of the British Isles and their Eggs*. 2 volumes. Warne, London.

Cox, J. B. 1987. Some notes on the perplexing Cox's Sandpiper. *S. Austral. Orn.* 30: 85-97.

Cox, J. B. 1989. Notes on the affinities of Cooper's and Cox's Sandpipers. *S. Austral. Orn.* 30: 169-181.

Cox, J. B. 1990. The enigmatic Cooper's and Cox's Sandpipers. *Dutch Birding* 12: 53-64.

Cramp, S. & Simmons, K. E. L. (eds.) 1977. *The Birds of the Western Palearctic*. Volume I. Oxford University Press, Oxford.

Cramp, S. & Simmons, K. E. L. (eds.) 1980. *The Birds of the Western Palearctic*. Volume II. Oxford University Press, Oxford.

Cramp, S. & Simmons, K. E. L. (eds.) 1983. *The Birds of the Western Palearctic*. Volume III. Oxford University Press, Oxford.

Cramp, S. (ed.) 1985. *The Birds of the Western Palearctic*. Volume IV. Oxford University Press, Oxford.

Cramp, S. (ed.) 1988. *The Birds of the Western Palearctic*. Volume V. Oxford University Press, Oxford.

Cramp, S. (ed.) 1992. *The Birds of the Western Palearctic*. Volume VI. Oxford University Press, Oxford.

Cramp, S. & Perrins, C. M. (eds.) 1993. *The Birds of the Western Palearctic*. Volume VII. Oxford University Press, Oxford.

Cramp, S. & Perrins, C. M. (eds.) 1994a. *The Birds of the Western Palearctic*. Volume VIII. Oxford University Press, Oxford.

Cramp, S. & Perrins, C. M. (eds.) 1994b. *The Birds of the Western Palearctic*. Volume IX. Oxford University Press, Oxford.

Dathe, H. & Neufeldt, I. A. 1987. *Atlas der Verbreitung palaearktischer Vögel*, 14. Berlin.

Dawson, R. 1992. Blood, sweat and petrels. *Birding World* 5: 443-444.

Deignan, H. G. 1957. The races of the longtail, *Prinia polychroa* (Temminck), with the description of a new race from southern Vietnam. *Bull. Brit. Orn. Club* 77: 24-25.

Delacour, J. & Zimmer, J. T. 1952. The identity of *Anser nigricans* Lawrence 1846. *Auk* 69: 82-84.

Dementiev, G. P. & Gladkov, N. A. (eds.) 1954a. *Birds of the Soviet Union*. Volume 5. (In Russian.) Moscow.

Dementiev, G. P. & Gladkov, N. A. (eds.) 1954b. *Birds of the Soviet Union*. Volume 6. (In Russian.) Moscow.

Devillers, P. 1978. Distribution and relationships of South American skuas. *Gerfaut* 68: 374-417.

Devillers, P. & Potvliege, R. 1981. Le Goéland leucophée *Larus cachinnans michahellis* en Belgique. *Gerfaut* 71: 659-666.

Diamond, A. W. (ed.) 1987. *Studies of Mascarene Island Birds*. Cambridge University Press, Cambridge.

Dittmann, D. L., Zink, R. M. & Gerwin, J. A. 1989. Evolutionary genetics of phalaropes. *Auk* 106: 324-326.

Dolgushin, I. A., Korelov, M. N., Kuz'mina, M. A. Gavrilov, E. I., Kov'shar, A. F. & Borodikhin, I. F. 1972. *Birds of Kazakhstan*. Volume 4. (In Russian.) Alma-Ata.

Dowsett, R. J. & Dowsett-Lemaire, F. 1980. The systematic status of some Zambian birds. *Gerfaut* 70: 151-199.

Dowsett, R. J. & Dowsett-Lemaire, F. (eds.) 1993. *A Contribution to the Distribution and Taxonomy of Afrotropical and Malagasy Birds*. Tauraco Research Report No. 5, Tauraco Press, Liège.

Dowsett, R. J. & Forbes-Watson, A. D. 1993. *Checklist of Birds of the Afrotropical and Malagasy Regions*. Volume 1: Species limits and distribution. Tauraco Press, Liège.

Dresser, H. E. 1902. *A Manual of Palearctic Birds*. Part I. London.

Dubois, P. J. 1985. Considérations sur le Goéland d'Arménie *Larus armenicus* Buturlin en Israël. *Alauda* 53: 226-228.

Dubois, P. J. & Yésou, P. 1986. *Inventaire des espèces d'oiseaux occasionnelles en France*. Paris

Duff, A. G. 1979. Sauchets du Cap *Anas smithii* au Maroc. *Alauda* 47: 216-217.

Durand, A. L. 1963. A remarkable fall of American land-birds on the 'Mauretania', New York to Southampton, October 1962. *Brit. Birds* 56: 157-164.

Dyrnev, Y. A., Siroklin, I. N. & Sonin, V. D. 1983. Materials to the ecology of *Delichon dasypus* (Passeriformes, Hirundinidae) on Khamar-Daban (south Baikal territory). (In Russian.) *Zool. Zh.* 62: 1541-1546.

Eck, S. 1980. Intraspezisische Evolution bei Graumeisen. *Zool. Abh. Staatl. Mus. Tierkde. Dresden* 36: 135-219.

Eck, S. 1987. Zur Vikarianz der chinesischen Häherlinge *Garrulax ocellatus* und *Garrulax maximus* (Aves, Timaliidae). *Beitr. Natkde. Nieders.* 40: 153-170.

Eck, S. 1988. Gesichtspunkte zur Art-Systematik der Meisen (Paridae) (Aves). *Zool. Abh. Staatl. Mus. Tierkde. Dresden* 43: 101-134.

Elzen, R. van den. & Wolters, H. E. 1978. Ornithologische Ergebnisse einer Sammelreise nach Senegal. *Bonn. zool. Beitr.* 29: 323-359.

Erard, C., Guillou, J. J. & Mayaud, N. 1986. Le héron blanc du Banc d'Arguin *Ardea monicae*, ses affinités morphologiques, son histoire. *Alauda* 54: 161-169.

Fernandez-Cruz, M., Araujo, J., Teixeira, A. M., Mayol, J., Muntaner, J., Emmerson, K. W., Martin A. & Le Grand, G. 1985. *Situacion de la avifauna de la Península Ibérica, Baleares y Macaronesia*. Madrid.

Filchagov, A. V. 1993. The Armenian Gull in Armenia. *Brit. Birds* 86: 550-560.

Filchagov, A. V. & Shemashko, V. Y. 1987. Distribution and ecology of the west-Siberian Herring Gull (*Larus argentatus heuglini* Bree, 1876) in the Kola Peninsula. (In Russian.) *Byull. Mosk. Ova. Ispyt. Otd. Biol.*, 92 (3): 37-42.

Filchagov, A. V., Yésou, P. & Grabovsky, V. I. 1992. Le Goéland du Taïmyr *Larus heuglini taimyrensis*: répartition et biologie estivales. *L'Oiseau et R. F. O.* 62: 128-148.

Flint, V. E., Boehme, R. L., Kostin, Y. V. & Kuznetsov, A. A. 1984. *A Field Guide to Birds of the USSR*. Princeton University Press, Princeton.

Ford, J. 1983. Speciation in the ground-thrush complex *Zoothera dauma* in Australia. *Emu* 83: 141-151.

Fry, C. H. 1984. *The Bee-eaters*. Poyser, Calton.

Fry, C. H. & Fry, K. 1992. *Kingfishers, Bee-eaters & Rollers: a Handbook*. Christopher Helm, London.

Fry, C. H., Keith, S. & Urban, E. K. 1988. *The Birds of Africa*. Volume III. Academic Press, London.

Gallagher, M. & Woodcock, M. W. 1980. *The Birds of Oman*. Quartet Books, London.

Gaston, A. J., Garson, P. J. & Pandey, S. 1993. Birds recorded in the Great Himalayan National Park, Himachal Pradesh, India. *Forktail* 9: 45-57.

Gavrilov, E. I. 1965. On the hybridisation of the Indian and House Sparrows. *Bull. Brit. Orn. Club* 85: 112-114.

Gebauer, A. & Kaiser, M. 1994. Biologie und Verhalten zentralasiatischer Schneefinken (*Montifringilla*) und Erdsperlinge (*Pyrgilauda*). *J. Orn.* 135: 55-71.

Gill, F. B., Funk, D. H. & Silverin, B. 1989. Protein relationships among titmice (*Parus*). *Wilson Bull.* 101: 182-197.

Glutz von Blotzheim, U. N. (ed.) 1991. *Handbuch der Vögel Mitteleuropas*. Band 12/II. AULA-Verlag, Weisbaden.

Glutz von Blotzheim, U. N. & Bauer, K. M. (eds.) 1982. *Handbuch der Vögel Mitteleuropas*. Band 8/I. Akademische Verlagsgesellschaft, Weisbaden.

Gonzalez, L. M., Hiraldo, F., Delibes, M. & Calderon, J. 1989. Zoogeographic support for the Spanish Imperial Eagle as a distinct species. *Bull. Brit. Orn. Club* 109: 86-93.

Gooders, J. (ed.) 1970. *Birds of the World*. Volume 6 (part 7). IPC Magazines, London.

Goodman, S. M. & Meininger, P.L. 1989. *The Birds of Egypt*. Oxford University Press, Oxford.

Goodwin, D. 1957. Remarks on some genera of Turdinae. *Bull. Brit. Orn. Club* 77: 110-113.

Goodwin, D. 1970. *Pigeons and Doves of the World*. British Museum (Natural History), London.

Goodwin, D. 1982. On the status of the Green Pheasant. *Bull. Brit. Orn. Club* 102: 35-37.

Goodwin, D. & Vaurie, C. 1956. Are *Luscinia pectardens* (David & Oustalet) and *Luscinia obscura* (Berezowsky & Bianchi) colour phases of a single species? *Bull. Brit. Orn. Club* 76: 141-143.

Gore, M. E. J. & Won Pyong-Oh. 1971. *The Birds of Korea*. Royal Asiatic Society, Seoul.

Goroshko, O. A. 1993. Taxonomic status of the Pale (Sand?) Martin *Riparia (riparia) diluta*.(Sharpe et Wyatt 1893). *Russ. J. Orn.* 2: 303-323.

Granadeiro, J. P. 1993. Variations in measurements of Cory's Shearwaters between populations and sexing by discriminant analysis. *Ringing & Migration* 14: 103-112.

Haffer, J. 1977. Secondary contact zones of birds in northern Iran. *Bonn. zool. Monogr.* 10.

Haffer, J. 1989. Parapatrische Vogelarten der paläarktischen Region. *J. Orn.* 130: 475-512.

Hall, B. P. & Moreau, R. E. 1970. *An Atlas of Speciation in African Passerine Birds*. British Museum (Natural History), London.

Hancock, J. & Kushlan, J. 1984. *The Herons Handbook*. Croom Helm, London.

Harrison, C. J. O. 1964. The taxonomic status of the African Silverbill *Lonchura cantans* and the Indian Silverbill *L. malabarica*. *Ibis* 106: 462-468.

Hazevoet, C. J. in press. *The Birds of the Cape Verde Islands*. British Ornithologists' Union, London.

Helb, H.-W., Bergmann, H.-H. & Martens, J. 1982. Acoustic differences between populations of western and eastern Bonelli's Warblers (*Phylloscopus bonelli*, Sylviidae). *Experientia* 38: 356-357.

Hepp, G. R., Novak, J. M., Scribner, K. T. & Stangel, P. W. 1988. Genetic distance and hybridization of Black Ducks and Mallards: a morph or a different color? *Auk* 105: 804-807.

Herremans, M. 1990. Taxonomy and evolution in redpolls *Carduelis flammea-hornemanni*; a multivariate study of their biometry. *Ardea* 78: 441-458.

Hiraldo, F., Delibes, M. & Calderon, J. 1976. Sobre el status taxonomico del aguila imperial iberica. *Doñana Acta Vertebr.* 3: 171-180.

Hirschfeld, E. 1992. More gulls with bill bands. *Birding World* 5: 116.

Hirschfeld, E. & King, R. 1992. The status of some escaped species of birds in Bahrain. *Phoenix* 9: 11-13.

Hockey, P. A. R. 1982. The taxonomic status of the Canary Islands Oystercatcher *Haematopus (niger) meadewaldoi*. *Bull. Brit. Orn. Club* 102: 77-83.

Höhn, E. O. 1969. *Die Schneehuhner*. Wittenberg Lutherstadt.

Hollom, P. A. D., Porter, R. F., Christensen, S. & Willis, I. 1988. *Birds of the Middle East and North Africa*. Poyser, Calton.

Holyoak, D. T. & Thibault, J.-C. 1976. La variation géographique de *Gygis alba*. *Alauda* 44: 457-473.

Hoyo, J. del. 1992. *Handbook of the Birds of the World*. Volume 1. Lynx Edicions, Barcelona.

Hüe, F. & Etchécopar, R. D. 1970. *Les oiseaux du Proche et du Moyen Orient de la Méditerranée aux contreforts de l'Himalaya*. Boubée, Paris.

Husain, K. Z. 1959. Taxonomic status of the Burmese Slaty-headed Parakeet. *Ibis* 101: 249-250.

Imber, M. J. 1985. Origins, phylogeny and taxonomy of the gadfly petrels *Pterodroma* spp. *Ibis* 127: 197-229.

Inskipp, C. & Inskipp, T. 1991. *A Guide to the Birds of Nepal*. 2nd edition. Christopher Helm, London.

Inskipp, T. P. & Round, P. D. 1989. A review of the Black-tailed Crake *Porzana bicolor*. *Forktail* 5: 3-15.

Inskipp, T. P. & Sharrock, J. T. R. 1992. English names of West Palearctic birds. *Brit. Birds* 85: 263-290.

Isenmann, P. & Bouchet, M.-P. 1993. L'aire de distribution française et le statut taxonomique de la Pie-grièche méridionale *Lanius elegans meridionalis*. *Alauda* 61: 223-227.

Ishihara, T. 1986. The Amami Ground Thrush distinct from the White's Ground Thrush. *Strix* 5: 60-61.

Jamdar, N. & Price, T. 1990. Simla Black Tit *Parus rufonuchalis* and Rufousbellied Crested Tit *Parus rubidiventris* breeding sympatrically in Kashmir. *J. Bombay Nat. Hist. Soc.* 87: 302-303.

Jepson, P. R. & Zonfrillo, B. 1988. Bird notes from Madeira, Summer 1986. *Bocagiana* 117: 1-10.
Jobling, J. A. 1991. *A Dictionary of Scientific Bird Names*. Oxford University Press, Oxford.
Johansen, H. 1944. Die Vogelfauna Westsibiriens. I. Teil. *J. Orn.* 92: 145-204.
Johansen, H. 1961. Die Superspecies *Larus canus*. *Vogelwarte* 21: 152-156.
Johnsgard, P. 1988. *The Quails, Partridges and Francolins of the World.* University of Nebraska Press, Lincoln.
Keith, S., Urban, E. K. & Fry, C. H. 1992. *The Birds of Africa*. Volume IV. Academic Press, London.
Kennerley, P. R. & Leader, P. J. 1992. The identification, status and distribution of small *Acrocephalus* warblers in Eastern China. *Hong Kong Bird Rep. 1991*: 143-187.
Kennerley, P. R. & Leader, P. J. 1993. Identification of Middendorff's and Styan's Grasshopper Warblers. *Dutch Birding* 15: 241-248.
Kessel, B. & Gibson, D. D. 1978. *Status and Distribution of Alaska Birds*. Studies in Avian Biology, No. 1. Cooper Ornithological Society, Los Angeles.
King, B. 1989. The avian genera *Tesia* and *Urosphena*. *Bull. Brit. Orn. Club* 109: 162-166.
Kirwan, G. 1993. Malachite Kingfisher presumed breeding in Yemen. *Phoenix* 10: 2.
Kistchinski, A. A. 1980. *Birds of the Koryak Highlands*. (In Russian.) Moscow.
Kistchinski, A. A. & Flint, V. E. 1983. Taxonomic relations within the group of the black-throated divers. (In Russian.) *Ornithologiya* 18: 112-123.
Kistchinski, A. A. & Lobkov, E. G. 1979. Spatial relationships between some bird subspecies in the Beringian forest-tundra. *Moskov. Obs. I Spyt. Prirody, Otd. Biol. Biull., nov. ser.*, 5: 11-23.
Knox, A. G. 1987. Taxonomic status of 'Lesser Golden Plovers'. *Brit. Birds* 80: 482-487.
Knox, A. G. 1988a. Taxonomy of the Rock/Water Pipit superspecies *Anthus petrosus, spinoletta* and *rubescens*. *Brit. Birds* 81: 206-211.
Knox, A. G. 1988b. The taxonomy of redpolls. *Ardea* 76: 1-26.
Knox, A. G. 1990. The sympatric breeding of Common and Scottish Crossbills *Loxia curvirostra* and *L. scotica* and the evolution of crossbills. *Ibis* 132: 454-466.
Knox, A. G. 1993. Richard Meinertzhagen – a case of fraud examined. *Ibis* 135: 320-325.
Lamarche, B. 1988. *Liste commentée des oiseaux de Mauritanie*. Association des Naturalistes Sahariens et Ouest-Africains, Nouakchott.
La Touche, J. D. D. 1930. *Birds of Eastern China*. Volume 1. Taylor & Francis, London.
Livezey, B. C. 1991. A phylogenetic analysis and classification of recent dabbling ducks (Tribe Anatini) based on comparative morphology. *Auk* 108: 471-507.
Lockwood, W. B. 1984. *The Oxford Book of British Bird Names*. Oxford University Press, Oxford.
Lörhl, H. & Thaler, E. 1980. Das Teneriffa-Goldhähnchen. Zur Biologie, Ethologie und Systematik. *Bonn. zool. Beitr.* 31: 78-96.
Loskot, V. M. 1982. *Parus hyrcanus* Sar. et Loud.: a distinct species. (In Russian.) In Gavrilov, V. M. & Potapov, R. L. *Ornithological studies in the USSR*. Zool. Inst., USSR Academy of Sciences, Moscow.
Loskot, V. M. 1991. *Phylloscopus collybita caucasica*: new subspecies of Chiffchaff (Aves, Sylviinae). *Vestnik Zoologie* 3: 91.
Louette, M. & Herremans, M. 1985. Taxonomy and evolution in the bulbuls (Hypsipetes) on the Comoro Islands. *Proc. Int. Symp. Afr. Vert., Zool. Forsch., Mus. A. Koenig, Bonn*: 407-423.
Ludlow, F. 1951. The birds of Kongbo and Pome, south-east Tibet. *Ibis* 93: 547-578.
Madge, S. C. 1985. Vocalisations and *Phylloscopus* taxonomy. *Brit. Birds* 78: 199-200.
Madge, S. C. & Burn, H. 1993. *Crows and Jays: a guide to the Crows, Jays and Magpies of the World*. Christopher Helm, London.
Mahe, E. 1985. *Contribution à l'étude scientifique de la région du Banc d'Arguin. 21°20N/19°20N. Peuplements avifaunistiques*. 2 volumes. Thèse. Acad. Montpellier.
Marchant, S. & Higgins, P. J. (eds.) 1990. *Handbook of Australian, New Zealand & Antarctic Birds*. Volume 1, part B. Oxford University Press, Melbourne.
Marien, D. 1951. Notes on the bird family Prunellidae in southern Eurasia. *Amer. Mus. Novit.* 1482.

Marion, L., Yésou, P., Dubois, P. J. & Nicolau-Guillaumet, P. 1985. Coexistence progressive de la reproduction de *Larus argentatus* et de *Larus cachinnans* sur les côtes atlantique françaises. *Alauda* 53: 81-87.

Marshall, J. T. 1978. Systematics of smaller Asian night birds based on voice. *Orn. Monogr.* 25.

Martens, J. 1975. Akustische Differenzierung Verwandtschaftlicher Beziehungen in der *Parus* Gruppe nach Untersuchungen im Nepal-Himalaya. *J. Orn.* 116: 369-433.

Martens, J. 1980. Latäußerungen, verwandschaftliche Beziehungen und Verbreitungsgeschichte asiatischer Laubsänger *Phylloscopus*). *Z. Tierpsychol.* Suppl. 22.

Martens, J. 1981. Latäußerungen der baumlaufer des Himalaya und zur akustischen evolution in der gattung *Certhia*. *Behaviour* 77: 287-318.

Martens, J. 1982. Ringförmige Arealüberschneidung und Artbildung beim Zilpzalp, *Phylloscopus collybita*. Das *lorenzii*-Problem. *Z. zool. Syst. Evolutionsforsch.* 20: 81-100.

Martens, J. 1988. *Phylloscopus borealoides* Portenko - ein verkannter Laubsänger der Ost-Paläarktis. *J. Orn.* 129: 343-351.

Martens, J. & Eck, C. 1991. *Pnoepyga immaculata* n. sp., eine neue bodenbewohnende Timalie aus dem Nepal-Himalaya. *J. Orn.* 132: 179-198.

Martens, J. & Meincke, C. 1989. Der sibirische Zilpzalp (*Phylloscopus collybita tristis*): Gesang und Reaktion einer mitteleuropäischen Population im Freilandversuch. *J. Orn.* 130: 455-473.

Massey, B. W. 1976. Vocal differences between American Least Terns and the European Little Tern. *Auk* 93: 760-773.

Mauersberger, G. 1971. Ist *Emberiza leucocephalos* eine Subspecies von *E. citrinella*? *J. Orn.* 112: 232-233.

Mauersberger, G. 1972. Über den taxonomischen Rang von *Emberiza godlewskii* Taczanowski. *J. Orn.* 113: 53-59.

Mayr, E. 1938. Birds collected during the Whitney South Sea Expedition, XL. Notes on New Guinea birds, V. *Amer. Mus. Novit.* 1007.

Mayr, E. & Bock, W. J. 1994. Provisional classifications *v* standard avian sequences: heuristics and communication in ornithology. *Ibis* 136: 12-18.

Mayr, E., & Cottrell, G. W. (eds.) 1986. *Check-list of Birds of the World.* Volume XI. Museum of Comparative Zoology, Cambridge, Massachusetts.

Mayr, E., & Paynter, R. A. (eds.) 1964. *Check-list of Birds of the World.* Volume X. Museum of Comparative Zoology, Cambridge, Massachusetts.

Mayr, E. & Short, L. L. 1970. Species taxa of North American birds. *Publ. Nuttall Orn. Club.* 9: 1-127.

Mayr, E. & Vuilleumier, F. 1983. New species of birds described from 1966 to 1975. *J. Orn* 124: 217-232.

McAllen, I. A. W. & Bruce M. D. 1988. *The Birds of New South Wales.* Biocon Research Group, Turramurra.

Mead, C. J. 1975. Variation in some characters of three palaearctic *Certhia* species. *Bull. Brit. Orn. Club* 95: 30-40.

Mearns, B. & Mearns, R. 1988. *Biographies for Birdwatchers: The Lives of Those Commemorated in Western Palearctic Bird Names.* Academic Press, London.

Mees, G. F. 1981. The sparrowhawks (*Accipiter*) of the Andaman Islands. *J. Bombay Nat. Hist. Soc.* 77: 371-412.

Meyer de Schauensee, R. 1984. *The Birds of China.* Smithsonian Institution Press, Washington.

Mild, K. 1993. Die bestimmung der europäischen schwarzweissen fliegenschnäpper *Ficedula*. *Limicola* 7: 221-276.

Molau, U. 1985. Gråsiskkomplexet i Sverige. *Vår Fågelvärld* 44: 5-20.

Montagu, G. 1802, *Ornithological Dictionary.* London.

Morioka, H. & Shigeta, Y. 1993. Generic Allocation of the Japanese Marsh Warbler *Megalurus pryeri* (Aves: Sylvidae). *Bull. Natn. Sci. Mus., Tokyo, Ser.* A, 19(1): 37-43.

Morlan, J. 1981. Status and identification of forms of White Wagtail in western North America. *Continental Birdlife* 2: 37-50.

Naik, R. M. & Parasharya, B. M. 1983. Sequence of plumage changes and polymorphism in the Indian Reef Heron *Egretta gularis*. *Sandgrouse* 5: 75-81.

Naurois, R. de. 1972. The Kites of the Cape Verde Islands (*Milvus milvus fasciicauda* and *Milvus migrans migrans*) and a hypothesis about speciation and geographical distribution in the genus *Milvus*. *Proc. XV Int. Orn. Congr.*: 671-673.

Naurois, R. de. 1988. *Ardea (purpurea) bournei* endémique de l'Isle de Santiago (Archipel du Cap Vert). *Alauda* 56: 261-268.

Nazarenko, A. A. 1978. On species validity of *Anthus rubescens* Tunstall (Aves: Motacillidae). (In Russian.) *Zool. Zh.* 57: 1743-1744.

Nazarov, Y. N. & Shibaev, Y. V. 1983. On the biology and taxonomic status of the Pleske's Grasshopper Warbler, *Locustella pleskei* Tacz., new for the U.S.S.R. (In Russian.) *Trudy Zool. Inst. Leningr.* 116: 72-78.

Nechaev, V. A. 1975. [On the biology of the Daurian Jackdaw *Corvus dauuricus*.] (In Russian.) *Trudy Biol.-pochvenn. Inst. Akad. Nauk SSSR* 29 (132): 114-160.

Neufeldt, I. A. & Netschajew, W. A. 1977. Vergleichende untersuchungen an kontinentalen und insulären Reisenschwirler, *Locustella fasciolata* (Gray). *Mitt. zool. Mus. Berlin* 53 (Suppl.) Ann. Orn. 1: 91-116.

Niethammer, G. & Niethammer, J. 1967. Neunachweise für Afghanistans Vogelwelt. *J. Orn.* 108: 76-80.

Nikolaus, G. 1987. Distribution atlas of Sudan's birds with notes on habitat and status. *Bonn. zool. Monogr.* 25: 1-322.

Olsson, U. 1987. The identification of snipes. *Proc. 4th Int. Identification Meeting (Eilat)*: 25-27.

Oman Bird Record Committee. 1994. *Oman Bird List*. 4th edition. Muscat.

Orenstein, R. I. 1979. The systematic position of the water redstarts, *Chaimarrornis* and *Rhyacornis*. *Ibis* 121: 220-224.

Ornithological Society of Japan. 1974. *Checklist of Japanese Birds*. 5th edition. Gakken, Tokyo.

Ouellet, H. 1993. Bicknell's Thrush: taxonomic status and distribution. *Wilson Bull.* 105: 545-572.

Paludan, K. 1959. On the birds of Afghanistan. *Vidensk. Medd. Dansk Naturh. For.* 122: 1-332.

Panov, E. N. 1983. *Die Würger der Paläarktis*. Die Neue Brehm-Bücherei, no. 557. Ziemsen-Verlag, Wittenburg Lutherstadt.

Panov, E. N. 1986. New data on hybridization of *Oenanthe pleschanka* and *O. hispanica*. *Zool J.* 65: 1675-1683.

Panov, E. N. 1989. *Gibridizatsiya i etologicheskaya izolyatsiya u ptits*. Moscow.

Panov, E. N. 1992. Emergence of hybridogenous polymorphism in the *Oenanthe picata* complex. *Bull. Brit. Orn. Club Centenary Suppl.* 112a: 237-249.

Parkes, K. C. 1982. Nomenclatural notes on the phalaropes. *Bull. Brit. Orn. Club* 102: 84-85.

Parmalee, D. F. 1988. The hybrid skua: the southern ocean enigma. *Wilson Bull.* 100: 345-356.

Payne, R. B. 1974. Species limits and variation of the New World Green Herons *Butorides virescens* and Striated Herons *B. striatus*. *Bull. Brit. Orn. Club* 94: 81-88.

Payne, R. B. & Risley, C. J. 1976. Systematics and evolutionary relationships among the herons (Ardeidae). *Misc. Publ. Mus. Zool. Univ. Mich.* 150: 1-115.

Paynter, R. A. 1963. Taxonomic notes on some Himalayan Paridae. *J. Bombay Nat. Hist. Soc.* 59: 951-956.

Pearson, D. J. & Backhurst, G. C. 1988. Characters and taxonomic position of Basra Reed Warbler. *Brit. Birds* 81: 171-178.

Pearson, T. G. 1936. *Birds of America*. Doubleday, New York.

Pennant, T. 1785. *Arctic Zoology*. London.

Piatt, J. F. 1994. Status of a 'new' rare alcid, the Long-billed Murrelet. *Pacific Seabirds* 21: 47-48.

Piechocki, R. & Bolod, A. 1972. Beiträge zur Avifauna der Mongolie. Teil II. Passeriformes. *Mitt. zool. Mus. Berlin* 48: 41-175.

Pitelka, F. A. 1950. Geographic variation and the species problem in the genus *Limnodromus*. *Univ. Calif. Publs. Zool.* 50: 1-108.

Pratt, H. D., Bruner, B. L. & Berrett, D. G. 1987. *A Field Guide to the Birds of Hawaii and the Tropical Pacific*. Princeton University Press, Princeton, New Jersey.

Quinn, T. W. G., Shields, F. & Wilson, A. C. 1991. Affinities of the Hawaiian Goose based on two types of mitochondrial DNA data. *Auk* 108: 585-593.

Randi, E., Meriggi, A., Lorenzini, R., Fusco, G. & Alkon, P. U. 1992. Biochemical analysis of relationships of Mediterranean *Alectoris* partridges. *Auk* 109: 358-367.

Ray, J. 1678. *The Ornithology of Francis Willughby*. Translated into English, and enlarged by J. Ray. London.

Ray, J. 1691. *A Collection of English Words*. 2nd edition. London.

Redman, N. J. 1992. Little-known bird: Blue-fronted Robin. *Bull. Oriental Bird Club* 16: 33-35.

Richardson, C. 1990. *The Birds of the United Arab Emirates*. Hobby Publications, Dubai.

Richardson, C. 1992. Escapes and introductions in the United Arab Emirates. *Phoenix* 9: 13-15.

Richman, A. D. & Price, T. 1992. Evolution of ecological differences in the Old World leaf warblers. *Nature, Lond.* 355: 817-821.

Ripley, S. D. 1958. A note on the Firethroat and the Black-throated Robin. *Postilla* 37: 1-3.

Ripley, S. D. 1961. *A Synopsis of the Birds of India and Pakistan*.Bombay Natural History Society, Bombay.

Ripley, S. D. 1977. *Rails of the World: a Monograph of the Family Rallidae*. M. F. Feheley, Toronto.

Ripley, S. D. 1982. *A Synopsis of the Birds of India and Pakistan together with those of Nepal, Bhutan, Bangladesh and Sri Lanka*. 2nd edition. Bombay Natural History Society, Bombay.

Ripley, S. D. & King, B. 1966. Discovery of the female of the Black-throated Robin, *Erithacus obscurus* (Berezowsky & Bianchi). *Proc. Biol. Soc. Wash.* 79: 151-152.

Ripley, S. D., Saha, S. S. & Beehler, B. M. 1991. Notes on birds from the Upper Noa Dihing, Arunachal Pradesh, Northeastern India. *Bull. Brit. Orn. Club* 111:19-28.

Roberts, T. J. 1991. *The Birds of Pakistan*. Volume 1. Oxford University Press, Karachi.

Roberts, T. J. 1992. *The Birds of Pakistan*. Volume 2. Oxford University Press, Karachi.

Roberts, T. J. & King, B. 1986. Vocalizations in the owls of the genus *Otus* in Pakistan. *Orn. Scand.* 17: 299-305.

Roselaar, C. S. 1992. A new species of mountain finch *Leucosticte* from western Tibet. *Bull. Brit. Orn. Club* 112: 225-231.

Roselaar, C. S. 1994. Notes on Sillem's Mountain-finch, a recently described species from western Tibet. *Dutch Birding* 16: 20-26.

Salomon, M. 1987. Analyse d'une zone de contact entre deux formes parapatriques: Le cas de pouillots véloces *Phylloscopus c. collybita* et *P. c. brehmii*. *Rev. Ecol. (Terre Vie)* 42: 377-420.

Satat, N. & Laird, B. 1992. The Armenian Gull. *Birding World* 5: 32-36.

Saunders, H. 1899. *An Illustrated Manual of British Birds*. Gurney & Jackson, London.

Schubert, M. 1982. Zur Lautgebung mehrerer zentralasiatischer Laubsänger-Arten (*Phylloscopus*; Aves, Sylviidae). *Mitt. zool. Mus. Berlin* 58: 109-128.

Schwartz, C. W. & Schwartz, E. R. 1951. An ecological reconnaissance of the pheasants in Hawaii. *Auk* 68: 281-314.

Serventy, D. L., Serventy, V. & Warham, J. 1971. *The Handbook of Australian Seabirds*. A. H. & A. W. Reed, Sydney.

Sheldon, F. H. 1987. Phylogeny of herons estimated from DNA-DNA hybridization data. *Auk* 104: 97-108.

Shirihai, H. (in press.) *Birds of Israel*. Academic Press, London.

Sibley, C. G. & Ahlquist, J. 1990. *Phylogeny and Classification of Birds*. Yale University Press, New Haven.

Sibley, C. G. & Monroe, B. L. Jr. 1990. *Distribution and Taxonomy of Birds of the World*. Yale University Press, New Haven.

Sibley, C. G. & Monroe, B. L. Jr. 1993. *A Supplement to Distribution and Taxonomy of Birds of the World*. Yale University Press, New Haven.

Simpson, J. A. & Weiner, E. S. C. (eds.) 1989. *The Oxford English Dictionary*. 2nd edition. Oxford University Press, Oxford.

Sluys, R. & van den Berg, M. 1982. On the specific status of the Cyprus Pied Wheatear. *Orn. Scand.* 13: 123-128.

Smith, N. 1966. Evolution of some arctic gulls (*Larus*): an experimental study of isolating mechanisms. *Orn. Monogr.* 4.

Smith, N. 1969. Polymorphism in Ringed Plovers. *Ibis* 111: 177-188.

Smythies, B. E. 1986. *Birds of Burma.* 3rd edition. Nimrod Press, Liss.

Snell, R. R. 1989. Status of *Larus* gulls at Home Bay, Baffin Island. *Colonial Waterbirds* 12: 12-23.

Snow, D. W. 1978. *An Atlas of Speciation in African Non-passerine Birds.* British Museum (Natural History), London.

Stagg, A. 1992. Mountain Nightjar: a new breeding bird for Arabia. *Phoenix* 9: 5.

Stainton, J. D. A. 1972. *Forests of Nepal.* John Murray, London.

Stepanyan, L. S. 1967. *Calandrella cheleënsis* Swinhoe a valid species. *Acta Orn.* 10: 97-107.

Stepanyan, L. S. 1972. A new species of the genus *Locustella* (Aves, Sylviidae) from the East Palearctic. (In Russian.) *Zool. Zh.* 51 (3): 1896.

Stepanyan, L. S. 1983. *Nadvidy i vidy-dvoniki v avifaune SSSR.* Moscow.

Stepanyan, L. S. 1990. *Conspectus of the Ornithological Fauna of the U.S.S.R.* (In Russian.) Academy of Sciences, Moscow.

Stokes, T. & Hinchey, M. 1992. Which small noddies breed at Ashmore Reef in the eastern Indian Ocean? *Emu* 90: 269-271.

Stresemann, E. & Arnold, J. 1949. Speciation in the group of Great Reed-Warblers. *J. Bombay Nat. Hist. Soc.* 48: 428-443.

Stresemann, E., Portenko, L. A. & Mauersberger, G. (eds.) 1967. *Atlas der Verbreitung palaearktischer Vögel*, 2. Berlin.

Stresemann, E., Portenko, L. A. & Mauersberger, G. (eds.) 1971. *Atlas der Verbreitung palaearktischer Vögel*, 3. Berlin.

Stresemann, E., Portenko, L. A. & Mauersberger, G. (eds.) 1974. *Atlas der Verbreitung palaearktischer Vögel*, 4. Berlin.

Stresemann, E. & Stresemann, V. 1972. Die postnuptiale und die praenuptiale Vollmauser von *Pericrocotus divaricatus* Raffles. *J. Orn.* 113: 435-439.

Summers-Smith, D. 1984. The rufous sparrows of the Cape Verde Islands. *Bull. Brit. Orn. Club* 104: 138-142.

Summers-Smith, D. 1988. *The Sparrows: a study of the genus Passer.* T. & A. D. Poyser, Calton.

Svensson, L. 1987. More about *Phylloscopus* taxonomy. *Brit. Birds* 80: 580-581.

Svensson, L. 1992. *Identification Guide to European Passerines.* 4th Edition. Stockholm.

Svensson, L. 1994. Booted or Sykes's Warbler. *Birding World* 6: 492-493.

Symens, P., Newton, S. F., Winkler, H. & Stagg, A. J. 1994. Mountain Nightjar *Caprimulgus poliocephalus* in Arabia: identification, status, and distribution. *Sandgrouse* 14 (2): 81-92.

Thibault, J.-C. 1983. *Les oiseaux de la Corse.* Parc Naturel Regional de la Corse, Ajaccio.

Thielcke, G., Wüstenberg, K. & Becker, P. H. 1978. Reaktionen von Zilpzalp und Fitis (*Phylloscopus collybita*, *Ph. trochilus*) auf verschiedene Gesangsformen des Zilpzalps. *J. Orn.* 119: 213-226.

Tomkins, R. J. & Milne, B. J. 1991. Differences among Dark-rumped Petrel (*Pterodroma phaeopygia*) populations within the Galapagos Archipelago. *Notornis* 38: 1-35.

Traylor, M. A. 1967. A collection of birds from Szechwan. *Fieldiana: Zool.* 53: 1-67.

Udagawa, T. 1953. The avifauna of Teuri and Yagishiri islands, Hokkaido. *Tori* 1953: 68-85.

Urban, E. K., Fry, C. H. & Keith, S. 1986. *The Birds of Africa.* Volume II. Academic Press, London.

Urban, E. K. & Jefford, T. G. 1974. The status of the cormorants *Phalacrocorax carbo lucidus* and *Phalacrocorax carbo patricki*. *Bull. Brit. Orn. Club* 94: 104-107.

Urdang, L., Long, T. H. & Hanks, P. (eds.) 1979. *Collins Dictionary of the English Language.* Collins, London.

Vaurie, C. 1949a. A revision of the bird family Dicruridae. *Bull. Amer. Mus. Nat. Hist.* 93: 199-342.

Vaurie, C. 1949b. Notes on some Asiatic finches. *Amer. Mus. Novit.*, 1424.

Vaurie, C. 1949c. Notes on the birds genus *Oenanthe* in Persia, Afghanistan and India. *Amer. Mus. Novit.*, 1425.

Vaurie, C. 1950a. Notes on some Asiatic titmice. *Amer. Mus. Novit.*, 1459.

Vaurie, C. 1950b. Notes on some Asiatic nuthatches and creepers. *Amer. Mus. Novit.*, 1472.

Vaurie, C. 1954a. Systematic notes on Palearctic birds. No. 5. Corvidae. *Amer. Mus. Novit.*, 1668.

Vaurie, C. 1954b. Systematic notes on Palearctic birds. No. 6. Timaliinae and Paradoxornithinae. *Amer. Mus. Novit.*, 1669.

Vaurie, C. 1954c. Systematic notes on Palearctic birds. No. 9. Sylviinae: the genus *Phylloscopus*. *Amer. Mus. Novit.*, 1685.

Vaurie, C. 1954d. Systematic notes on Palearctic birds. No. 12. Muscicapinae, Hirundinidae and Sturnidae. *Amer. Mus. Novit.*, 1694.

Vaurie, C. 1955a. Systematic notes on Palearctic Birds. No. 16. Troglodytinae, Cinclidae, and Prunellidae. *Amer. Mus. Novit.* 1751.

Vaurie, C. 1955b. Systematic notes on Palearctic birds. No. 18. Supplementary notes on Corvidae, Timaliinae, Alaudidae, Sylviinae, Hirundinidae and Turdinae. *Amer. Mus. Novit.*, 1753.

Vaurie, C. 1956. Systematic notes on Palearctic birds. No. 20. Fringillidae: the genera *Leucosticte*, *Rhodopechys*, *Carpodacus*, *Pinicola*, *Loxia*, *Uragus*, *Urocynchramus*, and *Propyrrhula*. *Amer. Mus. Novit.*, 1786.

Vaurie, C. 1957a. Systematic notes on Palearctic birds. No. 26. Paridae: the *Parus caeruleus* complex. *Amer. Mus. Novit.*, 1833.

Vaurie, C. 1957b. Systematic notes on Palearctic birds. No. 28. The families Remizidae and Aegithalidae. *Amer. Mus. Novit.*, 1853.

Vaurie, C. 1959a. *The Birds of the Palearctic Fauna.* Passeriformes. Witherby, London.

Vaurie, C. 1959b. Systematic notes on Palearctic birds. No. 38. Alcedinidae, Meropidae, Upupidae, and Apodidae. *Amer. Mus. Novit.*, 1971.

Vaurie, C. 1961. Systematic notes on Palearctic birds. No. 45. Falconidae: the genus *Falco* (Part 1, *Falco peregrinus* and *Falco pelegrinoides*). *Amer. Mus. Novit.* 2035.

Vaurie, C. 1965a. *The Birds of the Palearctic Fauna.* Non-Passeriformes. Witherby, London.

Vaurie, C. 1965b. Distribution regionale et altitudinale des genres *Garrulax* et *Babax* et notes sur leur systematique. *L'Oiseau et R.F.O.* 35 (suppl.): 141-152.

Vaurie, C. 1972. *Tibet and its Birds*. Witherby, London.

Weprincew, B. N., Leonowitsch, W. W. & Netschajew, A. W. 1989. Zur Lebensweise von *Phylloscopus borealoides* Portenko und *Phylloscopus tenellipes* Swinhoe. *Mitt. zool. Mus. Berlin* 65: Suppl.: *Ann. Orn.* 13: 71-80.

Weprincew, B. N., Leonowitsch, W. W. & Netschajew, A. W. 1990. On species status of the Sakhalin Warbler - *Phylloscopus borealoides* Portenko. *Ornithologiya* 24: 34-42.

Viney, C. & Phillipps, K. 1994. *Birds of Hong Kong*. 6th edition. Government Printer, Hong Kong.

Voous, K. H. 1977. *List of Recent Holarctic Bird Species*. British Ornithologists' Union, London. (Reprinted, with revisions, from *Ibis* 115 (1973): 612-638 and *Ibis* 119 (1977): 223-250, 376-406.)

Voous, K. H. 1986. Striated or Green Herons in the South Caribbean Islands? *Ann. Naturhist. Mus. Wien* (Ser. B) 88/89: 101-106.

Voous, K. H. 1988. *Owls of the Northern Hemisphere*. Harper Collins, London

Voous, K. H. & Marle, J. G. van. 1953. The distributional history of the Nuthatch, *Sitta europaea* L. *Ardea* 41 (extra nummer): 1-68.

Watson, G. E. 1962. A re-evaluation and description of a difficult Asia Minor *Phylloscopus*. *Ibis* 104: 347-352.

Wattel, J. 1973. Geographical differentiation in the genus *Accipiter*. *Publ. Nuttall Orn. Club* 13: 1-231.

Wells, D. R. 1982. Biological species limits in the *Cettia fortipes* complex. *Bull. Brit. Orn. Club* 102: 57-62.

Whistler, H. 1945a. Materials for the ornithology of Afghanistan, Part II. *J. Bombay Nat. Hist. Soc.* 45: 61-72.

Whistler, H. 1945b. Materials for the ornithology of Afghanistan, Part III. *J. Bombay Nat. Hist. Soc.* 45: 106-122.

White, C. M. N. & Bruce, M. D. 1986. *The Birds of Wallacea*. Brit. Ornithologists' Union, Check-list no. 7, London.

Williamson, K. 1967. *The genus Phylloscopus*. Identification for ringers, 2. British Trust for Ornithology, Tring.

Wilson, A. & Bonaparte, C. L. 1831. *American Ornithology; or the Natural History of the Birds of the United States*. 4 volumes. Constable, Edinburgh.

Wolters, H. E. 1967. Über einige asiatische Carduelinae. *Bonn. zool. Beitr.* 18: 169-172.

Wunderlich, K. 1991. *Aegithalos bonvaloti* Oustalet. In Stresemann, E. & Portenko, L. A. *Atlas der Verbreitung Palaearktischer Vögel*, 17. Berlin.

Yamashina, Y. & Mano, T. 1981. A new species of rail from Okinawa Island. *J. Yamashina Inst. Orn.* 13: 1-6.

Yates, B. & Taffs, H. 1990. Least Tern in East Essex—new Western Palearctic bird. *Birding World* 3: 197-199.

Yésou, P. 1991. The sympatric breeding of *Larus fuscus*, *L. cachinnans* and *L. argentatus* in France. *Ibis* 133: 256-263.

Zino, P. A. & Zino, F. 1986. Contribution to the study of the petrels of the genus *Pterodroma* in the archipelago of Madeira. *Bol. Mus. Mun. Funchal* 38: 141-165.

Zonfrillo, B. 1994. The soft-plumaged petrel group. *Birding World* 7: 71-72.

Zusi, R. L. 1978. The interorbital septum in cardueline finches. *Bull. Brit. Orn. Club* 98: 5-10.